GEOLOGIC FIELD METHODS

HARPER'S GEOSCIENCE SERIES

CAREY CRONEIS, EDITOR

GEOLOGIC
FIELD METHODS

by
JULIAN W. LOW

RESEARCH GEOLOGIST
THE CALIFORNIA COMPANY

HARPER & BROTHERS · PUBLISHERS · NEW YORK

C O N T E N T S

VI. STRUCTURAL FIELD WORK

EDITOR'S INTRODUCTION

Julian W. Low's *Geologic Field Methods* is a companion volume
to his *Plane Table Mapping* published in Harper's Geoscience
Series in 1952. Like that earlier successful manual, Low's *Geologic
Field Methods* is an intensely practical, down-to-earth volume
designed with the single-minded purpose of being helpful to students, geological trainees, and younger technical employees of companies dealing with economic resources. Its usefulness, however, is
likely to be more broadly based. Not only embryonic earth scientists
but seasoned professional geologists commonly discover that their
academic training in field methods has been inadequate, and that
they have overestimated their practical knowledge of the basic
logistics of field procedure. Ordinarily this discovery comes late and
proves embarrassing to everyone concerned.

Although the foregoing observations would have been sound a
score of years ago, they have even sharper pertinence today. This
is true because geology is becoming more and more an "exact"
science, at least in the sense that precise laboratory experimentation
has been increasing while old-fashioned field work has been somewhat on the decline. It thus happens that even under average circumstances an otherwise highly competent modern geologist may
have had almost no independent field experience. Yet it is quite
possible that such a man may some time be expected to organize
and direct a field expedition of considerable complexity. If and
when the assignment is made, living and working on the ground in
the field will be a necessity despite any or all of the new equipment
and methods for conducting every type of areal, stratigraphic,
structural, and mineral survey.

Low's manual thus is designed to be a handbook for experienced
as well as inexperienced party chiefs. In addition, it should be
helpful to party personnel with various levels of training and with
different degrees of familiarity with the "country." In fact, the
manual is a sort of high level do-it-yourself guide which makes it
possible for either the field veteran or the field tyro to follow the

step-by-step procedures discussed with very little trouble. The subjects covered have been selected by a master of field methods on the basis of his own rich academic and commercial experience; and Mr. Low has further simplified his straightforward discussions by including scores of highly instructive line drawings, mostly from his own pen.

It is a rare textbook which has been prepared on an outline that will satisfy a majority of teachers of the subject treated. Similarly, manuals used for the instruction of trainees in geology commonly are arranged to suit their authors, not the trainees or their tutors. Hence a serious attempt has been made to make each chapter of the present book essentially independent so that students, teachers, and professional geologists can readily rearrange *Geologic Field Methods* to suit their own ideas of logical development or presentation.

It has long been apparent to the editor that geology must and will place more and more reliance on the exact sciences; but if, in attempting to do so, it inadvertently puts less and less emphasis on meticulously winnowed field data, the results can only range between the mildly misleading and the aggressively worthless. Low's *Geologic Field Methods,* carefully followed, however, should make it possible for quantitative laboratory methods to be based on the soundest of all foundations—accurate field data.

CAREY CRONEIS

The Rice Institute

PREFACE

Geology is primarily a science of correlation, integration, and interpretation; and, like the legs of a tripod, it is supported by the basic sciences of physics, chemistry, and biology, to which we give the geologic names geophysics, geochemistry, and paleontology. In these fields are dozens of worthwhile books and countless papers; and the literature pertaining to them, or more specifically to geology, is growing at an ever increasing rate. No one could hope to read and assimilate all that has been, and is being, published on the subject, and the practicing geologist or student can spend only a small portion of his reading time on subjects not immediately related to his work. It would appear, then, that a new book stands small chance of being read by a substantial number of geologists whose time is so limited, but this is not necessarily so. Every book in geology incorporates much subject matter contained in others. This manual is no exception, for in it can be found little that has not at some time been published. But it is the author's belief that periodically the matter pertaining to one subject should be gathered from many sources, appraised, and then put into a single volume that is "tailored" to fulfill the needs of practicing geologists and students. This applies especially to methods and techniques which have a perplexing habit of becoming lost or forgotten.

The sources of material in this manual are indeterminate. The methods and practices set down here have been collected over a 30-year period of field work, and it would be impossible to recollect those which the writer has improvised and those which have been passed on to him, either by word of mouth or from the written article. In either case, the methods have proved to be practical, and they are hereby passed on to those whose experience and opportunities have been more limited in the applications of field methods.

An attempt is made to present text matter from the viewpoint of the inexperienced man *in the field,* unable to obtain help in the solution of immediate problems. Two objectives have been sought: to limit the dimensions of the manual to a size such that it might easily be carried in a pocket or notebook case, and to display the solutions to various problems in a manner that could readily be correlated with ordinary field situations.

Perhaps too much space has been given to the obvious. If the writer has erred in this respect, it is the result of a desire to reach the man in the field who *most* needs the help. It has been observed that the failure to carry out an assignment effectively often rests not so much on ignorance of the overall plan or background education as on lack of familiarity with minor aspects of methods and procedures. In short, a sharp distinction is made between the *collection* of accurate field data and their ultimate utilization.

This book would have failed to reach one of its primary objectives—small size—if the field *recognition* of geologic phenomena were treated in any detail. It is assumed that various courses in geology will have prepared the novice field geologist in characteristics of geologic phenomena and that his general knowledge will provide the means of distinguishing one type of feature from another. Once the feature is recognized, the methods described will come to his aid in making the necessary measurements. Clearly this manual is not intended to supplant other standard text books on structure, stratigraphy, or the broad subject of field geology. As the title states, this is a manual of methods, and therefore it supplements other standard works.

A realistic appraisal of field work must consider all factors that materially affect the performance of field personnel. The main problems of conducting a survey may not be geological, yet their solution determines to a large extent the success of the venture. This fact is proffered as justification for including such subjects as organization, selected subsurface methods, and outdoor work. Some geologists have never cooked a meal or spent a night in wilderness country; and when faced with these necessities, they find the problems related thereto far surpass those concerned with geology.

Many persons have contributed something to the writer's "bag of tricks," but in most instances the "trick" and the identity of the donor have become separated. Although these associates cannot be specifically named, they have indirectly contributed to the effort. Especial thanks are due Robert H. Carpenter, who prepared Chapter VIII on field methods for mineral exploration. Many of the figures in the chapter treating field mapping methods were taken from *Plane Table Mapping* (Harper, 1952). Other photographic illustrations were provided by Joe L. Low, and L. W. LeRoy, who are aware of my appreciation.

J. W. L.

March, 1957

GEOLOGIC FIELD METHODS

CHAPTER I

Introduction to Surface Geological Investigations

1. General Remarks

Geology is, literally, as "broad as the earth and as high as the sky." As a science it borrows from, and rests upon, all the other natural sciences, and thus it is as complex as the other sciences are complex. Advances in any of the basic sciences directly or indirectly affect the science of geology; and for this reason the ramifications of geologic work must extend into the depths of fields such as astronomy, chemistry, nuclear physics, and biology for newly discovered facts that might aid in solving geologic problems.

In an effort to reduce the vast complexity of geologic science to simpler terms and better organized methods of attack, certain categories of endeavor have developed. Unfortunately, these categories are not founded on common basic principles, and as a result they are not of the same system of classification. Nevertheless, the subdivisions do have a useful and practical purpose, both in the conduct of investigations and in discussion of geologic events and processes. It is well to keep in mind that sedimentation is the result of some tectonic event, that the *expression* of structural processes may vary according to changes in the sedimentary rocks involved in deformations, that climate has a bearing on the types and quantities of sediments deposited and the distribution of existing rocks, and that the chemistry of the seas and the atmosphere will have had considerable effect on the rocks and their organic constituents.

It is evident that stratigraphy is concerned primarily with the characters and relationships of sedimentary rocks and that structure applies to their deformation. These terms, and many others, have geologic connotations. But when we speak of *surface* geology and *subsurface* geology, we are referring to *methods* and realms of observation. The boundaries between the two are broad and indefinite, and geologic interpretations recognize none. In the strictest sense surface geology deals with outcropping bedrock, and subsurface geology with the rocks that are concealed by alluvium, soil, and other recent mantle materials. In practice, however, surface geology may incorporate observations of bedrock made in pits, trenches, mines, and shallow wells; whereas subsurface geology relies almost wholly on data gotten from relatively deep wells. Each method has its advantages and its limitations. In outcrops the characters of rocks over some lateral distance can be observed directly. Unconformities, lithologic changes, lenticularity, degree of dip, and direction of strike are commonplace observations. But rocks at the surface are subject to drastic alterations, depending on the type of rock, climate, topography and other factors. Furthermore, the actual depth of observation is determined by the amount of topographic relief, and the stratigraphic depth to which examinations may extend is limited by surface relief and structure and particular relationships between the two. In contrast, wells drilled for oil are now reaching depths in excess of 20,000 feet. There is no place on the surface of the earth where a *vertical* column of sedimentary rocks approaching such a thickness can be viewed, and it is far from a proved fact that some of the great *compiled* surface sections actually are representative of a restored vertical section at any one point.

The task of the surface geologist does not end with a record of only directly observable features. Dips and strikes and elevations on recognizable stratigraphic units may constitute all that is required as field data for a structural map of an area; but from these data, the geologist must project into the *subsurface*. It should be emphasized that all geologic relationships below the surface—structural and stratigraphic—are inferential, and that a number of assumptions are made in order to project surface observations into the subsurface. Although the extension of surface geology to moderate depths has often produced a remarkably accurate subsurface picture, thickening or thinning of formations, unconformities, and other unseen relationships have likewise led the surface geologist far astray in his interpretations. Geologic problems are much the same no matter what method of attack is employed. Surface geology utilizes certain kinds of data and subsurface, different kinds. No thoughtful geologist would attempt to use one method exclusively where both methods could be combined.

2. The Field Geologist

The term *field* or *surface* geologist is used here with reservations, for, as intimated in foregoing remarks, the prefix *surface* indicates nothing more than emphasis on particular types of data and the methods of collecting and processing these data. A field geologist, therefore, is one who seeks, measures, records, analyzes, and interprets data obtained from outcrops. If his abilities were limited to the recognition and measuring of field features, he would indeed be handicapped in the final appraisal of his field observations. Fortunately, most geologists are sufficiently versatile to apply their knowledge and skills to many areas of investigation, field geology being only one phase of inquiry.

Beginning geologists and students of geology commonly look upon work in the field as a career—a career which affords the opportunities of professional prestige and scientific exploration in wilderness regions. There are few, if any, organizations at the present time which offer such a career. The value of field work in geologic education and experience should not be minimized; under favorable conditions much more geology can be learned in the field in a given length of time than in any other branch of geologic endeavor. However, the total amount of time spent in field work, and the number of geologists getting field assignments are steadily decreasing relative to the effort and time spent in laboratory and office work. Therefore, a field assignment should be considered as an opportunity that most geologists do not have.

In most organizations the geologist is chief of the field party, which may consist of himself, one or more assistants, and several helpers, such as axmen, packers, and cooks. It is the responsibility of the chief of party to maintain amicable relationships among the group and to administer the diversified duties of the party impartially. He should also plan the field program well in advance of actual operations. These plans must include, in addition to technical operations, such things as living accommodations, provisions, and deployment of the field personnel. Complete notes on daily progress and accurate records on expenditures are necessary for periodic progress reports which he may be called upon to make to his superior or employer. The chief of party cannot expect to finish his day's work in eight hours, though others in the group often do so, nor should he resent the fact that he has less freedom from the demands of the project. The chief of party must keep all phases of the project in balance and up-to-date regardless of the amount of time required.

3. Field Methods

The term *field methods* refers to the detailed step-by-step procedures employed in collecting and presenting the basic data obtained from outcrops. This phase of investigation is vital, for on it will rest all succeeding conclusions. The field measurements, maps, and graphs constitute the framework around which far-reaching concepts are developed. Economically, the success or failure of extremely costly operations may rest entirely on the reliability of the field man's work. Unlike subsurface or laboratory work, completed field surveys are not easily repeated.

In areas where the geology is complex, it is often necessary for the geologist to do a considerable amount of measuring, recording, mapping, and computing before he can gain a clear concept of the basic data. This situation is common where complex structure or stratigraphy is associated with sparse, isolated outcrops. Measurements must be reliable even though their significance is not immediately apparent. It is a common, though erroneous, belief that measurements need not be precise in areas where available control is widely spaced. The converse is true, for these few points are the anchors on which the geology of the region must be tied. In areas where control is abundant a grossly erroneous measurement will be apparent.

The field man must be able to measure and record field data in a manner that fully expresses his observations and is comprehensible to others. In some instances laboratory determinations may be necessary before the field man can grasp the significance of the field problems; therefore, his work should take this factor into consideration.

The competent field geologist will select the method which will yield the desired results without unwarranted expenditure of field time. The word *select* implies *alternative*. It follows that in order to be selective in the application of field methods, one must have extensive knowledge of methods and procedures. The man who is familiar with several methods of doing a given task holds a decided advantage over one who can employ only one method.

4. Types of Field Investigations

There are many types of geologic field projects and the methods used vary greatly. For this reason, it is important to classify each project and to decide upon the methods that will be most adaptable and economical of time and money. The objectives of a survey should be defined clearly, and methods should be chosen with regard to reaching those objectives without unnecessary effort, yet with the assurance that all essential data will be obtained. The following topics illustrate the difference in emphasis on certain methods and preparations for various kinds of surveys.

TOPOGRAPHIC MAPPING

In preparation for field work whose purpose is to construct a plane table topographic contour map, the topographer should compile available data that will be useful in the field. The positions of fixed recoverable points, such as land corners, bench marks, and triangulation stations should be plotted on the plane table sheets or on vellum for later transfer to the sheets. Lists of elevations determined by prior surveys should be compiled. If the field man has not used the plane table for a considerable length of time, he should thoroughly review all conventional procedures of this method. Likewise, the general geology and especially the geomorphology of the region should be reviewed. Topographic forms will be expressed more clearly if the topographer is aware of their geomorphologic significance.

AREAL GEOLOGICAL MAPPING

Geologic structure and topography determine the areal distribution of stratigraphic units at the surface of the ground; however, they are individually effective only under certain circumstances. For example, an anticline may occur at the surface within the area occupied by one stratigraphic unit but not be reflected in the areal boundaries of the unit; nevertheless, facts pertaining to the regional structure should be assembled in preparation for field mapping of areal geology. Topographic maps and aerial photographs should be taken into the field to aid in sketching formational boundaries. The width of an outcrop band may vary according to the thickness of the formation; therefore, measured or drilled thicknesses of the surface formations may aid materially in determining the positions of boundaries under alluvium cover. All reports referring to lithologic characteristics and surface manifestations of the formations should be studied. Elevations and the means of determining elevation are important only in localities where formational boundaries cannot be seen and, therefore, must be projected.

STRUCTURAL MAPPING

The importance of elevation in structural mapping is relative. Where structural relief is low, elevations are determined with considerable precision and the methods used in establishing elevations must insure accuracy. On the other hand, where dips are steep and structural relief is high, particular attention must be accorded the methods of determining horizontal position, and those dealing with elevations are relatively less important. Of course, reports on regional and local structure should be reviewed. Regional and local structural trends sometimes can be interpreted from a combination of topographic and areal geologic maps.

STRATIGRAPHIC INVESTIGATIONS

Investigations pertaining specifically to stratigraphic problems are extremely diverse and involve many field techniques. Often the field technique is dictated by laboratory requirements, as for example, the collecting of samples for thin section or paleontological analysis. The field procedures employed in this case would be quite different from those used for no other purpose than to determine the thicknesses of stratigraphic units. Planning preparatory to field work is especially important in stratigraphic exploration.

5. The Significance of Outcrops

The mere existence of an outcrop has geologic significance apart from lithologic or other details of the rock itself. Rocks crop out as a result of some geologic event, or events. Had all orogenic processes ceased early in geologic time, there would be little to observe in rocks at the surface, for the surface rocks would be the product of just the latest period. The significance of an outcrop may be stratigraphic, structural, or locally topographic. In attempting to explain the reasons for isolated or anomalous outcrops the field geologist may find the answer to a problem of greater importance. In any case, explanations of geologic phe-

nomena of a region should be consistent with the reasons for the
outcrops.

6. Topographic Expression of Geologic Features

The field geologist can gain much from a systematic study of
the topography of the region. If topographic contour maps are
available, they should be studied in the field to relate specific
forms to geologic features. An attempt should be made to learn
the topographic response to various types of rocks and structures.
Certain rocks are highly resistant to erosion where lying essentially
horizontal, but more susceptible where dipping at a steep angle.
Thinly laminated shales often exhibit this characteristic. Other
rock types, such as some varieties of limestone, may show opposite
tendencies. The response of a given rock type to the agents of
erosion is frequently related to climatic conditions; therefore, in
order to utilize topography as a tool of geology, it is necessary to
determine the relationships locally by observation.

The pattern of surface drainage is commonly controlled by
either lithologic variations or structure, or both. Faults having
small displacements have been traced for many miles by deflected
courses of minor streams crossing them. Once a feature of this
kind has been interpreted from the topography, the geologist can
go directly to the critical points in the field for verification by
examination of the rocks. Aerial photos are especially helpful
when used in conjunction with topographic maps.

7. Preliminary Examination of Aerial Photos

The uses of aerial photographs in geological work are so well
known as to scarcely need an introduction. In order to take full
advantage of photographs it is necessary to know the fundamentals
of aerial photogrammetry. Nevertheless, the beginner will find
them extremely useful in various phases of a project even though
his lack of technical knowledge limits their full exploitation.

When photos are viewed stereoscopically shadows caused by
topographic relief can readily be distinguished from other dark
portions of the photo. Where light and dark portions not caused

by relief form definite trends or patterns they may have geologic significance. Alternating beds of shale and sandy shale may show on the photos as alternate light and dark bands. On the ground these beds may be covered by a thin mantle of soil or sod, but the photographic film is generally more sensitive to minute differences in tone or color than are the average person's eyes; therefore, the film records subtle differences in either the color of the soil or the vegetation that grows on it. Samples of the subsoil or bedrock will generally verify the photos.

Geologic boundaries can be traced directly on the aerial photographs, and approximations of dip and strike can be made by inspection of the stereoscopic view. Photos are valuable for quickly acquiring the regional aspects of the geology and topography and for planning ground methods to be used in the field.

8. Application of Plant Ecology

The selective association of certain plants with exclusive types of rocks has long been recognized as a valuable aid to the field geologist. Soils derived from underlying bedrock vary in character and fertility according to the differences in chemical and mineralogical constituents of the rock, its physical attributes, and the relative effectiveness of erosive agents. A soil that is sterile for one class of plants may be quite fertile for another, and the looseness of soil required by one type of plant limits the growth of a different type. Some rocks yield soils that, for one reason or another, are unsuitable for all wild plants in the region. The presence of such rocks at or near the surface is indicated by sparseness or absence of plant cover.

Porous beds often carry sufficient water to support luxuriant plant growth in regions where vegetation is normally scanty. The surface trace of these aquifers can usually be seen in aerial photographs as a distinct difference in tone, although the distinction may not be detected on the ground. This phenomenon is quite common in plains regions that are entirely covered with wild grasses.

Wild mustard grows profusely in soils derived from bentonite or bentonitic shales; in many regions of the West piñons and juniper grow in abundance only in sandstone soils, and in a few instances, only the soils from specific sandstones; in western Cuba and other tropical climates sparse pine forests and grasslands occupy areas underlain by tuffs and sandstones, and palms and tropical shrubbery grow in limestone-derived red soils. There are innumerable examples of plant and rock associations similar to those mentioned. Such associations should be observed in all areas where outcrops are isolated and widely scattered, for the distribution of vegetation may help to bridge over the covered areas. When plant and rock associations have been established, the geologist is better prepared to select sites for digging pits to obtain samples of bedrock or to determine the dip and strike.

In mountainous regions botanic zones may be controlled largely by elevation above sea level. Certain varieties of plants are quite sensitive to elevation and consequently the lines of demarcation are sharp. It has been observed that the same botanic boundaries are commonly lower on north and east slopes than they are on south and west exposures. In arid climates the densest growths are invariably on the northerly and easterly slopes. These facts must be considered when interpreting types of bedrock from vegetation patterns.

9. Springs and Seeps

Springs and seeps are different manifestations of the same process. Seeps are springs without discernible current. Both may be important to the field geologist in various ways. Where bedrock is covered by soils the positions of porous beds, such as sandstones and limestones, may be revealed by damp or muddy ground or by flowing springs. During dry periods when no water reaches the surface, the effect of earlier effluences may be seen as soil discolorations by iron oxides or alkalies. The associations of plants with aquifers has been mentioned.

Fault lines concealed by soil cover are commonly traceable by series of springs and seeps. Such alignments may be quite conspicuous on aerial photographs. Deep-seated faults in a sedimentary rock succession may be indicated by abnormally high temperatures of the water issuing from springs. High concentration of dissolved minerals generally associated with igneous rocks in some cases indicates deep faults.

When interpreting geologic conditions from springs it is necessary to distinguish between waters related directly to the bedrock and those held in the mantle or subsoil. Generally, springs from near-surface waters will tend to conform to the topography, and those stemming from bedrock may emerge in alignments without regard to topographic trends.

10. Climates and Erosion Processes

The field geologist is much concerned with erosion processes, for outcrops may either exist or be obliterated as a result of erosion. The processes of erosion and their effects in modeling the surface of the earth are fully treated in a number of textbooks on geomorphology. It is good practice for the field geologist to review such books periodically in order to keep the principles of this subject fresh in mind. However, in addition to principles, he should, at the outset of a field project, acquaint himself with details and peculiarities of erosion in the vicinity of his work. It is the specific resistance to erosion of rocks and structures that will be of direct and immediate interest, though broader aspects of geomorphology should not be neglected.

Climate has much to do with the relative effectiveness of erosion agents, such as water and wind. Water is more effective as an agent of the mechanical destruction of rocks in regions where temperatures fall far below the freezing point; but it is generally more destructive, chemically, in warm humid regions where abundant humus contributes various organic acids to surface waters, which, in turn, attack soluble rocks. Wind is an effective erosive agent when carrying large quantities of dust and sand grains; therefore, it is more important in arid or desert climates where dry particles are readily picked up off the ground.

In a general way (there are exceptions) certain lithologies exhibit characteristic responses to a specific erosion agent according to the type of climate of the region. Because of this fact it is necessary to determine the reactions of the rocks locally in order to use geomorphology most effectively as a tool of field geology.

Microscopic variations in lithology may not be directly observable in the field, but weathering characteristics caused by certain lithologies are sometimes so diagnostic that the field geologist has no difficulty in identifying and tracing them in the outcrops. Laboratory analysis of a carbonate bed in the Pennsylvanian of eastern Wyoming has demonstrated that where the rock is dolomitic it weathers to a distinctively "beaded" surface; where it is not dolomitic, the surface weathers smooth. The two lithologies cannot be differentiated with a hand lens in the field, but the changes in surface texture of the rocks are clearly evident and mappable.

The susceptibility of a given rock to breakdown varies, not only according to its climatic environment, but also with the bed's structural attitude and the types of lithologies in beds closely associated with it.

In the Black Hills region of South Dakota and in parts of southeastern Wyoming thick beds of gypsum occurring in the red shale sequence of the Permo-Triassic form locally prominent benches on the rolling plains and gentle slopes of hills. The exposed surfaces of the gypsum become tough and leathery and more resistant to erosion than the enclosing shales. In the same regions, gypsum and anhydrite occurring as beds adjacent to porous carbonates in the Permo-Pennsylvanian series rarely are seen in outcrops despite the fact that they are present in the subsurface throughout the region. Brecciated carbonates indicate their former presence in the surface sections. Thick beds of anhydrite in the Devonian dolomites of western Montana are likewise represented in the outcrops by brecciation of the closely associated carbonate rocks. Many other similar examples could be cited. It is apparent that gypsum and anhydrite are readily dissolved where they lie adjacent to porous beds capable of carrying

When making plans for an extensive survey all factors which bear on operations in the field should be written down, appraised, and provided for prior to active field work. Some of the factors to be considered are discussed in following articles. However, no theoretical rules can be used to anticipate the requirements of all projects, and each undertaking must be considered according to the peculiarities of topography, geology, personnel, and climatic conditions. All plans should be started well in advance of the initiation of field work in order to avoid hasty last-minute preparations.

14. Specifications for a Geologic Survey

When setting up specifications for a geologic field project many factors are weighed and balanced in relation to each other. Before any detailed plans can be made, it is first necessary to determine precisely what is required from the field work. One must distinguish between *minimum requirements* to meet the objectives and information that would be desirable to have for general knowledge, but not essential to the success of the project. These minimum requirements in quality and quantity of geologic data to be obtained serve as a basis for selecting appropriate field methods. Generally speaking, the detailing or precise methods require more time and a higher degree of skill and experience than do approximate methods. Also, there are fewer alternatives from which to choose, thus permitting less flexibility to adapt the method to fit the circumstances. Therefore, field methods and procedures should be outlined on the basis of minimum requirements. The principle of minimum requirements should be applied to all phases of the work, such as type of horizontal control (plane table, air photos, topographic sheet, township plats), elevations (level, vertical angles, barometric, hand level), dips and strikes (Brunton, three-point), and precision in placing the positions of stratigraphic markers or determining thicknesses.

If the objective is primarily that of mapping structure, existing maps and reports should be perused for information relating to the amount of structural relief, extremes of dip, and the areas or breadths of local structures, for these will be determining factors in the selection of contour intervals and scales which will show the desired detail in the field maps.

When undertaking the measurement of stratigraphic sections, the *permissible error* in thickness must be decided upon before methods and procedures for field work can be selected or devised. For example, if the error in stratigraphic thickness must be kept within five percent, all phases of the work pertaining to the measurement of thickness must be limited accordingly. It is illogical when measuring moderate- to steep-dipping strata to strive for a high degree of precision in elevations if the scale of the map will not permit plotting horizontal distances to a comparable accuracy. (See Chapter IV.)

15. Specification Sheets for the Field Parties

A survey that has been carefully planned can be executed more faithfully if the detailed plans are constantly available to the men in the field. It is often difficult for the geologist to obtain all the data needed if he is not provided with adequate instructions. The specification sheets given to the field men should include permissible limits of error in all phases of the work—areal density of control (when not dependent on distribution of outcrops); the field methods permitted in instrumental operations; the type, quality, and quantity (per unit area) of data sought; and any other information that might enable the field man to conduct the survey in a commendable fashion. These instructions should be tabulated in a form that is convenient for use in the field. Experienced field geologists need only an outline which states the principal objectives, the sequential order of various operations, and definition of the accuracy required. Details of methods and procedures can be selected better by those who have intimate knowledge of field conditions. Conversely, if the personnel is relatively inexperienced, the instructions need to be more complete.

16. Organization of Field Parties

Any project involving diverse operations and a considerable number of men must be well organized in order to obtain the most in production and quality of work. Several phases of the project may have to be completed in a definite sequence, as, for example, primary vertical and horizontal control must precede detailing of geology or topography; stratigraphic sections may have to be measured at a number of localities before the structure of an area can be determined. The sequence of interdependent operations should be determined in advance of field work.

In isolated regions communication between the field units and the base of operations is a vital factor in organization. When assigning parties to different parts of the map area, they should be given exact instructions as to the time, place, and method of reporting progress or other pertinent information to the supervisor.

A first principle of organization (and one commonly ignored) is the *line of authority and responsibility*. Too frequently, a man is given certain burdensome responsibilities but a commensurate authority is withheld from him. This situation is extremely bad for the morale of the men and the overall efficiency of the crew. Even though several persons are essentially equal in experience and competency, it is necessary for the sake of unified effort that *only one* person be placed in charge of the field operations. Sometimes it is advantageous to rotate two or more men in the position of supervisor during the course of the field season. This procedure permits several persons to acquire experience in direction, yet retains a clear-cut line of authority.

The basic unit on a geological survey where the plane table is used consists of the geologist and the instrumentman. This unit may be modified in a number of ways, depending on the type of work and the organization of the crew as a whole; for example, the mapping unit may have one plane table man and two or three geologists and paleontologists. The party may contain an instrumentman, a geologist, and a number of assistants. Basically, a topographic field party is the instrumentman, who is also engineer and topographer, and a rodman. This unit is often expanded to topographer, recorder, two or more rodmen, and chainmen or "swampers." In geologic work, the geologist is party chief; in topographic work, the topographer (instrumentman) is party chief. Generally, the recorder and computer is second in authority because his work requires close and constant association with the party chief. The terms "party" and "crew" are used in various ways by different organizations. One organization may consider the crew as composed of several parties, while another applies the terms in the reverse positions.

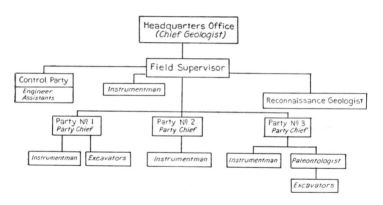

Fig. 1.   Chart showing the organization of a diversified field project.

The field supervisor coördinates the work of the field parties and serves as their direct contact with the headquarters office. All communications relating to the work pass over his desk. When it is more expedient for party chiefs to communicate with the head office directly, copies of the letters or memoranda should be sent to the supervisor so that he will be informed at all times on events that pertain to the project. When interim reports are required, the party chiefs should submit them to the supervisor for review or reorganizing before forwarding to headquarters, for he is in the best position to present the status of the project as a whole, and may be able to supply a few comments that will make the reports more comprehensible to those who are not in direct contact with daily operations.

Figure 1 is a personnel organization chart for a comprehensive geological survey. This chart shows the lines of authority and responsibilty for all members of the crew. It is a good plan to provide the members of the crew with copies of the organization chart with pertinent annotations in order to acquaint them with the reasons for certain procedures which otherwise might be construed as bothersome routine without real purpose. When a large number of men comprises the crew there is always some danger of confusion in handling important information and communications. Tables and charts aid materially in reducing possibilities of misunderstanding.

17. Scheduling Field Work

All field projects are limited in one way or another by various conditions, such as costs, length of field season, background of personnel, number of men available, and so on. Therefore, it is advisable in the early planning stages to determine as closely as possible just what the limiting factors are, and then to work out schedules and specifications that take them fully into account. One must not compromise primary objectives, but rather, find means of circumventing apparent limitations which at first seem to thwart attainment of the objectives. For instance, if the training and experience of the field men are inadequate for performing "standard" procedures, select or devise methods that will be within the grasp of the men, yet will accomplish the main purposes of the survey.

The process of scheduling consists of a series of estimates and approximations. Experience in field work and knowledge of the country in which the survey is to be made play an important part in the accuracy of estimating the many variables that must be evaluated. But equally important is the means by which estimations are attained. Projects involving many operations must be broken down into the component parts. Each task performed, each line surveyed, or each section measured is evaluated separately, and from these analyses the overall schedule for the season's work is derived. The scheduling of work is most important when *time* is the principal limiting factor; but it is a worthwhile phase of any extensive project. Following paragraphs briefly describe a

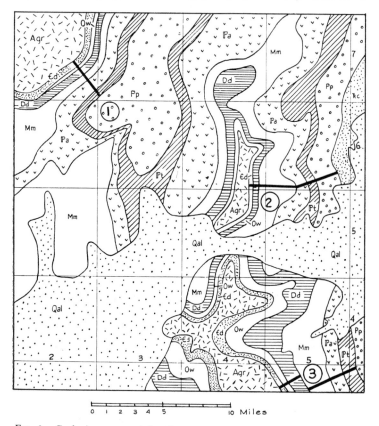

Fig. 2. Geologic map used for the purpose of locating and estimating the lengths of traverses needed in measuring stratigraphic sections.

method of scheduling a stratigraphic project where the length of the field season is a primary limiting factor.

Figure 2 is a portion of a standard U.S. Geological Survey geologic map on a scale of 1:500,000 on which are plotted the locations of stratigraphic sections. Corresponding numbers appear in the table where various physical and geologic conditions are shown.

Data Used in Scheduling Field Project

Section	Location	Maximum Difference in Elevation	Number of Samples	Average Rate of Dip	Length of Traverse	Estimated Thickness	Party-Days
1	7N,2E	100 Ft.	295	$10°$	3.2 mi.	2950 Ft.	5.5
2	6N,5E	150	303	$5°$	6.5	3030	
3	4N,4E	100	234	$5°$	5.1	2340	
Totals			832		14.8	8320	

NOTE: Compute the party-days required for sections 2 and 3.

Approximate lengths of traverses are scaled on the geologic map, which is also used for selecting areas in which sections are to be measured. Estimates of the rates of dip are obtained from published reports and study of air photographs. The length of time required to complete the measuring and sampling of the sections is stated in party-days, a party consisting of a geologist and an assistant who operates the plane table. Similar tables may be made for various phases of the work, and the total time required for the project is determined from the tables.

In estimating the time required to complete a given project, actual timing of operations over a period of a few days provides the best data. Experience in similar work and a general knowledge of the country and geology are important. Much can be learned by reviewing the records of other projects and compiling the amount of work done and the number of man-days required.

Referring again to the figure and table cited earlier: The length of traverse needed for Section 1 is about 3.2 miles (scaled on the geological map). The scale of the plane table sheet is to be 200 feet to the inch, and the backsight method is to be employed. The terrain is open and topographic relief is low. Lengths of sights are limited to 600 feet in order to maintain an accuracy of two feet in stadia distances. Instrument stations must be located near outcrops so the instrumentman can help in sampling the rocks. Stadia rod points are to be located about 100 feet apart across the section. Thus, there will be approximately 10 instrument stations and 50 rod stations per mile. Under the conditions stated the average time required to establish an instrument station is about 12 minutes, or 2 hours per mile of traverse. Side shots average about 3 minutes, or $2\frac{1}{2}$ hours per mile. The total time spent in instrumental observations and plotting on the plane table sheet is $4\frac{1}{2}$ hours per mile. Where differences in elevation are large, additional time for traveling from station to station, determining horizontal distances, and computation of difference in elevation must be taken into account. If the dips average 10 degrees, the thickness of section traversed in one mile is about 920 feet. The composite sample interval (see Chapter VII) is to be 10 feet; therefore, 92 samples will be collected and labeled for each mile of traverse. Collecting, labeling, and recording descriptions averages about 5 minutes per sample, or 8 hours per mile (920 feet of section).

It is difficult to estimate the time that will be spent in determining dips and strikes and the various small tasks associated with field work, but normally it would be in the order of one hour.

It is evident that a two-man party requires from 13 to 15 hours per mile to measure and sample a section under the conditions described in the preceding paragraphs. Stated in other terms, this amounts to 3380 feet of traverse or 600 feet (thickness) of strata per day. Even under most favorable conditions of weather and terrain, a certain amount of time is lost because of unavoidable circumstances. Experience has shown that approximately 10 percent should be added to the time of most projects, which, in the example, reduces the effective results to approximately 3050 feet of traverse or 540 feet of section per day.

Applying the methods briefly outlined, a large oil company scheduled a summer's work for four plane table stratigraphic parties in Montana, Wyoming, Colorado, and Arizona. All sections except one were completed as scheduled, and only one party was as much as one week off schedule during the entire season. Because of the impossibility of knowing beforehand the precise conditions that would be encountered in the field, all parties at various times were somewhat behind or ahead of the predicted stage of the project, but the estimated average for the season could hardly have been more accurate.

Although a stratigraphic project is used here as an example to illustrate the method of breaking down a project into its component operations for the purpose of estimating total time requirements, the method is by no means limited to such ventures. The method of break-down can be applied to any extensive field operation, though details will differ according as the conditions, technical and otherwise, vary from the given example.

Scheduling is an important step in any extensive project. Much commercial work is done by consultants on a contract basis. It would be difficult for either the contractor or the company who employs him to arrive at an equitable rate of payment if it were not possible to estimate with reasonable accuracy the number of days or weeks required to complete a project. When field parties must work far from a base of supplies, the materials, such as sample bags, and provisions needed for a number of weeks in the field have to be gauged with considerable accuracy. When a project has been broken down into the various elements and carefully scheduled, the parties in the field can better judge their own progress. Likewise, the supervisor can quickly recognize persistent defections in any of the parties in time to take remedial action before delays in progress jeopardize the project. If the progress of a party falls below average, an examination of each phase of the work in comparison with the schedule break-down may soon reveal the source of the trouble and thus permit corrective measures to be taken in a direct way.

18. Assignment of Areas

Field parties should be assigned areas, stratigraphic sections, or specialized phases of work according to (1) equitable division of work, (2) efficient distribution of the mapping parties, (3) the relative experience or competency of the field men, and (4) the relative dependency of one operation on another. Division of work often depends largely on the estimates of man-days or party-days required to complete certain portions of the project. By using the time schedule, assignments can be made so that completion of areas or phases of the project will be timed to the best advantage. For example, horizontal and vertical control must be timed to stay well in advance of the detailing. Where it is necessary for all parties to operate from the same base camp, distances to remote sectors must be taken into consideration, for the time needed to go to and from the map area may be a significant portion of the day. The field supervisor commonly assumes a portion of the map work; therefore, the parties should be distributed so that communication can be maintained without undue burden on the supervisor.

The primary control for many surveys consists of transit triangulation and traverse, plane table triangulation, and level lines. Detailing should not begin until the primary control has been tied in and, if necessary, adjusted. Early in the season the men destined to do the detailing may be used to advantage in reconnaissance work or to help in setting up the primary control. As the control is completed and adjusted in certain sectors, the detailing parties are organized and started on the mapping work. This procedure is advantageous to the supervisor in that he can devote more personal guidance to each party in the initial stages of the work.

Figure 3 is a portion of a "bar" graph which shows the scheduling of three field parties over a period of three months. Rates of progress are determined by methods described earlier and the bars are drawn on the basis of expected progress. With such

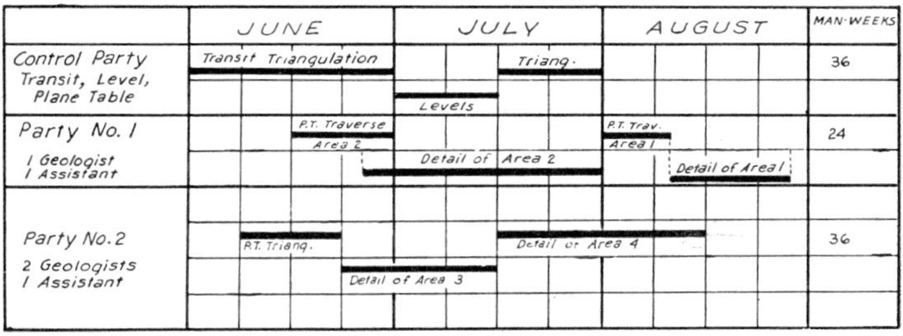

	JUNE			JULY			AUGUST			MAN-WEEKS
Control Party Transit, Level, Plane Table	Transit Triangulation				Triang.					36
				Levels						
Party No. I 1 Geologist 1 Assistant		P.T. Traverse Area 2			Detail of Area 2		P.T. Trav. Area I	Detail of Area I		24
Party No. 2 2 Geologists 1 Assistant	P.T. Triang.		Detail of Area 3			Detail of Area 4				36

Fig. 3. A form of bar graph used in scheduling and programming the work of a three-party survey. Notice that the detail work of Party Number 1 is begun before all traversing is completed.

a graph, the supervisor and chiefs of parties can better appreciate the interdependency of the field units and departments of the work. By referring to the chart periodically each can follow progress of the work in relation to the original plan. If one party consistently falls behind the predicted rate of progress while another is constantly ahead of schedule, minor shifts in personnel may bring about the desired production.

19. Progress Reports

The field supervisor and all party chiefs may be required to submit progress reports or letters at intervals of one or two weeks or one month. Generally, such reports are irksome to the field men, who are directly responsible for and interested in the details of day-to-day field problems. Nevertheless, progress letters are an essential part of large projects, and the field man must prepare them with the same care and accuracy that he employs in the conduct of technical work, for the overall direction of the project may be guided primarily on reports from the field. Periodic reports are very helpful to the man who prepares them. They force the recording of observed facts and interpretations of geologic phenomena at frequent intervals. When interim reports are not required, conclusions regarding the geology of the area may be postponed until the end of the season after all the field work is completed. Often, it is only then discovered that certain data should have been obtained, but the discovery comes too late for

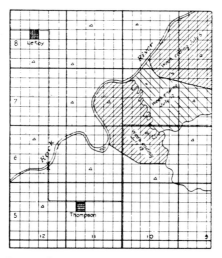

FIG. 4. Small scale index map indicating weekly progress of the detailed mapping. Such maps are submitted to the supervisor in periodic progress reports.

the necessary additional field work. If, on the other hand, the work must be reviewed each week the absence of critical data soon becomes apparent. Also, ideas on the geology evolve little-by-little at a time when the geologist is in a position to substantiate or abandon them on the basis of further observations of field conditions.

Progress letters are made much easier for both the man in the field and the directors of the project if a standardized form can be used. The forms for the letter or report can be printed by mimeograph or multigraph. The headings for tabulated data should be determined by the type of work being done. When periodic reports are received from a number of field units, the task of tabulation or compilation of results in the office is greatly simplified if certain classes of information appear in the same order on all the reports.

Progress on general mapping projects, such as areal geology, structural geology, or topography can best be shown on a small-scale base map. These maps should be letter-size ($8\frac{1}{2} \times 11$ inches) for convenience in filing and mailing. Figure 4 is such a base on which is shown the weekly progress of a general geologic survey. From these progress maps it is a simple matter for those in the office to chart the course of the work. The field man can keep carbon copies of all maps and reports submitted, thus avoiding lengthy descriptions in correspondence concerned with problems of the work or modifications of original plans.

20. Final Reports

At the end of the field season it may be necessary or desirable to prepare a comprehensive and detailed report on the summer's work. Much of the preparatory work can be done toward the end of the season while the field work is still in progress. A file of weekly or semimonthly letters is invaluable in preparing the final report.

The style of the report is usually determined by the company or organization sponsoring the project. In almost any circumstance, however, an outline should be made before actual writing of the report is begun. Main topics, such as topography, stratigraphy, and structure, are listed first. Under each of the main topics are subdivisions, as for example, under the main section of stratigraphy would be regional aspects, local peculiarities, formational relationships, lithologies, and other features related to the subject. It is a good plan to construct an outline for preparing the report even though the topics listed are not retained as headings in the report, for outlining of subject matter forces one to organize the material collected throughout the field season. The preparation of a report tends to develop ideas and concepts concerning the map area. When all the data are reviewed in detail, certain relationships may become apparent, because it is only at the end of the season that the geology can be studied in its entirety. The preparation of reports of one kind or another is a part of the field man's job, and the manner in which he presents the season's work reflects his awareness of the importance of organization. A poorly organized and carelessly written report suggests poorly organized field work. The report is the vehicle by which the field man can express his grasp of geological concepts and his ability to visualize an entire three-dimensional segment of the sedimentary column revealed only in scattered outcrops.

CHAPTER III

Living and Working Out of Doors

21. Introduction

Field geology, as the term implies, is an outdoor exploratory occupation, often requiring a mode of living quite foreign to the training and habits of most graduates from colleges of geology. Commonly, the greatest deterrent to progress in the field is, not lack of geological preparation but, rather, the strangeness of the environment in which the geologist must work. Sometimes the intellectual attributes of a man are of little moment in appraising field situations and making decisions that are concerned with the comfort, well-being, or safety of himself and others in the field party. When reviewing the qualifications of men in preparation for field assignments, one should carefully examine certain qualities in the individual which may have no direct relation to technical ability. The thoroughness of such an inquiry should be gauged by the nature of the assignment; that is, means of travel, climate of the region, remoteness from civilization, type of terrain, speed of outside communication, and so forth.

Of primary importance in the selection of men for field (especially camp) assignments is the mental attitude of the candidate toward life in the field. Although field assignments are attractive to most novice geologists, they are abhorrent to others. One who is psychologically unsuited to living and working under the variable conditions encountered in the field may not perform as effectively as one who is somewhat less skilled technically, but more adaptable to the inconveniences or discomforts of outdoor life.

Camp life poses many problems, not least of which is the encouragement and maintenance of congeniality among members of the field party. No group hampered by conflicts of personalities or temperaments can operate effectively. Of necessity, camp life is intimately communal. Men must work, eat, and often sleep together for many weeks or months. Minor differences in personal traits and professional opinions become greatly exaggerated as a result of constant close associations, and sometimes tolerance in these matters deteriorates and is gradually replaced by resentment or belligerency. In order for a camping project to succeed, continual effort must be made to reduce friction among members of the party.

Camp life in the "back country" can be comfortable and enjoyable, or it can be a series of hardships and deprivations. Certainly a man who is reasonably comfortable and adequately nourished is more effective in his work than one who is not. Critical studies of the causes of failure of a number of noted expeditions have shown the principal one to have been inadequate nourishment. Because of food shortage or poorly balanced diets, members of the expeditions became too lethargic or weak to do a full day's work, or they became the victims of various illnesses and disease, thus contributing directly to eventual failure of the project. Aside from any sympathetic motive, it is simply in good administrative judgment to plan camping assignments with a view to keeping the morale and physical and mental conditions of the men at high level.

PART I. TEMPERATE AND ARID REGIONS

22. General Remarks

Within the continental United States conditions obtaining during the different seasons at various latitudes and elevations nearly duplicate for short periods those found anywhere in the world. In the Rocky Mountains, Sierra Nevadas, and in northernmost latitudes winter temperatures may go below -50 degrees Fahrenheit—comparable to the intense cold of Arctic regions. In the canyon and desert country of the Southwest, summer temperatures exceed 125 degrees in the shade, and are greatly higher under the direct rays of the sun where the geological work must be done. The relative humidity of the atmosphere is often very near zero percent. These conditions are similar to those on the great desert regions of Africa, Arabia, and elsewhere. The swamplands of the Gulf Coastal areas, with temperatures and relative humidities near 100, are quite similar to tropical and subtropical regions the world over.

In some respects, the middle latitudes contain more dangers for the explorer than the extreme latitudes, because of daily and seasonal variations, which become less pronounced near the equator and the Arctic. Occasionally, the temperatures in mountain regions range from 50 to -25 degrees within a 24-hour period. Similarly, a shift in the direction of the wind may cause a temperature drop of 40 degrees within an hour. Such radical variations are often disastrous to one who has gone into the field inadequately prepared.

23. Preparations for Camping

Generally speaking, there are two types of camps; one is the semipermanent kind where parties may stay for periods of several weeks or an entire field season; the other, sometimes called a "fly camp" is occupied only from one night to two or three weeks, at which time the camper returns to the base of supplies. It is the temporary or "fly" camp with which the following discussions are primarily concerned, though both types are considered.

The first step in preparation for a camping project is to obtain detailed information directly from persons or agencies familiar with the region. When making such inquiries, it is well to prepare a list of topics beforehand so that important information will not be omitted. The following brief outline suggests certain categories generally considered important, though much variation would be apparent in different regions.

Character of terrain (plains, mountains, canyons, etc.):
    Extremes of elevation, vegetation, water supply, wood, trails and roads, natural shelter, etc.
Population density:
    Villages, farms, and general degree of isolation; local supply of camp necessities; availability of guides, horses, etc.
Fish and Game (for camp use):
    Game laws, permits, licenses; reliability of this source of food; methods of temporary preservation of meats; best types of tackle and calibers of firearms.
Medical facilities:
    Locations, completeness of facilities, such as staffed hospitals, nursing services, and so forth; distances and routes to these points from various parts of the map area.
Venomous and disease-carrying pests:
    Means of protection, innoculations, etc.
Character of climate:
    Dates of seasons and characteristic seasonal weather, including extreme temperature range and normal precipitation, normal daytime and nighttime temperature range for duration of the project.
Clothing requirements, including beds, temporary shelter, etc.

With a written outline similar to the foregoing many needs will be provided for in advance. When specific information is received detailed check lists pertaining to each category should be made in order to insure the procurement of all necessary items.

24. Arid or Desert Regions

Within the United States the only extensive desert regions are in the West and Southwest. Much of this region is also characterized by extremely rugged canyon and mountainous terrain. Remote areas can be worked only from camps, because of the great distances from towns or ranches. Vast areas contain no habitation, no roads or wagon trails, and little or no water on the surface of the ground. Geologic work in such regions is hazardous even for experienced men; it is doubly so for the neophyte. One must not take long chances in this type of country, for the price of failure may well be his life.

25. Water Supply

In desert country the most important matter is a reliable supply of potable water. This is also the principal factor in selecting the site for a camp. In the Southwest many of the canyons which contain permanent streams are rimmed with high cliffs, and routes of descent, even by foot, may be tens of miles apart. Springs, seeps, and natural cisterns exist above the canyon rims, but in some (rare) cases the water is corrosive, due to large concentrations of various dissolved salts; therefore, it is necessary to ascertain that the water is potable, though somewhat brackish, before setting up a camp. Often the only solution to the problem of water supply is to haul it to the campsite in cans or steel drums.

In some areas it may be necessary to create a small water supply by opening existing seeps or digging shallow wells. When searching for the most likely sites for near-surface water, the following criteria are helpful.

DIRECT INDICATIONS

Moist ground along drainage courses in desert country is an indication of a water-bearing sand near the surface. Water can often be found only a few feet below the surface in intermittent stream channels at a low spot near the outside of a bend, as shown in Fig. 5. Water may, or may not, appear immediately upon penetrating the sand. If the sand appears to be increasingly wet with depth, dig until an impervious layer is reached, such as bedrock or a layer of clay. Clean out the hole and place a perforated can deep into the sand. A gallon preserve or fruit can with small nail holes one inch apart over the sides and bottom is very good

for the purpose. Accumulated water can then be dipped out
without roiling.

Seepages sometimes occur in porous strata of the bedrock along
stream courses. If there is free water on the surface of the rock,

Fig. 5. Locations in a dry stream bed where
subsurface water may be found by digging. The
slope of the stream bed is toward the foreground.

a moderate supply of water may be obtained with a little work.
First, find the fracture, joint, or lamina from which the water
issues. With a hand pick or chisel, chip away the surface of the
rock, which may be more completely cemented than the subsurface. Cut grooves to channel the seepage into one stream. From a
piece of sheet metal (e.g. a tinned can) fashion a small trough and
place it so that the water flows directly into a vessel. Water seeping only one drop at a time does not appear to be a significant
flow, yet water *dripping* at a moderate rate will yield 10 to 20
gallons every 24 hours. In other words, a dripping seepage properly collected will supply the needs for two or three men in camp.

ANOMALOUS VEGETATION

Most deserts support a wide variety of plants, grasses, and
scrubby trees that are well adjusted to the dry environment. The
local profusion of such vegetation does not necessarily reflect
recoverable subsurface water. Certain types of plants obtain suffi-

cient water through shallow, but very extensive root systems; others, through tap roots which may extend to depths greater than 50 feet. Occasionally, certain forms of plant life, such as cottonwood trees, which require more water than is generally found in the desert environment, do occur locally. The appearance of these forms of plant life is almost a certain sign of a near-surface water supply.

ANIMAL SIGNS

Wild animals have become adapted to desert conditions so that they may go for two or three days on only the water obtained from plants and dew-covered grass. However, if a pool exists in the vicinity, animals will visit it once or twice a day and in doing so will tend to form distinct trails. Such trails may be followed directly to a watering hole. Birds need water more frequently than do many kinds of animals. A congregation of more than a usual number of birds may indicate a nearby pool or a small seepage.

It may be as important as life itself for one exploring desert regions to know and heed certain facts regarding the dangers of water shortage, especially when combined with high temperature and physical exertion. The U.S. Air Force has conducted much research into the means of survival under various climatic conditions. This research resulted in fundamental changes in old ideas concerning the hazards and safety measures of desert travel, as stated in some of the following articles.

26. Precautions

Most of the dangers of desert work in summertime can be avoided by strict adherence to a few rules.

(1) Do not go alone far into the desert (or any other wilderness country). Your companion should be one familiar with the country; but even another "stranger" may stand between you and a dangerous situation, such as a disabling accident, heat exhaustion, and the like. This admonition cannot be too strongly stressed.

(2) If available, *always* take a map or air photos of the area, and locate yourself frequently in regard to landmarks and corresponding map points. Stop occasionally and study the landscape while facing *toward* the camp; for this is the view that will be seen on the return trip. When working a circuit from the base camp, watch the changing *relative* positions of landmarks as viewed from different points.

(3) Check compass bearings toward camp from time to time when not tracing your course on a map or photo. If the return trip is made after dark, landmarks may not be recognizable. *When you are lost in desert or canyon country, you are in serious trouble.* If you should become lost, turn around and follow your own tracks back to some point from which you can reorient yourself, or if necessary, backtrack to camp even though the way is longer.

(4) Keep in mind the fact that it is as far *back* to camp as it is out to an objective point in the desert, and your physical reserve diminishes with each passing hour. When possible, plan the day's walk so that the return trip is begun early in the afternoon.

(5) When undertaking a full day's walk during hot weather, always carry a canteen of not less than two-quart capacity. As will be shown later, the distance you can travel afoot in hot desert weather is determined by the amount of water you drink.

(6) The amount of water required by the body is dependent on the amount lost by perspiration. The rate of loss is controlled by the temperature of the air and the heat developed in the body by exertion. When one is walking in high temperatures the loss is greater than it would be if one were at rest. Therefore, if the water supply is small and the distance to be travelled is long, it is better to walk at night and rest in the shade during the heat of the day.

(7) If work is being done by any motor vehicle, a large can of water should be carried at all times; for slow cross-country travel is likely to cause the water to boil out of radiators. All such vehicles are subject to mechanical failure, and in such an

event, it may be necessary to strike out afoot for camp or some nearer point where help can be obtained. For this reason, a large canteen for every person in the car is an essential piece of equipment.

(8) Physical efficiency is governed by the "water balance" of the body. This balance can be restored or maintained by drinking much water while in camp. It has been proved that the sensation of thirst is not a reliable criterion of water deficiency. The safest course is to drink *more* water than the quenching of thirst alone demands. This fact should be kept in mind before leaving camp on a long trek or before abandoning a vehicle in the desert.

(9) Contrary to old beliefs, it is now known that strict rationing of a short water supply is the wrong procedure. Except for lessening the anguish of intense thirst, water taken in very small quantities is essentially wasted. The Air Force advises desert personnel to "ration your sweat, not your water." Move slowly with as little exertion as possible.

(10) Do not take chances in the desert in the hot part of the summer. When possible let others know where you will be working. If you get into trouble and fail to return, searchers can confine their efforts to a specific area, and thus reach you more quickly.

27. Desert Winters

The foregoing discussions pertain to hot summer weather when the greatest danger or discomfort derives from shortage of water. Deserts in the middle latitudes, such as in Utah and northern Arizona are subject to intense cold during winter months. The scarcity of water is often alleviated in some deserts by moderately heavy snows, but often there is no precipitation even though the temperatures are very low.

In very cold weather, the primary problem may be shelter and fuel, for water requirements are not so pressing as in summer. Camping in cold climates is discussed farther on. Most phases discussed apply also to desert regions.

28. Preservation of Foods

Because of the extreme dryness of desert air, bacteria which cause organic matter to decompose are very scarce. For this reason it is not difficult to prevent spoilage of ordinary foods to the extent that they become unfit for use. However, any food which contains free liquids, such as bread, vegetables, fruits, and meats will rapidly dehydrate. Dehydration does not materially affect the nutritional properties of most foods, though it does make them less palatable. Jars and cans with tight covers will prevent excessive drying.

Certain foods deteriorate rapidly if kept at prevailing summer temperatures. Where large camps are established with motor communications gas or kerosene types of refrigerators can be operated conveniently and economically. If such conveniences are not available, an effective cooler can be built with a few common materials, as shown in Fig. 6. The cooler should be set in the shade but out in the open where breezes can pass through the moist burlap. The open framework is covered with window screen.

FIG. 6. Screened air cooler. A. Showing open drop-door and sand-covered roof. B. Method of placing wet burlap in pan of water to cool air inside.

A simpler type of cooler can be made by burying an open-end box in a shady bank. A trench is dug into the bank, or if the bank is nearly vertical, a cave-like hole large enough to accommodate the box may be easier. The outer open end of the box is covered with a tight-fitting screen door to keep small animals and insects away from the food, as shown in Fig. 7. If sufficient water is available, saturate the soil in and above the hole or trench. Hang saturated soft burlap over the front of the cave with the lower or side edges resting in pans of water.

The box may be removed morning and evening to permit rewetting of the walls of the cave. A brush lean-to considerably larger than the cave, set directly above, will aid greatly in reducing the ground temperature if the cave is located where the sun can beat down upon it for a number of hours a day.

FIG. 7. Cave cooler used to preserve foods in hot regions. Burlap curtain is opened at night, closed during the day. The cave should face in the direction of least direct sunshine.

Meat can be kept for a surprising length of time in only a moderately cool place, provided (1) it has not previously been processed in cold storage, (2) it *is* exposed to the circulation of fresh air, and (3) a dry, skin-like crust is permitted to form over the entire surface. This leathery skin is the result of dehydration; the meat is not spoiled; but it is well to trim the crust away before cooking the meat. Where nights are reasonably cool, it is common practice among ranchers of the "Canyon Country" of western United States to hang meat out in the open air at night and in the early morning to wrap it in several layers of cool canvas, such as a tarpaulin, and then lay it on the ground in the coolest place available.

Uncooked vegetables and certain kinds of fruits may be kept from several days to two or three weeks if treated in the following manner: (1) wrap the individual plants or fruit (tomatoes, apples, etc.) in waxed paper or place in a soft plastic bag; (2) over the waxed paper (or plastic) wrap several layers of water-saturated newspaper or paper towelling; (3) lay the wrapped fruit in a dampened cooler and spread several layers of wet newspaper or wet burlap over the entire stack. Dampen the cover at least once a day and examine the contents of the packages to ascertain that no spoilage is occurring.

It is important to conserve all foods when the camp is far from a base of supplies. This necessitates *frequent* checking. Many fruits and vegetables can be saved by cooking when they have become over-ripe or have lost their firmness due to dehydration in the dry desert air. The skins on citrus fruits become as dry and hard as wood, but the inside will remain juicy and fresh for weeks.

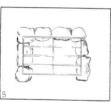

FIG. 8. Stone firebox. A. The U-shaped stone box, facing into prevailing wind. B. An iron grill placed on the box to support cooking vessels. Where stones are not available, the grill may be placed over a small fire pit.

29. Cooking in Camp

Field geologists and engineers often must prepare their own meals. Very good meals can be prepared with a minimum of effort if procedures are properly organized and the physical set-up is made convenient.

THE FIREPLACE

It is worth the effort to build a simple fireplace with stones even for the preparation of one meal. Figure 8A illustrates a box-type fireplace that can be built in 5 to 10 minutes. The open end of the box should face into the prevailing wind. A grill is almost indispensable in camp cooking. The grill is laid on the top of the stone fireplace, as shown in Fig. 8B.

The inexperienced camper usually builds a fire that is too large. The best procedure where a fireplace is used and wood is plentiful is to remove the grill and start the fire in the open stone box. Lay on moderately large pieces of wood (2 to 4 inches in diameter) and let this burn down briskly until a deep bed of live coals accumulate. Replace the grill and cook over the coals, which will produce sufficient heat with little or no annoying smoke. It may be necessary to add a few small dry sticks occasionally. When wood is scarce, *do not start the fire* until preparations for cooking are complete. Build a *small fire* and begin cooking immediately over the flames.

Several brands of light two-burner gasoline stoves have proved their worth through many years of use. They are economical of fuel and are compact and light; hence they are ideal for camping where supplies do not have to be packed in afoot or where wood is scarce.

Cooking Utensils

Only a few pertinent suggestions need be made regarding camp cooking ware. Frying pans should have long handles so that they extend back from the fire. The old-fashioned pressed steel "spider" is best. Wooden, horn, or plastic handles on any cooking vessel are sure to be damaged or lost to flames. Kettles and pots with bails are better than those with "ear-type" handles. Similarly, the coffee pot should have a bail. The Dutch oven is a utensil that has been used in this country for generations and probably has been in use in various parts of the world for centuries. The Dutch oven is a cast iron kettle, with a rounded bottom, some types having three small legs, and a flat recessed lid, also of cast iron. Because of the heavy walls and bottom the degree of heat within the kettle is quite uniform, even with considerable variation in the intensity of the camp fire. Biscuits, bread, and certain pastries can be baked satisfactorily in the following way.

(1) Build a rather large fire with hardwood (scrub oak, ironwood, etc.) or green softwoods to obtain a quantity of large live coals.

(2) Put the dough in a small, thin metal pan (or several small pans) and set this in the Dutch oven.

(3) Put the lid on the Dutch oven, set it on the bed of embers, and heap live embers on the lid. Before removing the lid, rake off the embers and ashes and fan or blow away the fine ashes.

Pot roasts with vegetables are placed directly in the Dutch oven.

Every camping outfit should include several rolls of aluminum foil. It has many uses around a camp, including the construction of cooking vessels, which are discarded after serving their purpose.

(1) Potatoes may be greased with bacon fat, rolled completely in foil, and laid in a bed of embers to bake.

(2) The foil can be pressed into a frying pan or pot as a close-fitting lining so that food does not come in contact with the pan. When the food is removed the lining is lifted out, leaving the supporting vessel clean. This procedure not only eliminates the need for washing the pan, but also conserves water, which may be a very important consideration in desert camps.

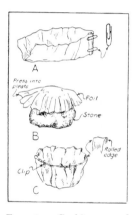

FIG. 9. Cooking vessel made from aluminum foil. A. Boat-shaped, rolled and clipped at ends. B. Pleated and formed over rock. C. Edge rolled and clipped over a wire rim.

(3) Serviceable utensils can be made from aluminum foil alone, and for this reason it is especially useful for "fly" camps where equipment and supplies for a few days must be back-packed. When employed in this way, a few paper clips may be used effectively to hold the folded foil together, as indicated in Fig. 9. Inasmuch as the foil is easily punctured, care should be taken that the vessel is not set upon protruding sticks or twigs in the fire. When a grill is not used, the fire should be allowed to burn down to a bed of embers before the foil container is placed upon it. Food should be dipped out of foil utensils before they are removed from the fire, otherwise there is danger of the thin material tearing and thereby losing the contents.

30. Desert Shelter

Although one should foresee the need for protection against the rare, but occasionally violent, thunderstorms that occur in the desert, the most pressing need in the summer is shelter from the burning sun. Canvas tents fulfill the former requirement, but they are exceedingly hot when set up under the sun unless a tent fly is used. A fly is a plain rectangle of canvas with eyelets and tie ropes along two opposing sides. The fly is stretched across the ridgepole of the tent but at a somewhat flatter slope than that of the tent roof. This arrangement permits air to circulate between the two. The object of the fly is to cast a shadow across the roof of the tent.

An effective sun shelter can be erected quickly and easily from a long sheet of canvas, as shown in Fig. 10. The canvas may be folded back over a pole or a taut rope or wire. Anything that will cast a shadow over the top of the tent will aid materially in reducing the inside temperature. Light-weight wire netting ("chicken wire") may be stretched over

Fig. 10. Sun shelter made by stretching canvas over wire line. Space between the two layers helps to "break" the sun's rays.

a pole framework as a base upon which small twigs, grass, or brush is strewn in sufficient depth to cast a moderately dense shade.

Tents are cooler if the lower edges are tied up so that air can circulate across the floor.

31. Protection from Sun Rays

Summertime work in the desert can be uncomfortable or even hazardous unless precautions against over-exposure to direct rays of the sun are taken. Because of the sparseness of vegetation in desert regions, the sun's rays are reflected to a high degree from the surface of the ground, rocks, and cliffs, and for this reason one can acquire a painful burn without exposure to *direct* rays of the sun. So-called "windburn" is nothing more than sunburn from reflected rays, and it matters little whether the wind is blowing or not. It is not uncommon for one to suffer rather severe sunburn while riding all day in a car where *direct* sun rays cannot fall. If one is especially vulnerable to sunburn, precautions should be taken before the burn occurs.

Even though a sensation of coolness may result from exposing the body to the dry desert air, it has been proved much safer to wear light, loose clothing over the entire body. The Arabs' robe and burnoose are admirably suited to the desert environment, and clothing which simulates theirs is best. It is dangerous to work throughout the day under the hot sun without the protection of some sort of head covering, such as a sun helmet or light felt or straw hat. Sunstroke is caused by excessive heat on the head (not to be confused with heat exhaustion, which is caused by excessive loss of body fluids). A cool and generally effective headgear can be made from a piece of white muslin or broadcloth about 30 inches square, as illustrated in Fig. 11. Fold one edge over two

FIG. 11. Headgear made from a square of cloth. The edge is first rolled and then brought about the head and tied loosely.

or three times to make a band about 2 inches wide. Next, lay the open cloth over the head with the middle of the band across the forehead. Tie the two ends of the "band" over the cloth at the back of the head. Leave the cloth quite loose over the top of the head and arrange the edges below the band so that the neck and ears are protected from the sun. This type of headgear gives no protection to the face, eyes or forehead.

Brilliant desert sunlight is likely to be harmful to the eyes. Sun glasses should be worn when working over barren wastelands where there is much reflection of the intense light. These reflected rays, which cause sunburn, are especially dangerous for one may not be aware of their power until after some damage has been done to the retinas of the eyes. In lieu of ordinary sun glasses, several devices can be improvised from materials readily available.

Soft charcoal (made by burning a cork bottle stopper) applied beneath the eyes on the cheek bones greatly reduces the glare of reflected sunlight. Similarly, a strip of dark cloth passing over the bridge of the nose and tied at the back of the neck will afford considerable protection from glare.

A sun shield used by the Eskimos consists of a 2- by 5-inch strip of whalebone with narrow horizontal slots for peep holes. A similar shield can be made from any thin flexible material, such as cardboard. The construction of a slotted shield is shown in Fig. 12.

Fig. 12. Sunshield made by cutting narrow peep-hole slots in thin cardboard.

The devices described are serviceable in emergencies, but they are only poor substitutes for good sun glasses. Be sure to include sunglasses in the equipment for any desert assignment.

32. Protection from Ground Heat

Sand and rocks exposed to the intense rays of the sun become extremely hot and the heat is transmitted to anything in contact with the ground. When motor vehicles are used, the pressure in the tires must be checked from time to time throughout the day, for pressures may quickly build up to the danger point. It should be stressed that the tires must be checked during the hot part of the day, not just in the morning before going into the field.

When the work necessitates much walking, it is of paramount importance to pay particular attention to foot gear and to the care of the feet. Although the specific type of boot or shoe is largely a matter of personal preference, certain substantiated generalities should be heeded. The sole of the boot should be thick in order to provide greater protection from the hot ground. Leather is a better insulator than composition. Cloth or plastic fabric uppers are cool and generally serviceable but perforated material should be avoided because sand, dust, and certain insects (such as sand fleas) can enter the boot. A thick sock or two pairs of socks provide further insulation from the hot ground. Large metal hobnails conduct heat into the boot; it is better to use a boot having a cleat-type of outer sole and avoid the disadvantages of hob nails.

When working afoot in the desert your feet are constantly subjected to varying kinds and degrees of abuse. You cannot work effectively on sore feet. Keep boots in good repair, and start every day with fresh socks. Salts and acids from perspiration accumulate rapidly in socks and boots. These products attack the skin and will ultimately result in sore feet.

PART II. HIGH MOUNTAINOUS REGIONS

33. General Remarks

The following remarks are pertinent to regions in the middle or higher latitudes, such as the Rocky Mountains or Sierra Nevadas, where the seasons are sharply defined by wide variations in temperature and precipitation. Geological work is normally done during the summer months when the ground is free of snow. In early spring or early autumn, winter conditions may develop with sudden storms and catch the inexperienced camper poorly prepared for the unseasonal weather. In high portions of the Rockies and other mountains snowstorms may occur during any month of the year, though they are rare from late June to mid-August. These storms during "summer" months are of short duration and the snow quickly melts away; but they can cause considerable discomfort or hardship when one is prepared for only summer weather.

At high altitudes the summer sun may be quite hot, and this sometime leads one to believe that warm clothing or heavy blankets are unnecessary. However, the hottest days may be followed by very chilly nights, even in midsummer. When preparing for a full season's work in the mountains (from May or June to

September) clothing and bedding normally used only in winter at low elevations must be included in the equipment.

34. Location for a Camp

When selecting a site for camp the following factors should be considered.

ACCESSIBILITY

If cars are used for transportation, the camp site should be situated on or near a road or trail that can be traversed in all kinds of weather. It is somewhat disconcerting to have established a comfortable camp in dry weather only to find that it cannot be reached (or left) after a typical mountain storm. Pay particular attention to steep hills, swampy ground, and fords across normally small streams, for after a night of rain they may become impassable. It is always wise to inquire *locally* regarding the accessibility of a prospective camp site during periods of wet weather.

FUEL SUPPLY

Wood fires are commonly used in camps for cooking and as a source of heat in the chilly evenings. When the camp site is to be occupied for a period of several weeks it is well to ascertain that a supply of suitable wood is near at hand. Although wood may be hauled to the camp from some distant source, this chore should not be added to the many others connected with camp life if it can be avoided.

Dead *standing* trees are the best wood for camp fires. Wood lying on the ground is very likely to be damp even in dry weather, and damp wood produces an annoying smoke. In wet weather, moderately dry wood for fires will be found in lower dead branches of live trees. It is good practice to keep a supply of wood in a sheltered place, such as a cave or under an overhanging ledge, for starting fires in rainy weather. If no such natural shelter is available, keep a small supply of kindling wood in the tent.

WATER SUPPLY

The water in most high mountain streams is palatable and safe to drink. Nevertheless, the contemplated water supply should be checked for both quality and quantity. Determine whether there are any dwellings or stock corrals upstream from the camp site and if refuse drains into the stream. In selecting a camp site it is sometimes necessary to choose between one near a water and one near a fuel supply. Other factors being equal, select the site near water. It is much easier to haul wood than water, and storage facilities are not needed for wood.

Anyone who has had experience in camping on a very small stream or "water hole" is cognizant of the difficulty of dipping *two* successive bucketfulls of *clear* water. The surge caused by lifting out the first bucket disturbs the fine silt and mud so that the second is roily. A little work on the preparation of a water hole which reduces or eliminates this nuisance is well worthwhile. Two procedures are outlined in following paragraphs; others will become apparent according to the specific situation. These comments apply to very small brooks.

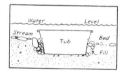

FIG. 13. Tub or pan placed in stream bed for dipping bucket and preventing roiliness.

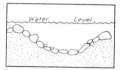

FIG. 14. Cobble-lined pit in stream bed for dipping bucket and preventing roiliness.

(1) Select a wide spot in the channel where the gradient is low and relatively free of large boulders. Dig a hole large enough to admit a galvanized tub, large bucket, wooden box, or any other large container available. Place the tub in the hole with the rim extending two to six inches above the stream bed, but below the surface of the water, as shown in Fig. 13. Fill the

space around the outside of the tub with gravel or sand. If the hole cannot be dug deep enough to sink the tub to the desired depth, punch a few holes below water level on the upstream side. Water can be dipped from the tub repeatedly without roiling. When no large container is available, dig a hole with gently sloping sides and line it with small boulders. Let the boulders extend somewhat above the stream bottom, as shown in Fig. 14.

(2) Often it is difficult to find a convenient water hole simply because of the high gradient of the stream. If the channel is narrow, perhaps the easiest way to create a pond is by damming the stream with rocks or logs and lining the dam on the upstream side with mud or sod.

TERRAIN AND THE WIND

As mentioned earlier, evenings in the high mountains may be uncomfortably chilly, even during fair weather in the middle of the summer. The chill of evening is accentuated by almost imperceptible breezes which are characteristic of mountain terrain. These light breezes generally blow up or down the valleys, depending upon whether there is a regional wind. When the air is essentially quiet, thermal currents tend to flow *down* the valley, and the coldest air is in the bottom of the valley. For this reason, the ideal place for the camp is on a terrace or bench considerably above the elevation of the stream. If regional winds are persistent in one general direction, keep this fact in mind when setting up tents or other open-end shelters. Always face the tent downwind.

EFFECTS OF TREES AND SHRUBS

Field geologists are usually not in camp during the warm hours of the day, but they are often required to work late at night on notes and maps in preparation for the next day's work in the field. Because of this fact the camp should be set up with a view to comfort in the cool or chilly evenings. All kinds of plants, but particularly the leafy types, tend to modify the temperature and humidity of the locality in which they grow in profusion. Do not be misled by the inviting coolness of a grassy grove at midday; it will be cold at night. However, a thick grove of trees is an excellent windbreak and full advantage of this fact should be taken when selecting the location for the camp. The peculiarities of mountain breezes have been discussed; set the camp on the generally leeward side of the grove, preferably in a clearing some yards away.

35. Setting up a Tent

Anyone can set up a tent after a fashion, and very likely it will remain essentially erect for a long time, so long as calm weather obtains. But tents must be set up correctly to withstand the strains of rain, high winds, or snow—any of which may occur with little warning in mountain country. A tent hastily erected in the morning may collapse upon its occupants in the midst of the confusion of a midnight squall. Set up your tent correctly in the first place, and avoid an unpleasant experience.

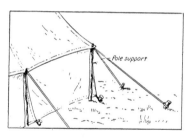

Clear the ground of sticks, weeds, small shrubs, and grass. Level off humps and hollows with a shovel. Green grass may make the interior unpleasantly damp. Bare ground well packed is the best floor.

Use long, strong stakes, and be sure that they are driven deeply. Stakes will loosen and cause the tent to sag during periods of wet weather when the ground is

Fig. 15. Staking a tent. Double corner guys support the tent against wind pressure from any direction. Short poles keep side walls taut.

soaked. Be especially careful to have solid anchors at the four corners and the guys bracing the ridge pole at the two ends. The distance between corner stakes should be somewhat greater than the length of the tent, as shown in Fig. 15.

Before staking the bottom edges, dig a small trench entirely around the tent and continue the trench from the lowest point to lower ground in order to prevent water from running into the tent in rainy weather. After the trench is prepared, set the stakes at the bottom edge. Soil should not be packed on or against the bottom edge for this will cause the canvas to rot. It is better to dig the trench a foot or two from the tent and make a ridge from the "spoil," as in Fig. 16.

Canvas and hemp ropes shrink while wet. The combination of greater tension on the ropes and a softening of the ground may cause the stakes to be pulled out. When the roof of the tent becomes quite taut during a rainstorm, the stake ropes should be slackened. Hemp or cotton tent ropes last longer and are more easily handled when wet if they are saturated with linseed oil.

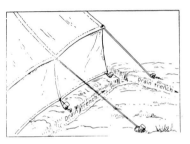

Fig. 16. Peripheral drain trenches keep inside of tent dry during heavy rains.

36. Open Fires for Heat

Fires for cooking should be small, because one must be able to reach and work with the food while it is cooking; but fires used primarily as a source of heat usually need to be somewhat larger, especially if they are to serve several persons. However, the effectiveness of a fire is greatly increased by a reflector, either natural or artificial.

The heat from a fire placed at the foot of an overhanging or vertical ledge, cliff, or bank is reflected outward. A reëntrant angle is even more effective.

If such a natural reflector is not conveniently situated, a crude stone wall can be erected in the form of a horseshoe, the fire being placed at the back side of the arc. Such a wall only two feet high will make a noticeable difference in the effectiveness of a small fire.

Logs may be used as reflectors, but, if dry, they have the unpleasant tendency to burn up. A lean-to pole reflector can be built in a short time. Green deciduous saplings, such as aspen, alder, or cottonwood are best for the purpose.

Considerable heat can be reflected into the open end of a tent from a fire located a few feet outside. Any of the constructions discussed are applicable.

PRECAUTIONS

Except in very wet weather, there is always some danger of fires getting out of hand. A responsible camper *never* permits this to happen. Keep in mind that relaxation of simple safety procedures may result in loss of equipment, loss of time, and possibly loss of life.

(1) Always clear away all woody debris and dead grass and weeds from the area *before* the fire is started.

(2) Beware of sudden gusts or shifting winds. A change in the direction of the wind may create a danger that was not apparent when the fire was started.

(3) Do not leave an unattended fire or go to bed with a fire burning, unless it is contained in some sort of noninflammable "box," such as a rock fireplace.

(4) Do not assume that a fire has burned out because there are no visible smoke or embers. A breeze may bring it to life. Drench the *entire* ash bed with water or bury it with sand.

(5) Wood smoke is irritating to the eyes. Inasmuch as mapping in direct sunlight, checking notes by lantern light, and other necessary tasks place an unusual burden on the eyes, an effort should be made to arrange the reflector or fireplace so that sufficient heat is obtained with little smoke.

37. Beds and Bedding

In high mountainous country, the temperature begins to drop in the late afternoon and continues falling until the small hours of

the morning. During clear, quiet weather the most chilling time
is from dawn until an hour or two after sunrise; for during this
time, strong cold breezes are created by unequal warming of the
air when the first rays of the sun strike across the valleys. It is
quite common at high elevations in midsummer for the temperature to drop from a high point of 85 degrees at 3:00 P.M. to 35
degrees at 3:00 A.M. Many a mountain camper has fallen asleep
in the comfort of late evening only to awaken hours before daylight thoroughly chilled. Several such nights may be endured
before the initiate finds a means of *staying* warm. A few principles, as stated below, will aid the novice in avoiding the misery
of a cold bed.

(1) When the sleeping bag or bed roll is spread on the ground,
select a place where the soil is dry. The earth may be stirred with
a pick or shovel, but do not turn up moist soil. An effective procedure used by pioneer "mountain men" (and still good) consists
in building a large fire of dry wood several hours before retiring.
Embers and ashes are then raked away and the bed is laid on
the warm, dry earth. A thin layer
of sand or fine dry soil may be
sprinkled over the firebed to prevent blackening of the bed roll.

(2) Place the head of the bed
near a windbreak, such as a large
boulder or log, so that cold
breezes cannot enter the bed at
the open end. A pillow aids greatly
in this respect. A strip of canvas, burlap, or similar material
stretched around stakes, as shown
in Fig. 17, is an effective windbreak.

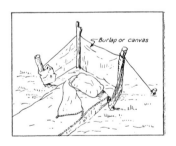

Fig. 17. Temporary wind guard
made from burlap or canvas.

(3) A sleeping bag or bed on a canvas (Army-type) cot is
colder than the same bed laid on dry ground. Be sure to insulate
the *bottom* of the bed. Cold air passing under a cot will cause the
bed to be cold. Let the bed covering hang down to the ground to
check the breeze. An air mattress provides good insulation against

cold, whether the bed is laid on a cot or on the ground.

(4) Beware of rubberized, plastic, or other watertight cot covers. Never spread such a cover directly *on* the bed in cold weather. Moisture given off by the body condenses on the under side of a tight cover, thus providing a good conductor to the cold outside air. When a waterproof cover is needed, arrange poles, ropes, or wires so that the cot cover or poncho is suspended slightly above the bed.

(5) Heavy woolen blankets are best for warm, dry beds. Cotton blankets retain moisture and thereby prevent the escape of body vapors.

(6) Whenever practicable, bedding should be hung or spread in the sunshine. A good night's rest in a fresh bed is sufficient reward for a small chore.

38. Clothing for Mountain Work

As stated earlier, clear mountain weather is characterized by warm to moderately hot days and cool to cold nights. Rainy weather is almost invariably cold anytime during the summer. Because field work in rugged country is generally strenuous, one's clothing frequently becomes damp from perspiration even in late afternoon, and this dampness may cause chilling when the sun has gone down. The rapid fall of the temperature with the setting sun also raises the relative humidity so that early dew is quite common. When selecting clothing for mountain work, these facts should be kept in mind. The following suggestions will serve as a guide to those unfamiliar with outdoor life in high country.

(1) Most mountain regions are covered with underbrush, which, in turn, is very destructive to clothing. Outer garments should be made of heavy, hard-finish cloth, such as denim or khaki. During "warm" weather, jackets of denim, poplin, or lightweight leather are most serviceable.

(2) A raincoat of tough material is an essential garment in regions where rainfall is fairly common.

(3) As for field work in other types of terrain, boots should be

of heavy leather. In rugged, rocky mountains the soles should have either a composition "tread" or steel hobnails. Hobnails are bad in cold weather when one is walking in snow, because of their high conductivity of heat from the feet. Heavy inner soles, worn inside the boots, aid in keeping the feet warm. If hobnails are removed, plug the holes with tight-fitting pegs cut from soft wood to prevent water from seeping through the soles. Greasing a boot helps to waterproof it, but oil or grease also makes a boot cold. Boots should be large enough to accommodate heavy woolen socks.

(4) Even though one is not accustomed to wearing gloves when doing field work, it is unwise to go on lengthy high-country assignments without them. The combination of dry air, intense sunlight, and wide temperature variation, causes the skin to chap and crack. Small scratches from underbrush become exceedingly sore and are slow to heal unless protected.

Any kind of glove is better than none; but because of the rough treatment they generally receive, the most serviceable are close-fitting "work" gloves made from horsehide or buckskin.

39. Miscellaneous Considerations

The only dangerous wild animals south of the Arctic in Canada and in the United States are grizzly bears and moose, and these animals are dangerous only when suddenly encountered at close quarters. One should exercise some caution in entering willow and poplar thickets in country where these animals are prevalent. Poisonous snakes do not exist above elevations of about 8000 feet or north of the central latitudes of the Canadian provinces. However, insect pests, such as mosquitoes, gnats, and a number of species of biting flies, are commonly so numerous that the air is filled with dense swarms of them, and work is impossible unless protective measures are taken. Generally speaking, mosquitoes and gnats are most prevalent in the larger valleys where stream gradients are low and grassy or swampy flats are common. This is a poor setting for a camp. Many types of voracious flies are bothersome at high altitudes.

Insect repellents, such as those used by the U.S. Army, are the most effective protection. A few yards of inexpensive mosquito netting to spread above the bed on a wire, sapling, or cord frame is the best night protection. Mountain workers often place a large square of cloth, such as a bandana handkerchief, under the hat so that the edges hang down to protect the ears and neck. Those who have attempted to operate a plane table under a distracting cloud of insects are aware of the importance of precautionary measures, and one day's experience will certainly convince the skeptic.

Large portions of the western mountains harbor wood ticks infected with Rocky Mountain spotted fever. This is a very dangerous and rapidly-developing malady. It is common practice for oil companies sending men into infected regions to provide inoculations two to three weeks prior to going into the field. Everyone should take this precaution.

Climbing at high altitudes is much more exhausting than at lower elevations. This factor should be taken into account in the planning and execution of a geologic investigation. Adjustment to high altitude work varies considerably among different individuals, but generally a rather complete adaptation is reached in a few days to a couple of weeks. Where the terrain and requirements of a project permit, it is better to begin work at the lower elevations and carry the work gradually into the higher portions of the area.

The two most serious hazards in mountain work are *physical injury* and a state of *panic* when lost in rugged terrain. The best remedy in either case is *prevention*.

As stated earlier, one should not venture far into wilderness areas alone because of the dangers of disabling accidents. If it is necessary to work alone, let others know *where* you intend to be and *when* you expect to return; then, within reasonable limits, attempt to follow the itinerary agreed upon. If you get into trouble, a search can be started early and directed toward the locality where you are working. One should recognize the fact that, regardless of his attitude toward his own safety, others' concern, effort, and time are also involved. Any member of a camping party who operates independently of the group is placing an unfair burden of responsibility on the others.

The greatest danger in being lost in the mountains is succumbing to irresponsible fear or panic. If you are lost, *do not do anything* until you have calmly appraised your situation and decided upon a sensible course of action that will get you out of trouble without causing others unnecessary anxiety or useless effort. It is not practicable here to outline the means by which one might find his way out when lost in rugged hills or dense timber; but it is important to have in mind the following facts *before* starting out alone into the hills.

(1) Danger of starvation is remote, but water is important for sustaining one's strength.

(2) The greatest immediate danger is unplanned, precipitous action.

(3) The large majority of mishaps resulting in extreme hardship or fatalities can be attributed primarily to exhaustion. It follows that this hazard can be circumvented by conservation of one's strength. Guard against fruitless expenditure of energy.

(4) Physical exhaustion prepares the way for injury by falls or exposure to cold.

(5) Travel by night or aimless wandering not only reduces one's ability to get reoriented, but greatly handicaps the efforts of searchers.

From these recognized facts, the correct course of action should be indicated. If water and shelter are available there is no need for haste. If you are so completely lost that you do not know the general direction of camp, and therefore wisely decide upon awaiting help, find a windbreak, such as a cave or ledge where you can rest at night, preferably near a ridge or prominent hill that can be seen from some distance in any direction. During the day maintain a *smoky* fire on the ridge to attract searching parties.

When preparing on expedition into remote, sparsely inhabited country, include an up-to-date manual on first aid from the American Red Cross. Read those portions applicable to local conditions so you will know what to do in an emergency. A first aid manual in camp does not help you when the site of an accident is miles away.

A responsible geologist is duty-bound to uphold the ethics of the profession and to respect the rights of others. A thoughtless or inadvertent act reflecting adversely on the profession or causing persons outside the profession inconvenience or unnecessary expense is to be deplored by all geologists. Much field geology is done in rural areas or stock range country where fences restrain sheep and cattle. Gates in these fences should be closed immediately upon passing through—not an hour or a few hours later. A few minutes interim between opening and closing a gate may permit the escape of stock and thus cost the rancher a great deal of extra time and work. Never cut the wires of a fence. In an emergency, if it is necessary to take a car across a fence between gates, pull (and save) the staples from the wires at several posts. Then press all the wires down close to the ground and staple them lightly. Drive the car over the wires, and restaple them in their correct position. It is much easier and less damaging to the fence to lower the wires where the fence passes over the crest of a hill. The property owner should be told of the event.

Whether you work for an agency of the Federal Government, a State Government, or a corporation, you have no legal right to work within the boundaries of a pasture, ranch, or farm without the permission of the landowner. Avoid misunderstanding by explaining the nature of the work to the property owner and obtaining his permission; then be sure to respect his wishes in the conduct of the work.

40. The Mountains in Winter

Generally speaking, geologic field work cannot be done in high mountainous country during winter months because of the snow cover over outcrops, the difficulty of travel, and extreme cold. In both spring and autumn seasons, snowstorms and low temperatures may alternate with seasonal warm weather for periods of a few days; hence, these are the seasons when the field geologist might get into serious trouble if he is unaware of, and inadequately prepared for, the characteristic abruptness of weather variations.

In many respects wintertime or winter weather in high mountains in the intermediate latitudes is similar to Arctic regions. During the fall and spring seasons one must always be prepared for severe storms which may occur with little forewarning. This is the time of year when days may be quite warm and nights exceedingly cold. At high altitudes the insulating effect of the atmosphere is very minor; so as soon as the sun disappears, evening cold sets in.

CHAPTER IV

Field Mapping

41. Introductory Remarks

The term "field mapping" is used here to distinguish between maps that are made almost entirely in the field and those constructed by common cartographic methods as practiced in the drafting room. The geologist is concerned primarily with the methods of mapping which he must utilize in the field. When topographic and other types of accurate base maps or air photographs are used in the field for the purposes of the geologist, only the rudiments of mapping methods need be known; but if such base maps are not available, the geologist must have a working knowledge of surveying, field map construction, and various procedures and practices that permit concurrent geologic and planimetric mapping.

The accuracy of geologic measurements and interpretations of geologic phenomena are often dependent to a considerable degree on the correct placement of outcrop data on a map. If points of geologic control are not accurately located on the map, these points do not have the same interrelationships as do the corresponding points on the ground. Therefore, any interpretations and conclusions derived by a study of the maps are bound to be in error.

The relative precision of various mapping techniques is affected by the methods and instruments employed, the care and skill in execution of field procedures, and the scale of the map. Each technique and instrument has its advantages and limitations, and very few can be condemned. Actually, it is only one's judgment in selecting an appropriate method that is subject to adverse criticism. In order to be efficient in the field, one must become familiar with many different methods of mapping, and thus be able to select those methods which best meet the needs of any given set of circumstances.

The following pages present only the fundamentals of a number of field mapping techniques—the limited space in this manual does not permit full treatment of each. Complete books are available on several of these techniques (e.g., photogrammetry and plane table surveying). Those who wish to pursue special methods in detail are advised to obtain these books. However, the outlines presented in the following pages should be sufficient for ordinary geologic field work.

42. Purposes of Geologic Mapping

Geologic maps of various types are made for either scientific or economic reasons, and it is sometimes important for the geologist to distinguish between the two and to conduct his work accordingly. When a geologist is sent into the field to define and evaluate a prospective oil structure, he should not engage in the pursuit of investigations not pertinent to the objective, even though such action might yield information of scientific value. The time spent in such scientific inquiry may be costly to the company in amounts far exceeding the expense of maintaining the survey party a few extra days in the field. In commercial work the timing of certain operations is often of vital importance and the field geologist must be cognizant of his responsibility to do whatever is necessary within the time limitations prescribed. Conversely, government or institutional projects often consider the time expended secondary to accuracy and thoroughness of the investigations. Clearly, the geologist must set up and carry out field assignments according to the primary objectives or purposes, and the methods must be selected according to accuracy, speed, or economy of operation. The most effective field work is that which leads most directly to the accomplishment of principal objectives.

43. Field Maps

As used in discussions throughout this book, the term *field map* refers to maps made for the most part in the field. In a sense, most maps could be placed in this category to the extent that they are constructed from data that have been acquired from field measurements, but a large number of these maps are principally the products of drafting room cartographic procedures and consist of compilations of preëxisting maps, which, in turn, may have been made in the field. The exploration geologist often works in regions which are poorly mapped or, perhaps, not mapped at all. In such areas the geologist must construct some sort of base upon which the geological features are plotted. These maps may range from a rough chart sketched while floating down a river in a boat to extremely accurate maps based on precise surveys.

44. Relative Quality of Geologic Maps

The quality of any type of geologic map is not necessarily measured by the accuracy with which positions and elevations of the control points have been established. There are many factors which affect the quality of the finished product, such as the frequency and distribution of outcrops, rate of dip, complexity of stratigraphy and structure, and nature of the topography. All such factors should be carefully weighed when selecting methods to be used in mapping. As a general rule, methods which insure a high degree of precision also consume more time. The greater accuracy in measurements may not be justified, especially if the geologic features are of such nature that sharp definition is difficult or impossible. For example, no advantage is gained by determining elevations to the nearest tenth of a foot in structural work where formational boundaries are gradational or otherwise indistinct. Similarly, if the strata are dipping very steeply (20 to 60 degrees), the plotted position of a control point should be in the same order of accuracy as the elevation of the point. Where beds dip at 45 degrees, an error of 10 feet in location has the same effect on a structure map as an error of 10 feet in elevation. When stratigraphic sections are measured with the plane table, it is sometimes necessary to use a large scale only for the purpose of obtaining more accurate horizontal distances on the sheet.

It would be quite impracticable to set up rules here for governing procedures in mapping projects; there are too many variables, and it is unlikely that all actual situations would be foreseen regardless of the space devoted to the subject. The quality of a geologic map is not necessarily determined by the precision of technical operations that go into its making. The ideal plan is one in which all departments of the work, including an appraisal of the outcropping rocks, are evaluated with regard to the finished product—the map. Each project should be considered on its own merits and the objectives to be attained. The key to such planning is *balance*. The mapping of a system of mines and tunnels usually employs only methods of fairly high precision and large map scales so that the plotting of points will be in the same order of accuracy as the determinations of distance and direction. In such a survey, *no* operation subject to large errors can be tolerated. On the other hand, a regional reconnaissance survey commonly employs approximate methods in all phases of the work.

In the following pages a number of common mapping methods is discussed briefly. The beginner should strive to master these methods through actual practice in the field, for it is only through practice with the instruments that one attains proficiency in the methods.

45. The Plane Table Method

The primary object in field mapping is to place lines, points, and areas upon the field sheet in the same relative positions that they bear to one another on the ground, and to do this within the limits of accuracy prescribed for the survey. It does not matter whether the map serves the purposes of geology, agriculture, or

industrial construction, the basic principles of mapping remain the
same. Therefore, when discussing the *methods* of field mapping
there is no need for distinguishing between geologic and other
types of maps.

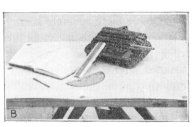

F ɪ ɢ. 18.   Plane table outfits.
           A. Johnson head tripod, plane table, explorer's and topographic
              alidades, and carrying cases.
           B. Notebook and pencil case, protractor, and scale.
           C. Left sides of explorer's and topographic alidades.
           D. Right side of topographic alidade and dismounted striding level.
(From Julian W. Low, *Plane Table Mapping,* Harper & Brothers, 1952.)

The most direct means of constructing an accurate map in the
field employs the telescopic alidade and plane table, terms which
have become almost synonymous with geologic mapping because of
their peculiar adaptability to this kind of work.

The *alidade* consists of a telescope having a magnification of 12 to 32 diameters, an eyepiece with stadia wires or a glass diaphragm on which stadia lines are engraved, and two or three spirit levels, all of which are mounted on a flat base whose edges are parallel to the line of sight through the telescope (see Fig. 18). The alidade is in no way attached to the tripod, but is free to be moved about on the map sheet in the course of map construction.

The *plane table* is a specially constructed drawing board about one inch thick and varying in plan dimensions from 15 x 15 inches to 24 x 31 inches. The board is equipped with thumb screws or clamps for holding the drawing paper on which the map is made. On the under side of the board is a plate with a threaded socket which screws on to the threaded stud of the tripod head.

Tripods generally used in geologic and topographic work are of two types: the rigid split-leg and the extension telescopic leg. There are several types of tripod heads, but the Johnson universal head is used practically to the exclusion of others. The Johnson head is shown in Fig. 19. By means of two wing nuts the plane table can be leveled and then rotated in a horizontal plane.

A *stadia rod* is a metal or wooden board varying in width from two to five inches, and in length from 10 to 16 feet. The board is painted in contrasting colors (usually white, black and red) in graduations of exactly one foot and decimals of one foot. Some stadia rods are graduated in the metric system, such as those used by the U.S. Coast and Geodetic Survey; but rods of this kind have very limited use, and are not discussed in this manual. Stadia rods vary greatly in the design of construction and pattern of graduation, depending largely on individual preference. Generally it is better to use only simple designs, such as alternate black and white feet, with the exception of the fifth and tenth feet, which are graduated in tenths of a foot.

Plane table sheets are made in a wide variety of grades from cheap engineering construction paper to paper-surfaced zinc or aluminum sheets—only two types are of general interest.

The *single-mounted* sheet consists of a high quality drawing paper tightly bonded to cloth. *Double-mounted* sheets are two layers of paper bonded on both sides of strong cloth. Cloth-mounted sheets are stronger and less subject to shrinkage than unmounted paper.

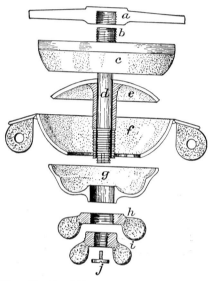

Fig. 19. Partially sectioned view of the Johnson tripod head assembly. (From Julian W. Low, *Plane Table Mapping*, Harper & Brothers, 1952.)

Considerable attention should be given to the *pencils* used on a plane table sheet, for the accuracy of plane table mapping depends to a large degree on accurate drafting. Only sharp, hard pencils should be used so that clean, fine lines are produced. Because the paper sheet becomes hard and abrasive in dry climates, pencils of hardness 9H are best. In humid climates, however, the 9H pencil may cut into the sheet. The correct pencil will make a gray mark (rather than black) without cutting the surface of the paper.

The materials and equipment mentioned in the foregoing paragraphs are essential for plane table work. Others, such as note-books, erasers, pens, and inks, also are important or essential for most projects, but the selection of types or brands is largely a matter of preference.

46. Principles of Plane Table Surveying

Surveying has been defined as the process of measuring the spatial relationships of features on or near the surface of the earth. These measurements are commonly referred to as *horizontal distance, bearing,* and *elevation,* or variations of these quantities. Plane table surveying is concerned primarily with the measurement of horizontal distance and difference in elevation, terms which are defined later. The plane table method of surveying is unique in the manner in which the directional relationships of lines or objects are determined. The procedure in plane table surveying is outlined briefly in the following articles.

47. The Starting Point

The starting (initial) point of a plane table survey may be plotted at any convenient position on the plane table sheet unless other points or lines have already been drawn on the sheet. The initial point can be any definite ground mark, such as a section corner, bench mark, road intersection, or an arbitrary location marked by a stake or cairn for the purpose of the survey. If section lines, triangulation stations, map projection, and the like are drawn on the sheet before field work is begun, the initial point must likewise be plotted in correct relationship to these lines. Of course, it is necessary that this point appear as a definite mark on the ground.

48. Setting up the Plane Table

Tighten the wing nuts on the tripod legs so that the legs fit snugly, but do not bind, on the tripod head. Press the points of two legs firmly into the ground, and level the table approximately by moving the third leg to the correct position, then press this leg into the ground. If the ground slopes, place one leg on the uphill side, two legs on the downhill. This arrangement provides the greatest stability for the table.

49. Leveling the Table

Loosen the two wing nuts at the center of the Johnson tripod head beneath the table (*h* and *i* in Fig. 19). This frees the table to rotate or tilt in any position in space. Place the alidade at the center of the table directly above the tripod head. Before releasing the alidade, grasp the edge of the table with one hand so that it cannot tilt and allow the alidade to skid to the ground. On the blade of the alidade is a circular universal (bull's eye) spirit level. Tilt the table until the bubble is centered. Hold the edge of the table with one hand and with the other tighten *only* the *upper* wing nut beneath the table (*h,* in Fig. 19). The plane table is now leveled, but is free to rotate about a vertical axis in the horizontal plane.

50. Orientation

The process of orientation consists in rotating the table about a vertical axis to a position such that lines on the sheet are exactly parallel to corresponding lines on the ground. Thus, a north-south section line on the map should be aligned exactly parallel to the actual section line on the ground. There are many ways or methods for orienting a plane table. Two are discussed in this manual; others may be found in books which treat the subject in detail.

Magnetic Orientation

The most widely used, and generally the safest, method of orientation is by means of the magnetic compass needle, which is mounted on the base of most alidades. A compass needle points toward the *magnetic* north pole, which is an electromagnetic field situated considerably south of the geographic pole. Because of the separation of the two "poles," the apparent north line toward the magnetic pole makes an angle with the true north line, or meridian, and the size of this angle is dependent on the geographical position from which the observation is made. The angle between a true meridian and a magnetic meridian is called the *magnetic declination.* In the eastern part of the United States is a sinuous line extending across the country in a direction somewhat west of north along which the compass needle points to true north. This imaginary line is called the *agonic* line. East of the agonic line, the needle points west of true north, and the declination is, therefore, *west.* West of the agonic line, the needle points east of true north, and the declination is *east.* It is necessary to know the direction and amount of declination in order to lay off on the field sheet the magnetic meridian which is the basis for orienting the plane table by means of the compass.

Table 1 in the Appendix is a map of the United States showing the amount of declination by a series of sinuous lines. Such a map is called an *isogonic chart.* The declination at any given point varies slightly from year to year—this variation is progressive and predictable. The annual variation on the isogonic chart is indicated by a set of dashed lines. Along the double dashed line there is no annual variation. North and east of this line the direction of change is to the east. South and west of the double line, the change is to the west. An example of the use of the chart is given in the table cited. By following the instructions given in the table, the amount and direction of declination can be determined for any locality or date.

The plane table may be oriented in the following manner.

(1) Draw on the sheet a line, preferably parallel to the edge, which represents a true north line. With a protractor, lay off the declination for the area as determined from the isogonic chart, or from any other reliable source, such as a standard U.S. Geological Survey topographic sheet. This magnetic meridian should be a thin, clear line as long as the base of the alidade. Indicate the north end by an arrow. Some instrumentmen prefer to draw a 2-inch line at each end of the base, instead of a con-

tinuous line which may interfere with map details, as indicated in Fig. 20.

(2) After the table is leveled as described in the preceding article, place the fiducial edge of the alidade base exactly on the

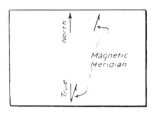

magnetic meridian, rotate the table until approximately oriented, and release the needle by lifting the locking arm. Check the alignment of the base on the line.

(3) Do not touch the alidade. Rotate the table to right or left until the south end of the needle is precisely coincident with the zero index mark on the compass box. The table is now oriented.

FIG. 20. True north and magnetic meridians indicated on the plane table sheet by short lines near the ends of the alidade base.

(4) Without disturbing the table, tighten the *lower* wing nut of the tripod head.

(5) Check the needle to ascertain that it still remains on the zero mark. If so, press the locking arm down before moving the alidade. The plane table is now leveled, oriented, and ready for surveying procedures.

BACKSIGHT ORIENTATION

This method is described in connection with triangulation.

51. Focusing the Telescope and Stadia Wires

Surveying telescopes must be focused exactly or certain errors are introduced in the observations. There are two separate operations in the adjustments of focus.

(1) Turn the telescope on some *distant* object and adjust the focusing knob until the object appears clear. Now tilt the telescope up into the northern sky somewhat above the horizon. The instrument is now ready for focusing the cross wires.

(2) Near the eyepiece is a small disk, or on some instruments a knurled ring around the telescope tube, which slides the cross

wire focusing mechanism. While viewing the wires through the telescope against the blank background of the sky, turn the eyepiece knob or ring back and forth to a position where the wires appear sharp and black.

(3) Point the telescope toward some sharply defined object, such as a stadia rod, some few hundreds of feet distant. Using the forward knob or knurled ring, bring the object into sharp focus. The stadia wires should still be black and clear. Move the eye backward and forward over the eyepiece while observing the position of one of the horizontal wires on the object. If the wire appears to move with respect to the object, the instrument is not in perfect focus. This condition is called *parallax*. Readjust the telescope focus slightly while testing for parallax. It may be necessary to readjust the eyepiece focus slightly if parallax is not completely eliminated. This test should be made on every observation when surveying, for large errors difficult to trace may result from an imperfectly focused instrument.

52. Sight Lines and Rays

The fiducial (beveled) edge of the alidade base is parallel to the line of sight through the telescope; therefore, when the vertical wire is aligned on a distant object, such as a stadia rod, the *direction* from the instrument station to that object is shown on the map by drawing a line along the fiducial edge. If a point representing the map position of the instrument station is plotted on the sheet, successive sights to rod stations around the instrument station are represented on the sheet by radiating lines. These lines are called *rays*.

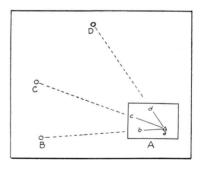

FIG. 21. Sight rays. The sight lines from the instrument station at *A* to ground points *B*, *C*, and *D*, are drawn on the sheet toward *b*, *c*, and *d*; *a* is the plotted position of *A*.

Figure 21 shows the relationships between ground points and rays on the plane table sheet.

53. Stadia Interval and Stadia Distance

Once the direction to a point is established, the map position can be determined by measuring the distance from the instrument station to the rcd point and then scaling the distance and plotting the point along the ray. Thus, if the map scale is 1 inch = 1000 feet, and the distance to the point is 850 feet, the map position of the point is 0.85 inch from the plotted position of the instrument station. The ground distance may be measured by any means, but in plane table surveying the stadia method is most commonly employed.

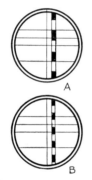

When you look through the telescope of an alidade, you will see a vertical wire and either three or four horizontal wires, the number depending on the type of reticle in the instrument. The vertical and middle horizontal wire are spoken of collectively as *cross wires*. The spacing of the horizontal wires has a fixed and constant relationship to any object viewed through the telescope. In modern instruments this relationship is such that when a graduated stadia rod is observed through the telescope, for each foot intercepted between the *upper* and *lower* wires, the rod is 100 feet distant from the instrument. Thus, in Fig. 22A, the intercept on the rod is 3.0 feet and the distance is $3.0 \times 100 = 300$ feet. In B of the figure the rod intercept between the upper and lower wires is 4.5 feet and the distance to the rod is, therefore, 450 feet. The rod intercept between the upper and lower wires is called the *stadia interval*.

FIG. 22. View of a stadia rod through the alidade telescope. In (A) the rod is 300 feet distant; in (B), 450 feet. (From Julian W. Low, *Plane Table Mapping*, Harper & Brothers, 1952.)

As the rod is moved farther away from the instrument, there

comes a point where the interval is too great for an intercept on the rod, as shown in Fig. 23. This situation often occurs in plane table mapping. In the figure cited, the upper wire is on the top of the rod and the lower wire falls below the base; consequently, a full interval intercept is impossible. However, the middle wire cuts the rod at a point 7 feet below the top. This is a half-interval intercept, and the computation of distance is $2 \times 7.0 \times 100 = 1400$ feet. If the distance is too great for a half-interval intercept, the *quarter-interval* is used and the observed intercept is multiplied by 4 instead of 2.

A reticle of new design consists of a glass diaphragm on which the vertical and horizontal "wires" are etched. The space between the upper and lower marks is three full intervals, and each interval is subdivided into tenths of an

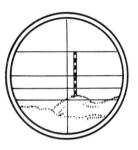

Fig. 23. The half-interval intercept as seen through the telescope.

interval. Although this type of reticle has many advantages over the cross-wire kind, it is not yet in wide use. Most of the alidades of the U.S. Geological Survey, Topographic Branch, are being equipped with the new reticle.

54. Stadia Interval Factor

In the preceding article it is assumed that the factor by which the stadia interval is multiplied to obtain the stadia distance is 100. Generally speaking, this is true, but occasionally, because of inaccurate placement of the stadia wires, the factor may vary from as low as 95 to as high as 105. If a factor of 100 were used in the calculations of distance from observations made with such an instrument, large errors in the survey would ensue. For this reason the *stadia interval factor* should be determined as follows.

Set up the plane table on flat moderately level ground. With a 50- or 100-foot tape (preferably steel or invar) carefully measure a line several hundred feet long from a point directly beneath the center of the alidade resting on the plane table. Set a stake at each 100-foot interval. Observe and record the stadia interval on a stadia rod held at each of the stakes along the measured line. Be sure the instrument is in proper focus for *each* observation. When determining the stadia interval factor, read the rod to the nearest 0.01 foot.

For the purpose of illustration, assume that the rod intercepts at the 100-foot stations are 1.02, 2.04, 3.06, 4.08, and 5.10, instead of the usual 1.0, 2.0, and so forth. It is evident that the stadia wires are incorrectly spaced, but this does not preclude doing accurate work with the instrument. Add the known (taped) distances from the instrument to each of the stations. Now add the observed intercepts, as shown in the accompanying table.

Distance	Intercept
100	1.02
200	2.04
300	3.06
400	4.08
500	5.10
1500	15.30

The correct stadia interval factor for this instrument is determined by dividing the sum of the distances by the sum of the observed intercepts.

$$\frac{1500}{15.30} = 98$$

All stadia intercepts observed with this instrument must be multiplied by 98 (instead of 100) to obtain correct distances.

55. Plane Table Traversing

The preceding articles have shown how to level and orient the plane table, how to determine the direction and distance to a rod point from the instrument station, and, finally, how to plot this point on the plane table sheet in the correct relationship to the plotted position of the instrument station. The next step in extending these principles is called *traversing*.

When the stadia rod is held on a point whose position is plotted on the sheet, the position of the instrument can be determined by reversing the process previously described.

In Fig. 24, the circle identified by the Roman numeral I is the ground location of a point which is also plotted on the plane table

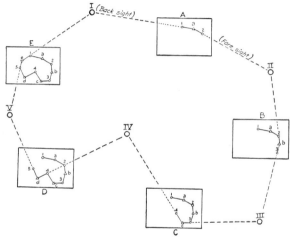

FIG. 24. Plane table traversing. Roman numerals and capital letters are ground positions. Arabic numbers and small letters are corresponding map points. The polygon *I* to *E* is the same as 1 to *e*, except that the scales are different. (From Julian W. Low, *Plane Table Mapping,* Harper & Brothers, 1952.)

sheet as the initial point of the traverse. The plane table is set up and oriented at the ground position *A*. The initial point is shown on the sheet as station 1. The edge of the alidade base is placed against this point and rotated until the rod on the corresponding ground point is cut by the vertical wire. A light line is now drawn along the base from station 1 *toward* the instrument station. The stadia distance is determined and the map position of the instrument station is scaled from 1 to *a*. Such a sight, which determines the position of the instrument, is called a *backsight*.

The alidade is now rotated about instrument station *a* until the cross wires are brought to bear on the rod which has been taken to position II. After determining the direction and distance from station *A*, the map location of II is plotted at 2. This point is called a *turning point,* or T.P., and the operations involved in establishing a T.P. are called *foresighting*.

The rodman stays on the turning point and the instrument is moved to position *B,* from which another backsight is taken to T.P. II, thus establishing instrument station *b* on the map. The procedure described is repeated for any number of alternating foresights and backsights. Such a sequence is called a *traverse.*

A closed traverse or loop is a traverse which terminates at the starting point, as shown in the figure cited. When the instrument station at *E* (*e* on the sheet) is established from a backsight on T.P. V (5 on the sheet), the rod is held on the initial point I. Now this sight is treated as a foresight from V, and the location as derived from this instrument station is plotted as 1', regardless of where it may fall on the sheet with respect to original plot of this point. If the traverse has been conducted without error, or if such errors as have been made compensate each other, the new determination of the location of station I will coincide with the starting point. If, on the other hand, errors have been made, the new plot will fall at some distance away from the original plot, and this discrepancy is called the *error of closure,* or *closing error.* If this error is too great, then remedial steps must be taken, either by adjusting the positions of all points in the traverse or by re-running the entire loop, or portions of the loop wherein errors might be suspected.

In the illustration, it is obvious that the polygonal figure defined by the traverse is exactly duplicated at a smaller scale on the plane table sheet.

56. Stadia, Slope, and Horizontal Distance

In foregoing discussions, distances obtained by stadia are considered as actual map distances; that is, the distance determined by stadia is plotted without adjustment on the plane table sheet. This may be done *only* when the line of sight is level or inclined at a low angle. When the telescope is steeply inclined toward a rod point a correction known as *conversion to horizontal distance* must be made.

Figure 25 represents a sight to a point much higher than the instrument. For reasons explained later, the rod must be held vertical no matter how steep the line of sight. As can be seen in the figure, the rod intercept (interval) is larger than it would be if the rod were presented at an angle normal to the line of sight, which would be the case in a level sight. Therefore, the term "stadia distance" is not necessarily synonymous with actual distance.

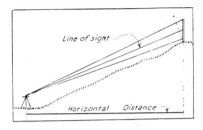

FIG. 25. Inclined sight. The rod is held vertical and the horizontal distance is computed from the observed stadia intercept.

The stadia distance is a quantity which can be converted to *slope distance* or *horizontal distance*. From Fig. 26 it is evident that the slope distance can be obtained from the stadia distance by the formula

$$S = i \cos \alpha \times F.$$

When S is the slope distance, i is the observed interval, α is the inclination of the telescope (vertical angle), and F is the stadia interval factor. For example, if the observed interval is 10.0 feet, F is 100, and α is 20 degrees, the slope distance is

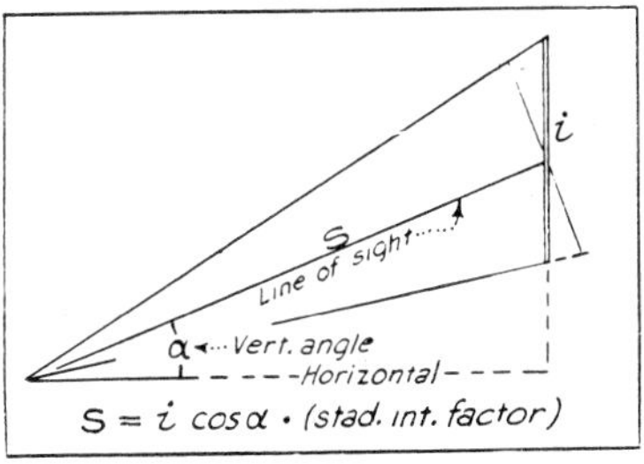

FIG. 26. Computation of slope distance from observed stadia intercept on a vertical rod.

$$S = 10.0 \times .940 \times 100 = 940 \text{ feet (Approx.)}$$

Fig. 27. Explorers' (expedition) alidade, showing the principal external parts. (From Julian W. Low, *Plane Table Mapping*, Harper & Brothers, 1952.)

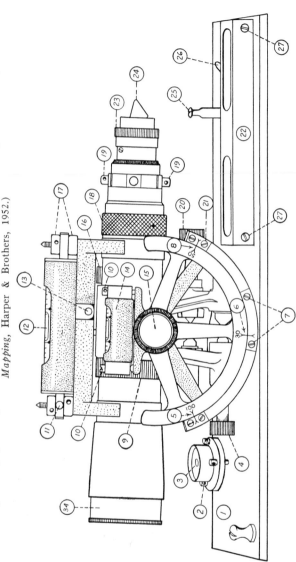

Principal external parts of the alidade as shown in Figs 27 and 28.

(1) Blade or base. (2) Adjustment screw for universal level. (3) Universal level center mark. (4) Vertical angle and Beaman arc index tangent screw. (5) Horizontal distance arc index. (6) Vertical angle arc index. (7) Vertical angle arc index adjustment plate. (8) Beaman arc index. (9) Knurled telescope holding collar. (10) Control level adjustment screw. (11) Lateral adjustment screw for striding level. (12) Striding level bubble vial. (13) Striding level spring lock. (14) Control level sleeve shield. (15) Telescope axis bearing. (16) Axis clamp (on right side of instrument). (17) Vertical adjustment capstan nuts of striding level. (18) Knurled focusing ring. (19)

Mapping, Harper & Brothers, 1952.)

Capstan adjustment screws for adjusting collimation. (20) Telescope tangent screw (with or without gradienter attachment). (21) Beaman arc index adjustment screws. (22) Magnetic needle box or trough. (23) Cross wire or eyepiece focusing ring. (24) Prismatic eyepiece on Fig. 12, inverting eyepiece on Fig. 13. (25) Keeper stud for striding level. Used when instrument is laid in case. (26) Needle lifting lever. (27) Compass box assembly screws. (28) Striding level stud. (29) Ring foot bearing for striding level. (30) Plunger opposing Beaman tangent screw. (31) Pedestal or standard of topographic type alidade. (32) Striding level spring lock releasing screw. (33) Finder sights on striding, not on all instruments. (34) Dust protector cap for objective lens

The distance plotted on the map, however, is the *horizontal* distance, or the vertical projection of the slope distance on to a horizontal plane. From the example given above, the horizontal distance would be

$$940 \times \cos 20° = 940 \times .940 = 884 \text{ feet (Approx.)}$$

Stadia conversion tables (see Table 2, Appendix) are computed on the basis of a *vertical* stadia rod; therefore, if the rod is inclined toward the instrument on steeply inclined sights a serious error is introduced. The use of the horizontal distance scale on the Beaman stadia arc is explained later.

57. Spirit Levels of the Alidade

Most alidades have three spirit levels that perform different functions.

UNIVERSAL LEVEL

This level, on the base of the alidade, is used for leveling the plane table, as mentioned previously.

STRIDING LEVEL

The striding level on most alidades is detachable and when not in use, is either clamped to the blade of the alidade or placed in a bracket in the instrument case. When in operation, the striding level sets over a stud on the top of the telescope, and its function is to indicate when the telescope is level.

AUXILIARY (ARC) LEVEL

This level is attached on the left side and above the vertical arcs of the alidade. It is used to set the arcs in such a position that vertical angles (or Beaman arc) are referenced to the arc index (Beaman 50, vertical angle 30°00′), thus facilitating the manipulations of the arcs when determining difference in elevation.

If the instrument is in perfect adjustment, the bubbles of the striding and auxiliary levels will be centered when the vertical angle arc reads 30°00′ and the Beaman arc reads 50. Refer to Figs. 27 and 28 for parts of the alidade.

58. Difference in Elevation

Most plane table surveys require the determination of the elevations or altitudes of all rod and instrument stations. The computation of elevation of a new station (rod or instrument) is based on the *difference in elevation* between the new station and the known elevation of the point sighted upon. Thus, if a new instrument station is being established by a backsight on a turning point whose elevation is 3250 feet, and by computation it is determined that the instrument is 95 feet higher, the elevation of the instrument is $3250 + 95 = 3345$ feet. Now, if a new rod station is established from this instrument station, and the *difference* in elevation is found to be 103 feet, and the rod point is below the instrument, the elevation of the new point is $3345 - 103 = 3242$ feet.

59. Ground Elevation, H.I., and Differential Leveling

In Fig. 29, the stadia rod is held on a bench mark (*A*) whose elevation is 3045.6 feet. The alidade is set up at some distance

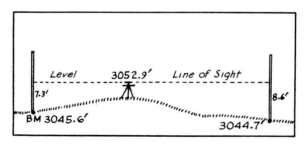

Fig. 29.   Differential leveling. Middle (level) wire readings.

away (*B*) and the telescope is sighted on the rod. By means of the striding level, the telescope is carefully leveled, and the position on the rod cut by the *middle* (level) wire is observed and recorded. This point in the figure is 7.3 feet. It is clear from the illustration that the center of the telescope is 7.3 feet above the bench mark; therefore, the elevation of the instrument is 3045.6 + 7.3 = 3052.9. The elevation of the *ground* at the instrument station is obtained by measuring the height of the instrument above the ground and subtracting this amount from the elevation just obtained. This height is sometimes referred to as the H.I., and the elevation of the instrument, as the E.I. However, common practice has so changed these original terms that E.I. is used by comparatively few, if any, organizations conducting plane table work, and H.I. is the generally accepted term for the *elevation* at the center of the telescope—it is used in this sense throughout this manual.

After establishing the H.I. elevation (3052.9), the rod is set up on a new point (*C*) whose elevation is to be determined. With the telescope leveled, the middle wire reading is 8.6 feet. Inasmuch as the known elevation is the H.I., which in this case is the higher of the two, the difference in elevation must be subtracted. The elevation of *C* is 3052.9 − 8.6 = 3044.3.

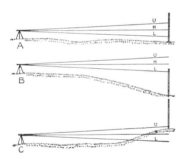

FIG. 30. Readings made with the telescope level: A. Middle wire. B. Lower wire. C. Upper wire. (From Julian W. Low, *Plane Table Mapping,* Harper & Brothers, 1952.)

The process just described may be continued through any number of H.I.'s and alternating turning points, in the same way that map locations are established by alternating instrument stations and turning points. This process is called *differential leveling,* and such a series is called a *level line.* In plane table mapping, both the locations and elevations of rod and instrument stations are determined from each instrument set-up.

60. Lower and Upper Wire Readings

It has been stated that the difference in elevation between the telescope and the rod station is obtained directly by reading the position of the *middle* wire on the rod when the telescope is level. If the rod point is considerably lower than the instrument, the middle wire may be above the top of the rod, as in Fig. 30B. However, if the lower wire falls on the rod, the difference in elevation can be computed. From the reading of the stadia intercept (distance) the stadia interval is known. The lower wire is one-half interval below the middle (or level) wire; therefore, the *difference* in elevation is the rod reading of the lower wire *plus* the half-interval.

EXAMPLE:

Stadia interval is 10.6 feet
Lower wire reading is 11.3 feet

Difference in elevation is $11.3+5.3=16.6$ feet.

The sign of lower (and middle) wire readings is minus for foresights and plus for backsights.

If the point sighted on is higher than the alidade the middle wire will be below the base of the rod, as in Fig. 30C. When the upper wire cuts the rod, the difference in elevation is the *difference* between the half-interval and the upper wire reading.

EXAMPLE:

Stadia interval is 10.6 feet
Upper wire reading is 1.5 feet

Difference in elevation is $5.3-1.5=3.8$ feet.

The sign of upper wire readings is plus for foresights and minus for backsights.

61. Vertical Angles

On the left side of the alidade is a silver arc graduated in degrees and half degrees. Minutes of arc are read on a vernier scale. The graduations on the vernier are arranged in a manner such that only one pair of lines can be coincident, regardless of the position of the arcs (Fig. 31). The vernier reads up to 30 minutes, and the vernier reading is added to the degrees and half degrees observed on the degree scale.

EXAMPLE:

> Vertical angle arc reading is 31° 30', plus
> Vernier reading is 15'
>
> Vertical angle is 31° 30'+15'=31° 45'

A vertical angle is the angle of elevation or depression of the telescope above or below, respectively, a level position. By means

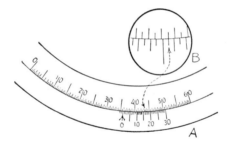

FIG. 31. Vertical angle arc and vernier. In B, the vernier is magnified to show the one coincident, and remaining offsetting lines. (From Julian W. Low, *Plane Table Mapping*, Harper & Brothers, 1952.)

of this angle and the stadia intercept, the difference in elevation can be computed, either by trigonometry or special stadia conversion tables presented in the Appendix.

The procedure for determining difference in elevation by this method is outlined below.

(1) From an instrument station whose elevation is known, the stadia distance to the rod is observed and recorded.

(2) By means of the striding level, the telescope is carefully leveled. The vertical angle arc is read (through a hand lens of about ×3 magnification) and the reading recorded in the notebook. All determinations should be to the nearest minute of arc. This (level) reading should be within a few minutes of 30 degrees, as from 29° 30′ to 30° 30′, the variation depending on how accurately the table is leveled.

(3) The telescope axis clamp is loosened and the telescope is trained on the rod. The clamp screw is tightened.

(4) The middle wire is set on some definite foot mark of the rod and the angle is again observed on the arc and recorded.

The *vertical angle* is the difference between the first (level) reading and the second. If the first reading is smaller than the second, the vertical angle is *plus;* if larger than the second, the angle is *minus,* thus indicating that the rod was at a higher or lower elevation than the instrument, respectively.

EXAMPLE 1:

First reading 29°48′: second reading 33°16′
Stadia interval 13.6 feet (middle wire on the 5-foot mark)
Vertical angle 33° 16′−29° 48′ = +3° 28′
Under 3° 28′ in the *Stadia Conversion Tables* (Appendix) find the factor 6.04.

Difference in elevation is $13.6 \times 6.04 - 5.0 = 77.1$ feet.

The five-foot rod correction is *subtracted* on *plus angle* sights because the middle wire is moved past the ground point at the rod station.

EXAMPLE 2:

First reading 29° 53′: second reading 26° 31′
Stadia interval 2×12.3 (middle wire 10.0 feet)
Vertical angle 29° 53′−26° 31′ = −3° 22′
Conversion factor for 3° 22′ is 5.86.

Difference in elevation is $24.6 \times 5.86 + 10.0 = 154.2$ feet.

The rod correction is *added* on *minus angle* sights because the middle wire is moved from the level position only to within 10 feet of the ground point.

In the first example the difference in elevation is *plus* on a foresight and *minus* on a backsight. The reverse is true for the second example.

62. The Beaman Stadia Arc

Toward one end of the vertical arc is a scale labeled "Beaman." Opposite this scale is a single index mark. On most instruments the Beaman arc is graduated from 10 to 90 and the arc reads 50 when the telescope is level. The principle of the Beaman arc is simple. The graduations are spaced so that as the telescope is elevated or depressed, the arc scale indicates the difference in elevation in terms of stadia intervals. Whether the sight is upward or downward is shown by the readings being greater or less than 50. Thus, a reading of 45 would correspond to a *minus* vertical angle. The sign is obtained by subtracting 50 from the arc reading with the telescope on the rod.

$$45 - 50 = -5$$
$$61 - 50 = +11$$

63. Field Procedure for the Beaman Arc

EXAMPLE 1 (Using the striding level):

(a) Determine and record the stadia interval (11.6).
(b) Level the telescope.
(c) With the arc tangent screw (front end, left side) set the Beaman arc *exactly* on 50. Use a hand lens.
(d) Release the telescope and place the middle wire approximately on the middle of the rod.
(e) Using the telescope tangent screw (right rear of alidade), set the arc on the nearest Beaman division. Do not touch the tangent screws hereafter.

(f) Read the position of the middle wire on the rod and record in the notebook (5.3 feet).

(g) Read the Beaman arc and record (54).

Difference in elevation is
$$11.6 \times (54-50=4)-5.3=46.4-5.3=41.1 \text{ feet.}$$

EXAMPLE 2 (Using the arc or index level):

(a) Read and record stadia interval (10.7 feet), and set the middle wire near the middle of the rod.

(b) Center the arc bubble by means of the *left front* tangent screw.

(c) With the *right* (telescope) tangent screw set the Beaman arc on the nearest graduation (42).

(d) Read and record the middle wire on the rod (9.5 feet).

Difference in elevation is
$$10.7 \times (50-42=8)+9.5=95.1 \text{ feet.}$$

The Beaman arc has a scale to be used in converting stadia distance to the horizontal equivalent. On some instruments the scale reads from 100 per cent downward. This is the percentage of the stadia distance that is to be plotted on the plane table sheet; thus, if the stadia distance on an inclined sight is 1250 feet and the scale reads 97.5, the horizontal distance is $1250 \times .975 = 1219$ feet. Some instruments have a scale that reads from 0 percent upward. This scale indicates the percentage correction to be applied to the stadia distance. For example, if the stadia distance is 1200 feet and the scale reads 3.5, the horizontal distance is $1200-(1200 \times .035)=1158$ feet.

64. Distance by the Gradienter, or Stebinger Screw

On the right tangent screw of most alidades is a drum graduated into 100 equal divisions (Fig. 32). One complete revolution of the drum moves the telescope through approximately one stadia interval; therefore, each peripheral graduation represents 1/100 interval of movement by the stadia wires. With some instruments, one revolution may not move the wires through *exactly* one interval; in other words, one interval may require turning the drum 98, 103, or some other number of divisions on the drum. For this reason, it is necessary to check the calibration of the drum and determine the factor by which distance and difference in elevation are computed. Two of the causes for variation in the factor are wear in the threads of the tangent screw and the axis arm, and the position of the thrust point on the axis arm. These conditions are generally unpredictable; hence, the computation factor should be determined each time the gradienter is used when it is known that the factor is appreciably different from 100. The gradienter is used for determining distance on long sights when a half- or quarter-interval intercept cannot be obtained. There are two common methods.

Fig. 32. The gradienter or Stebinger drum: *a*, eccentric adjustment nut; *b*, graduated drum; *c*, lock nut; *d*, telescope axis arm; *e*, drum revolution scale; *f*, tapered screw bearing; *g*, scale adjustment screw. (From Julian W. Low, *Plane Table Mapping*, Harper & Brothers, 1952.)

EXAMPLE 1:

(a) Set the middle wire on the 1-foot rod graduation.
(b) Read and record the drum reading (23).
(c) With the *right tangent screw*, move the middle wire up to the highest clearly visible rod graduation (13-foot).
(d) Record the drum reading (37).

From these figures it is evident that in turning the drum through 14 divisions $(37-23)$ the middle wire traversed 12 feet $(13-1)$ of rod. If the instrument is in perfect adjustment, the stadia distance is

$$12 \times \frac{100}{14} \times 100 \text{ (the stadia interval factor)} = 8571 \text{ feet.}$$

To determine the gradienter interval factor, set the upper wire on a rod graduation and read the drum (15). Now move the lower wire to this position on the rod and read the drum (17). The drum has been rotated through 102 divisions; therefore, in the observations given above the distance would be

$$13 \times \frac{102 \times 100}{14} = 9471.$$

EXAMPLE 2:

(a) Set the upper wire on the top of the rod and read the drum (drum, 23; rod, 14 feet).

(b) Move the middle wire up to the lowest clearly visible rod graduation and read the drum (drum 38; rod 2 feet).

$38 - 23 = 15$ drum graduations

$14 - 2 = 12$ feet difference in rod readings

The half-interval is represented by 12 feet plus the foot-equivalent of 15 drum divisions.

(c) While observing the drum, carefully turn 15 additional drum divisions in the same direction (clockwise) and read the position of the middle wire on the rod (9.5). This is the amount by which the half interval is deficient for a direct stadia reading of the interval.

Distance is $12.0 + (9.5 - 2.0) \times 2 \times 100 = 3900$ **feet.**

When the stadia interval factor, discussed earlier, is other than 100, this number is used instead of 100 in the examples of computation.

65. The Gradienter for Difference in Elevation

The gradienter is a fast and accurate means of determining difference in elevation if this difference is not large with respect to the full stadia interval. The method is most useful where the vertical angle is less than one-half degree. As has been stated earlier, each division on the drum is (approximately) 1/100 of an interval; consequently, the elevation or depression of the telescope from the level position can be measured in terms of hundredths of an interval. For example, assume the stadia interval is 12.6 feet. The telescope is leveled, but the stadia wires are below the base of the rod. In order to bring the middle wire up to the base of the rod, the drum is turned through 64 divisions. The difference in elevation is, therefore,

$$\frac{64}{100} \times 12.6 = 8.1 \text{ feet.}$$

Because of the fact that one complete revolution of the drum might not move the telescope through an exact interval, a factor for computation may have to be determined. Two methods for using the gradienter are given below.

EXAMPLE 1:

(a) Determine the stadia interval (18.4 feet), level the telescope and read the gradienter drum (21 divisions).

(b) Turn the right tangent screw until the upper wire (for a plus sight) is on the base of the rod, or a clearly discernible graduation near the base, and read the drum again (69 divisions). The drum is turned through $69 - 21 = 48$ divisions.

(c) Turn off 48 divisions in the same clockwise direction, and note the distance traversed on the rod (8.8 feet). This is the distance of the upper wire below the base of the rod when the telescope was level. Notice that readings were made on the upper wire, which necessitates a half-interval correction. Compute as follows:

Difference in elevation is $8.8 + 9.2$ (half-interval) $= 18.0$ feet.

In the case of a minus sight, start with the middle wire on the top of the rod, and note the number of divisions necessary to bring the telescope into the level position. The length of the rod must then be added to the difference in elevation as computed from the gradienter readings.

EXAMPLE 2:

(a) Determine the stadia interval (15.8), level the telescope, and read the gradienter drum (15).

(b) Turn the right tangent screw until the middle wire is on the base of the rod. Read the drum (87).

(c) Relevel the telescope, read the drum (16), and select any sharply-defined small object on the landscape that is cut by the upper wire.

(d) While looking through the telescope turn the right tangent screw clockwise until the lower wire cuts the object exactly as previously cut by the upper wire. Read the drum again (18). Steps (3) and (4) are taken to establish the interval factor for the instrument, which in this case is $118-16=102$ (instead of 100).

Difference in elevation is

$$\frac{87-15}{102} \times 15.8 = 11.1 \text{ feet.}$$

66. Intersection of Points

It has been shown that when a point is sighted through the telescope a line drawn along the edge of the base of the alidade represents on the sheet the direction to that point from the instrument station. The position of the point is therefore somewhere on this line. If such a sight line is drawn toward the same point

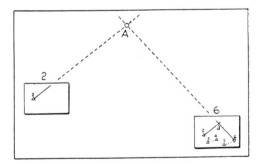

Fɪɢ. 33. Intersection. Ray to *A* first drawn from station 2; when ray is drawn from 6, an intersection is obtained at *a,* the map location of *A.*

from each of two established instrument stations in a manner such that the lines intersect, the point is located at the intersection, for this is the only position where directional requirements are satisfied for rays from both instrument stations. In Fig. 33, from station 2 a line (ray), is drawn toward a clearly defined object, such as a post, rock, or chimney. By traversing, station 6 is located, from which the object previously sighted is again in view. The ray drawn from station 6 intersects the one from station 2, thus locating the object on the map at *a*. A point located in this way is called an *intersected point*.

67. Resection

The position of the instrument may be determined by intersection from points previously located on the sheet. In Fig. 34, points 6 and 12 have been located on the sheet from a traverse.

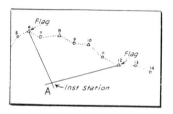

FIG. 34.   Resection. Ray is drawn from stations 6 and 12 to locate instrument at *A*.

These points have been marked on the ground so that they are visible from the desired instrument station in the vicinity of *A*. The plane table is first carefully oriented by the magnetic needle. The edge of the alidade base is placed at point 6 and rotated until the ground point is brought exactly into the line of sight and a line is drawn along the base toward *A*. This process is repeated for point 12, and an intersection results at *A*. This is the location of the instrument station. The procedure just described is called *resection,* and the station located is called a *resected station.*

68. Determination of Difference in Elevation

When one side and one angle of a right triangle are known, the other sides of the triangle can be computed by a simple trigonometric formula. After a point has been intersected (or resected) the *horizontal* distance is found by careful scaling between the points on the sheet, and the angle is obtained by observing a vertical angle to the ground point whose elevation is desired. Thus, if the scaled distance is 5720 feet and the vertical angle to the point is $1° 38'$, the difference in elevation is

$$5720 \times \tan 1° 38',$$

or

$$5720 \times .0285 = 163.0 \text{ feet.}$$

This difference in elevation is added or subtracted (depending on whether the sight is up or down) to the H.I. of the station from which measurements are made. Normally, the elevation of an intersected point is determined from two or more instrument stations in order to verify the computed elevation. The reverse procedure is employed when computing the elevation of a resected instrument station.

69. Plane Table Triangulation

The principles set forth in the preceding three articles are the basis for a form of surveying called triangulation. Assume that two points a and b in Fig. 35 have been located by intersection

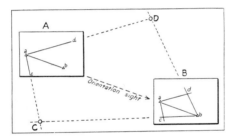

Fig. 35. Triangulation. Points c and d are located on the sheet by intersecting rays drawn from stations A and B.

from a traverse, as previously explained. The plane table is set up on point A, and oriented, then rays are drawn toward two additional points, C and D, as at a and b of the figure. In addition, a sight is taken on the established point b. This sight checks the orientation of the table and the plotted positions of both a and b, for if errors are present, the line from the instrument at a will not bisect the point b.

The instrument is now taken to point B and oriented, and rays are drawn to C and D. These rays intersect those drawn from station A, thus locating these points on the sheet at c and d. It is evident that the process described may be carried almost indefinitely from the points of origin, each new point established being occupied by the plane table in order to establish still other points farther afield. In the course of such operations a series of triangles having common sides is built up, and this skeleton of map control is called a *triangulation net*. The process is spoken of as *expanding the triangulation*.

70. The Base Line

In the preceding discussion and illustrations, intersections and resections were obtained from stations established by traversing. This method is very useful to the geologist for work in which extreme accuracy is not required. However, the triangulation net usually serves the purpose of primary control for the map, and in this case the triangulation is conducted somewhat differently, although the principles discussed are the same.

It has been shown that the locations (and elevations) of any number of points over an indefinitely large area can be established from an initial pair of points correctly plotted on the sheet. In triangulation, the straight line connecting these two initial points is called a *base line*. The measurement of the base line and the plotting of the base line on the plane table sheet are extremely important. Of equal importance is the orientation of the plotted line with reference to the line on the ground. In order to ascertain that all the initial steps are performed with an accuracy necessarily somewhat higher than that required in much of the subsidiary plane table work, common procedures are as given in following paragraphs.

The base line should be located somewhere in the central part of the area, in open, flat terrain which affords a clear view of surrounding country. The line on the ground should be measured carefully with a tape, as stadia determinations of distance are usually not sufficiently accurate. The process of taping, generally referred to as *chaining*, is performed as follows.

(1) Set up and carefully orient the plane table at one end of the proposed base line. Place a flag on the opposite end and align the alidade on the flag. Draw a line along the alidade base at the desired location on the sheet.

(2) Set a stake, stone, or other substantial marker at a point directly under the alidade. This will be the starting point for chaining.

(3) The *rear* chainman holds the zero end of the tape at the instrument. The *head* chainman takes the other end, and (with the help of the instrumentman) draws the tape taut along the line of sight. The instrumentman signals to the head chainman right or left to maintain a straight line of measurement. The head chainman carries a notebook in which he keeps a record of all measurements. He also carries a few sharpened stakes to set at each point of measurement. The recording of the head chainman can be checked periodically by counting the stakes recovered and carried by the rear chainman.

(4) If the ground slopes appreciably, the chain is held approximately level, the ground point being determined by dropping a plumb bob from the tape to the ground. Where slopes are steep, it may not be possible to hold the end of the tape sufficiently high to maintain a horizontal measurement. In this case, only a convenient portion of the tape is used.

(5) To check the base line measurement, it is retaped back to the instrument. For plane table triangulation, the base line measurement should check within 5 feet per mile. If within this figure, use the average of the two measurements.

(6) Plot the measured distance *very carefully* on the line previously drawn on the plane table sheet. Check the orientation of the table by placing the alidade base on the base line and sighting the flag at the opposite end of the line. The initial phase of triangulation is now complete.

71. The Base Net

During the early stages of setting up a triangulation net, *every* operation must be performed with great care, for errors are multiplied many times as the net is expanded. The base net is a figure composed of triangles in which the measured base line forms one side of each. Figure 36 is a common type of base net, and the

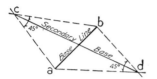

FIG. 36. Triangulation base net. Secondary base line is determined by intersection of *c* and *d* from the ends of the measured base line, *ab*. (From Julian W. Low, *Plane Table Mapping*, Harper & Brothers, 1952.)

procedure for setting it up on the ground and sheet is as follows.

(1) Set up the instrument on one end of the base line and orient by aligning the base along the line drawn on the sheet and then rotate the table until the signal at the other end of the base line is bisected by the vertical wire. Lock the Johnson head and recheck the orientation. This procedure is called *backsight orientation*.

(2) Refer to Fig. 37A. The plane table station is at *a*, and orientation was effected by sighting on *b*. The short scores *x* and *y*, are drawn on the sheet near the ends of the alidade base to provide a longer line for more accurate

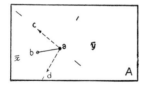
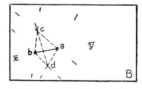

FIG. 37. Backsight orientation. A. When backsighting from *a* toward *b* short scores *x* and *y* are drawn near ends of alidade base. In B, similar scores are made for all sights. (From Julian W. Low, *Plane Table Mapping*, Harper & Brothers, 1952.)

alignment of the alidade. Such scores should always be used in the backsight method. Now pivot the alidade about point *a* until a point *c*, previously flagged, is exactly on the line of sight. Draw a ray to this point. Sight the flagged point *d* in the same manner.

(3) Set up the instrument on the opposite end of the base line

at *b,* and orient by *backsighting* on *a.* Draw rays from *b* to *c* and *d,* and obtain the intersections as shown in B of the figure.

72. Expanding the Net

While the instrument is set up at *a* and *b* (see preceding article) draw rays to any other flagged triangulation points that are visible. Label each ray so that it can be identified later. Vertical angles are determined and recorded on each station so that elevations can be computed later.

The second phase consists in setting up the instrument at *c* and *d,* orienting back on *a* and *b,* and drawing a second set of rays to points previously sighted from *a* and *b.* From stations *b* and *c,* rays to more distant points are drawn, and in like manner the system of triangles is expanded.

Although the intersection of two rays is the theoretical map position of the point, wherever possible a ray from a third station should be drawn for verification.

73. Earth Curvature and Refraction

A level line is a line parallel to the mean surface of the earth; therefore, it is not straight in the vertical plane, but is a circular curve. Short level sight lines may be considered as straight because the small segment of an arch whose radius is approximately 4000 miles is essentially a straight line. However, long sight lines commonly occur in triangulation, and for this reason, the curvature of the earth must be taken into account in the computations of elevations.

Owing to the decreasing density of the atmosphere with increasing altitude, horizontal light paths are slightly refracted. These paths also follow a circular curve whose radius is vastly larger than that of the earth. The effect on apparent elevation caused by earth curvature is partially compensated for by atmospheric refraction, which depresses the line of sight.

Figure 38 illustrates the relationships between curvature, refraction, and difference in elevation. The instrument is set up at *i* and leveled. At this point the level line of sight is horizontal, but because of refraction, at a distance iA, the sight line is depressed an amount r. This is the refraction *correction*. However, the

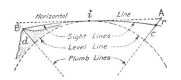

FIG. 38.   Exaggerated drawing showing relationships of curvature, refraction, horizontal and level lines. (From Julian W. Low, *Plane Table Mapping,* Harper & Brothers, 1952.)

curvature correction alone is $r+c$. It can be seen that, since the *line of sight* (or observed point) is distance r below the horizontal, the correction for reducing the line of sight to point A to a level line is the distance c.

On the left side of the figure cited, a "level" sight from station i cuts the top of a hill. It would appear, therefore, that the hill has the same altitude as the instrument. However, the actual difference in elevation is d, which in this case is the amount of the curvature and refraction correction.

Curvature is essentially a constant; but refraction varies slightly according to the general elevation at which observations are made. The formulas and values most commonly used for curvature and refraction are given in Table 3 in the Appendix.

The application of this correction to the *difference in elevation,* regardless of the sign of this difference (plus for foresights, minus for backsights), is as follows.

EXAMPLE 1 (Foresight):

> Apparent (computed) difference in elevation is $+200$ feet.
> Distance is 2.0 miles.
> Curvature correction is 2.3 feet.

> Difference in elevation is $+200+2.3 = +202.3$ feet.

EXAMPLE 2 (Foresight):

> Apparent difference in elevation is -15 feet.
> Distance is 10 miles.

Correction is 54.4 feet.

Difference in elevation is $-15+54.4=+39.4$ feet.

If the elevation of the instrument were being determined in the foregoing examples, all signs would be reversed.

74. The Three-Point Problem

Determination of the map position of an instrument station by *resection* from previously located points has been discussed. If such a station is correctly located by the intersection of two rays, the ray from a third control point will also pass through this intersection. The third ray serves as a check, and the process of locating the instrument station by this method is called *three-pointing*. A three-point location is shown in Fig. 39A. If the plane table is misoriented, the third ray will not pass through the intersection made by the other two rays, and a small *triangle of error* will be formed, as shown in B of the figure.

When a triangle of error occurs, the true location of the instrument station is *never* at any of the three intersections, and it can be concluded that the table is incorrectly oriented. The problem, therefore, is to reorient the table so that a three-point intersection is obtained. There are several methods for solving the three-point problem, but only one is discussed here. There are certain constant relationships between the three control stations, the triangle of error, and the true location of the instru-

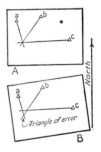

FIG. 39. Three-point location. A. Table is correctly oriented. B. Table is misoriented and a triangle of error is formed. (From Julian W. Low, *Plane Table Mapping*, Harper & Brothers, 1952.)

ment station. These relationships are briefly discussed in the following paragraphs.

From geometry it is known that a circle arc can be made to pass through any three points plotted at random on a sheet. In surveying, such an imaginary arc passing through three triangulation stations is called a *great circle* or *danger circle*. Straight lines connecting the three stations form what is commonly termed the *great triangle*, as shown in Fig. 40. It is important in solving the three-point problem to know approximately where the instrument is with regard to the great circle and great triangle.

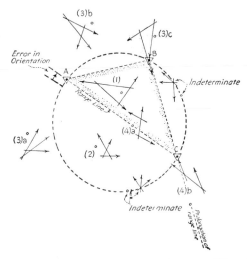

Fig. 40. Comparison of triangles of error at different locations with respect to the great circle and great triangle. Small circles are correct locations of the instrument stations. (From Julian W. Low, *Plane Table Mapping*, Harper & Brothers, 1952.)

There are several methods for determining the correct location (and orientation) of the plane table after a triangle of error has been obtained, but the most commonly used one is called Lehman's (Coast and Geodetic Survey) method. In actual practice, it is a "controlled" trial and error procedure.

Figure 40 shows three triangulation stations, *A, B* and *C,* the great triangle, and the great circle. Triangles of error are shown at a number of positions relative to the triangulation stations. The error in orientation is the same at all locations. It can be seen that the sizes of the triangles of error vary for a given error of orientation according to the relative location of the plane table station. The three-point location is *strongest* in the regions where the triangles of error are *largest*. The small circles near the triangles are the correct locations of the instrument. Examination of the figure will show the following relationships.

(1) When the plane table is within the great triangle, the correct location is within the triangle of error (1).

(2) When the station is in a segment between the great circle and great triangle, the ray to the *middle* triangulation station lies between the true location and the intersection of the other two rays (2).

(3) When the plane table is *outside* the great circle, the true location lies on the *same side* of the ray from the most distant triangulation station as the intersection of the other two rays (3)*a*, (3)*b*, and (3)*c*.

(4) When on, or near, a range line formed by two of the stations, a triangle of error is not formed (4)*a* and (4)*b*, and the desired location is on or near the range line.

(5) When the plane table is on or very near the great circle, a three-point location will be obtained when the table is misoriented; therefore, a perfect three-point intersection is no assurance of a correct location.

Figure 40 illustrates another fundamental relationship which aids in selecting a *trial point* for reorientation of the table. Consider location (1), within the great triangle. Let the perpendicular distance from the correct location to the rays from the stations be designated pa, pb, and pc, the second letters corresponding to stations A, B, and C, from which the rays originate. Let pA, pB, and pC be the distances from the instrument station to each of the triangulation points. By scaling these distances it can be shown that $pa/pA = pb/pC = pc/pC;$ or that the distance from the true location to the rays is proportional to the distance from the true location to the respective triangulation stations. Also, the ratio pa/pA, etc., is the same for all triangles of error derived from the same triangulation points for a given orientation error.

Applying the foregoing relationships, the three-point problem is solved in the following manner.

(1) Orient the table with the compass needle and resect from three triangulation stations.

(2) If a triangle of error is formed, first determine by inspection of the plotted stations whether the location is within the great triangle, outside the great circle, or in a segment between these two figures.

(3) Having decided which of the previously stated rules applies, select a trial point in the proper relative position with reference to the triangle of error; that is, if within the great triangle, plot the trial point within the triangle of error according to the rule of proportionate distances.

(4) Align the alidade along the trial point and the farthest triangulation station. Loosen the Johnson tripod nut and rotate the table until the vertical wire cuts the station signal. Lock the tripod head.

(5) Draw rays from the three stations. If a triangle is still formed, but smaller than the first, reorient the table slightly in the same direction and resect again. Experienced plane table operators will usually get a correct orientation on the second trial.

Three-point locations are based on the assumption that the triangulation stations are correctly plotted on the sheet. If one of these points is in error, the three-point method of locating the instrument will fail except in the one situation where the error in the plotted position is exactly along the line of sight to the station.

75. Errors and Precautions

The plane table provides a very precise method of mapping, but in order to attain precision, one must become adept in *all* phases of the work. Every observation should be checked before the rodman is signalled off the point. After orienting with the needle, hold a piece of iron or steel, such as a pocket knife, near the compass case to set the needle in motion, then ascertain that it again

comes to rest at the zero point. Do not attempt to carry two sets
of figures in your mind; record each observation in the notebook
as soon as it is made. Set up and practice a pattern, or routine,
for making observations in a definite sequence, for this procedure
reduces the danger of omitting an essential reading or recording.
Notes and plotted distances should be carefully checked every day
or more frequently if occasions arise. Much time and fruitless
effort are saved if errors are discovered and corrected before too
much subsequent work is affected. It is axiomatic in surveying that
it requires less time to employ precautions which reduce the
probability of errors than to correct errors resulting from careless
work.

76. Combining Plane Table Methods

Geologic mapping combines the various methods discussed in
preceding articles. Three-point locations may be obtained by resecting on three marked traverse stations. Much supplemental
control can be added to that obtained from rod stations by intersecting natural objects, such as rocks, trees, posts, and the like,
from traverse or triangulation stations.

Several methods for obtaining difference in elevation have been
described. The competent field man uses all these methods, but
the selection of any one involves an accurate and rapid appraisal
of the field conditions, requirements of precision and time, and
possibly other considerations. It is common practice to employ
only the more precise methods on main traverse lines and a
number of approximate methods for establishing points of secondary control. After one has acquired a sound understanding of
the principles of surveying and mapping and familiarity with the
instruments, judicious application of methods "pays off" in rapid
progress and accurate maps. For the field geologist these accomp-
lishments are worthy of considerable effort.

77. Field Adjustments of the Alidade

Minor adjustments of the alidade must be made from time to
time. Changes in temperature, constant manipulation, or occa-

sional jolts cause screw settings to loosen or tensions to develop in various parts of the instrument with consequent distortion.

THE STRIDING LEVEL

The adjustment of the striding level should be checked at least once a day, and preferably at each new set up. The reversal method for making the *vertical* adjustment is as follows.

(1) Place the striding level on the telescope and exactly center the bubble.

(2) Without disturbing the telescope, lift the level, reverse it end-for-end and carefully replace it on the telescope. If the bubble returns to center, the level is in correct adjustment; but if it comes to rest at some distance from the center position, an adjustment is necessary.

(3) Notice the position of the end of the bubble with reference to the centered position. By means of the right tangent screw, elevate (or depress) the telescope an amount such that the bubble comes to rest *midway* between these two positions. The *telescope* is now nearly, or exactly, level, but the bubble will still be somewhat off center. The object now is to adjust the level bubble to center without disturbing the telescope.

(4) Figure 41 shows the vertical adjustment end of the striding level. If this end of the level tube is to be lowered, loosen capstan nut *a* only a very small amount and then tighten *b* (the opposing nut) until snug, but not tight. To raise the adjustment end, first loosen *b,* then tighten *a.* Relevel the telescope and readjust the level screws until the bubble comes to center when reversed.

The longitudinal axis of the striding level should be parallel to the axis of the telescope, or the bubble will tend to "creep." The *lateral* adjustment is shown in Fig. 42. Remove the stud on the top of the telescope so that the striding level can be rotated about the barrel, as indicated in the figure. Proceed as follows in adjusting.

(1) Set the level exactly on the center of the telescope and bring the bubble to center.

(2) While keeping the feet of the striding level in contact with the rings on the telescope barrel, rotate the level slowly from one side to the other and notice if there is a tendency for the bubble to move toward either end of the tube; if so, an adjustment is necessary.

 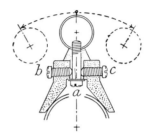

FIG. 41. Vertical adjustment of the striding level. (From Julian W. Low, *Plane Table Mapping,* Harper & Brothers, 1952.)

FIG. 42. Lateral adjustment of the striding level. (From Julian W. Low, *Plane Table Mapping,* Harper & Brothers, 1952.)

(3) Loosen screw a and tighten screw b. Replace the level on the telescope with the same end forward and rotate as before. If the bubble moves toward the same end, but farther, the adjustment has been made in the wrong direction; therefore, loosen screw b and tighten screw a. Repeat until the bubble stays in the center during rotation.

THE AUXILIARY LEVEL

Level the telescope with the striding level. Set the vertical arc exactly on 30° 00′. The auxiliary (arc index) level should come to center; if not, correct by means of the adjustment screw at the end.

THE BEAMAN ARC

When the vertical angle arc reads 30° 00′, the Beaman arc should be exactly on 50; if not, loosen the index mark plate and lightly tap it into position. Tighten the holding screws.

Other adjustments of the alidade are sometimes necessary; but unless one is quite familiar with the internal parts of the instrument they should not be attempted.

78. Air Photographs

Air (or aerial) photographs have become as commonplace in geologic mapping as the plane table or prospector's pick. In general, photos have largely replaced other methods in geologic reconnaissance and are widely employed in conjunction with other techniques in detailed surveys. An exhaustive treatment of the subject would require a book as large as this manual. Obviously, the space given here can do little more than introduce the subject. There are several good textbooks on aerial photogrammetry and the interpretation of air photographs. All geologists charged with field assignments should become familiar with the subject matter in these books in order to utilize photos in the field and office to greatest advantage.

There are two types of air photos—the oblique and the vertical. Only the vertical is considered in following discussions because it is used almost exclusively in geologic work. The vertical photo may be defined as one taken when the optical axis of the camera is vertical. In such a photo, distortions in the relative positions of terrestrial objects are caused only by relief (relative elevations) and minor aberrations of the camera lenses. However, it is not always possible to control the aerial camera sufficiently to prevent some inclination off the vertical, and a condition known as *tilt* is thereby introduced. Tilt in an aerial photo vastly complicates the process of construction of accurate maps.

79. Explanation of Photographic Displacements

A vertical air photograph of flat, level ground is a map having all the scale attributes of a map made by surveying methods. It can be seen in Fig. 43 that the relative positions of points on the photo are exactly the same as those on the ground. The directions of rays from points on the ground pass through the camera and on to the film without deviation; and, since the plane of the photo is parallel to the surface of the ground, the relations are simply those of similar triangles. However, if the surface of the ground is characterized by high relief, the positions of points on the photo

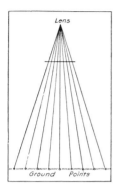

Fig. 43. Vertical air photograph of flat terrain. Points on the photo are in true map relationships.

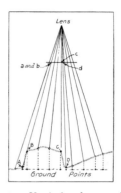

Fig. 44. Vertical photograph of rugged terrain. Interrelations of points on the photo are distorted, as distances between a, b, c, and d are obviously different from the orthographic projections A, B, C, and D.

vary with relation to one another according to (1) the difference in elevation between the points, and (2) the distance from the point to the center of the photo. Figure 44 shows these image displacements; and, by vertical projection to the base of the figure, the relative horizontal positions as would be shown on a map. A ray of light emanating from point A on the ground passes through point B before entering the camera lens. Inasmuch as rays from A and B are coincident, the picture images are also coincident, and only B will show on the photo at position b. Points C and D have the same elevations and intervening distances as A and B; but because they are situated more directly beneath the camera (nearer the picture center, or *principal point*), the error in position is much less. The error in position caused by topographic relief is called the *parallactic displacement*. This displacement is always along a *radial line* from the principal point. It is evident that air photos cannot be used directly as maps where topographic relief is high. However, there are methods whereby accurate maps can be constructed from photos having a large amount of relief distortion. These methods are discussed later.

80. Effects of Tilt in Air Photos

If the optical axis of the aerial camera is inclined when an exposure is made, as mentioned before, *tilt* is introduced in the picture. The effects of tilt are difficult to eliminate except through the use of expensive equipment not generally available to the geologist. Nevertheless, the field geologist using air photos as a base should be cognizant of tilt distortions in order to avoid errors in the construction of base maps.

The horizontal angles between *radial lines* to definite points on a vertical photo are the same as those obtained by sighting with an engineer's transit set up on the ground at the location of the principal point. This relationship holds regardless of the amount of *relief* distortion. However, if the photo is tilted, angles between radial lines are altered so that they no longer are equal to the true ground angles. In addition to changing angular relationships, tilt distorts the normal radial effect of parallactic displacements caused by relief. Occasionally only a few prints in a series will be noticeably tilted and will not match with adjacent overlapping prints. It is sometimes possible to discard such prints and construct the map by means of the surrounding overlapping prints.

81. Scale and Scale Variations

The scale of an air photo is a function of the altitude of the plane above the ground and the focal length of the camera lens. Figure 45 shows diagrammatically the derivation of the scale formula. Let H be the altitude of the plane, AB the distance on the ground, f the focal length of the camera lens, L the position of the lens, and *ab* the photo distance representing *AB*. From the diagram, the following relations are apparent:

$AB/ab = H/f$. Inasmuch as H and f are generally expressed in feet and inches, respectively, the scale fraction will be in these units.

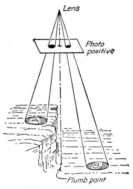

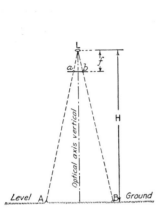

FIG. 45. Diagram showing derivation of the scale formula. (From Julian W. Low, *Plane Table Mapping,* Harper & Brothers, 1952.)

FIG. 46. Effects of ground elevation on the photo scale. Ground figures *A* and *B* are identical, but *A* appears larger on the photo because of its relative nearness. (From Julian W. Low, *Plane Table Mapping,* Harper & Brothers, 1952.)

EXAMPLE:

$H = 10,000$ feet, $f = 8$ inches;

The scale of the photo is $\dfrac{10,000}{8} = 1250$, or 1 inch = 1250 feet.

The scale of the photo varies inversely with the height of the plane above the ground; thus, in the preceding example, if the plane flies at 20,000 feet, the scale is 20,000/8 or 1 inch = 2500 feet. From these relationships, it should be clear that the scale will vary according to differences in the elevation of the terrain, as indicated in Fig. 46.

82. Air Photos as Plane Table Sheets

Air photos may be enlarged to any desired *average* scale for use on the plane table in place of the ordinary blank sheet. The principal advantage is that details which could be mapped only by time-consuming instrumental observations are already "located" on the photo, and elevations can be determined by alidade or barometer. Sometimes it is necessary to locate geologic control points in featureless localities on the photo where ground points cannot be identified. In these circumstances the alidade and stadia rod are used; however, unless the photo scale is exceptionally consistent, there is danger of large errors in position of points plotted on the photo from ground measurements.

83. Rectification

The simplest way to improve the scaling properties of a photo is by rectification, provided distortions are caused by tilt. There are several ways of rectifying a tilted photo, but one permits simultaneous enlargement to any desired *average* scale. This is the projection method, which requires at least three well-spaced points, identified on the photo and accurately located on the ground by surveying methods. These *ground control* points are plotted on a sheet of construction paper on a scale somewhat larger than that of the photo. If the points lie at about the same elevation, parallactic discrepancies are eliminated. The control sheet is fastened to the photographic enlarging table. The photo negative is placed in the enlarger and projected on to the sheet so that the three or more images fall exactly on the plotted positions of the corresponding ground points. If any of the images fail to coincide with their respective plotted positions, either the projector or the enlarging table must be *lowered, raised,* or *tilted* until all points coincide. Now, without disturbing any of the enlarging equipment, sensitized enlarging paper is laid on the table and exposed, as for conventional enlargements. The resulting print has had most of the effects of tilt removed, but if terrain relief is high, some residual tilt distortions still remain.

There are two objections to this method. The first is that it is necessary to have a negative for use in the projector, and often the negatives are not available. The only alternative is to photograph the air photo print with a large mapping camera. Some detail is lost in the process and additional distortions may be introduced. The second objection is that ground control must be obtained for the purpose of rectification and enlargement. Only under special circumstances is it practical to do this. The best method for establishing ground control for rectification is plane table triangulation on the scale desired in the photo plane table sheet.

84. Plotting Locations by Picture Images

For reasons evident in foregoing statements, the field geologist will usually have to use air photos with whatever scale and positional deficiencies as may be present. However, a knowledge of the character of distortions helps to circumvent most pitfalls. One must always keep in mind the fact that parallactic displacements are an expression of difference in elevation. A vertical photo exhibits *constant scale* between points at the *same elevation*. In country where the difference in elevation is large, the photo images are displayed on almost an infinite number of scales. If points were located on the same topographic contour, their relative positions would be comparable in accuracy to a good map; but the scales would be different, though equally accurate, along contours of higher and lower elevations. On any aerial photo, the higher the topographic elevation, the larger the scale. The greatest scale variations will be encountered near the margins of the photo between points having a large difference of elevation.

When using photos in the field, details of geology, wherever possible, should be located simply by identifying and marking on the picture those points which lie at or near the desired features. It is bad practice to make long-distance measurements by direct methods if shorter measurements from definite images can be made. In a general way, errors due to scale discrepancies are proportional to the distance; hence, the shorter the distance, the smaller the error.

It was stated earlier that one of the advantages in using air photos in the field is the wealth of detail shown. The field mapper should make fullest use of these details. Sometimes it is necessary to locate a point in a featureless portion of the photo where direct "spotting" by picture images is impossible. A convenient way to locate such a position relative to other photo details utilizes the alidade and a small piece of tracing paper, as follows.

Tape the tracing paper to the plane table and plot a point in the central part. It is not necessary to orient the plane table. Select three points lying at about the same elevation that are identifiable on the photos. With the alidade, sight and draw a ray to each from the plotted point. Try to select points that will produce horizontal angles in the order of 90 to 150 degrees between rays, as shown in Fig. 47. Now, place the tracing paper over the

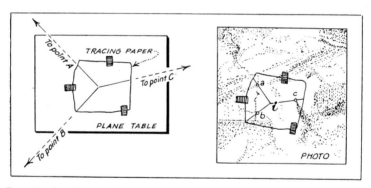

Fig. 47. Locating a point by the tracing paper method. Rays to *A*, *B*, and *C* are drawn on tracing paper by direct sights; tracing is then aligned with rays cutting corresponding points *a*, *b*, and *c* on the photo.

photo and carefully adjust until each ray cuts the corresponding picture image sighted upon. With a plotting needle, prick the central point through the vellum and into the photo at *i*. This process is identical to the tracing paper solution of the three-point problem in plane table surveying.

85. Use of the Plotting Scale on Air Photos

Inasmuch as the scale of a photo varies with elevation, it follows that the same plotting scale cannot be used *directly* for all parts of a photo exhibiting much surface relief. If the scale change is large, then a *scale factor* should be determined in the field according to the following two-stage procedure.

The first stage consists in comparing the scales at different levels of elevation. Set up the alidade on a well-defined picture point. There is no need to orient the table. Carefully measure the distances to other picture points, at about the same elevation, with either a tape or stadia. These sight lines should radiate, as shown in Fig. 48. Referring to the figure, the measured distances

are 450, 810, and 790 to points *a, b,* and *c,* respectively. Now, using a plotting scale most nearly approximating that of the photo, scale these distances on the photo. The scale distance to *a* is 470 feet, thus giving a scale ratio of 450 : 470. When the stadia is to be used for locating points on the photo at about the same elevation as the test, the measured distance must be increased in the relation of 450 to 470, or about 1.0 to 1.04. But this factor should

Fig. 48. Locating a point by proportional distances.

be checked by computing ratios to *b* and *c.* The scaled distance to *b* is 860 feet, and to *c* is 815, and the computed ratios to actual distances are 1.05 and 1.03, respectively; therefore, the average scale factor for this elevation is 1.04 or 4 feet per 100 feet of distance.

Having determined the scale ratio, distances scaled on the photo can be converted to actual distances on the ground. Say that the distance between two photo points, according to the plotting scale, is 1640 feet, and it is necessary to know the actual, or ground distance. From the ratios previously determined, it is known that the photo scale is somewhat larger than the plotting scale; therefore, the scaled distance is *reduced* in the amount of 100/104 and the photo distance of 1640 feet becomes 1576 feet, actual distance.

The foregoing illustration would apply only to measurements on or near the same elevation plane. If ground relief within the area of the photo is high, the scale factor should be determined at different elevations. A considerable error in scaling may be permissible. For this reason, the most practical field procedure is to first determine the ratios at the *highest* and *lowest* elevations. If the difference in these two ratios is small, there may be no need for establishing intermediate ratios.

The second consideration deals with the "lean," or radial parallactic displacement of points on the photo. The safest procedure in the field is to avoid measurements involving large differences in elevation. The computations of these displacements are quite involved, for the amount of displacement is dependent, not only upon the difference in elevation, but also upon the distance from the center of the photo.

86. Orienting Photos in the Field

If the plane table is set up at the ground location of the principal point (picture center) of a vertical photo, the photo may be oriented by aligning the alidade on this point and any other visible one, then rotating the table until the corresponding ground point is brought into the line of sight. This is exactly the same procedure as described earlier for backsight orientation in plane table surveying. Similarly, if the center location is marked by a flag or cairn, the photo may be oriented by setting the tripod on any identifiable outlying feature, aligning the alidade on this point and the principal point, and then rotating the table until the principal point is brought into view. When this alignment has been effected, all other points on the photo are correctly oriented *with reference to the principal* point; but their orientation with respect to each other is a matter of *relative elevation.* Figure 49 shows a photograph that has been oriented from the instrument station at *a* to the principal point, *c.* It is desired to locate a point by stadia at *x,* which lies at the same elevation as the plane table (the elevation of the principal point is immaterial). The direction from *a* to *x* can be located by direct sight and the distance along the instrument rays is plotted according to the correct scale fraction. Next, a second point is needed in a featureless part of the photo in the vicinity of *z.* This point, however, is much higher in elevation than the instrument; therefore, it is displaced radially outward from the center with reference to instrument station *a.* The true orientation of line *az* is *az'.*

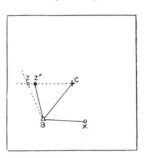

Fᴵᴳ. 49.   Air photo oriented from *a* along line to principal point at *c.* Point *x* is at the same elevation as *a.* Point *z* is higher than *a* and is displaced outward from *c.* Correct orientation is *az'.*

From the foregoing discussion it should be evident that a photo plane table sheet may be oriented by sighting from any definite point toward a mark at the center of the photo or a definite picture point *near* the picture center. The sheet may also be oriented by backsighting from an instrument station at one photo feature to any other photo feature provided the two points are at approximately the same elevation or lie roughly along a radial line. These procedures apply only to vertical (untilted) photographs.

87. Transferring Photo Data to the Base Map

The scale variations inherent in air photos of terrain exhibiting appreciable relief complicate the process of reducing all field data to the same scale. The simplest way to do this is by photo-projection. Several drafting room machines now available embody adjustments for scale variation and some provide for projecting from the plane of the photo to an inclined map plane, thus making it possible to transfer work directly from a distorted portion of a photograph on to a true scale base map. These methods, however, are not adaptable to many field operations; so the field man must resort to more laborious methods. In preparation for this type of work, the base map should be drawn on cellulose acetate or similar material having a high degree of transparency. Vellum and tracing linen are not suitable because they do not permit a clear view of the gray-toned features of the photograph.

In order to transfer photo data to a base map it is essential that a number of points on each print be correctly located on the base. In other words, ground control is necessary. It is common practice to use section and township lines for this purpose. These lines usually show on the photos as trails along fences or roads on the section lines. If the land grid has not been established by plane table surveying, it can be plotted from township plats obtainable at small cost from the U.S. General Land Office, or from county surveyors.

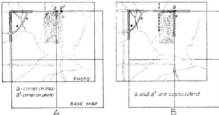

FIG. 50. Adjusting scale differences by shifting tracing from position *A* to position *B*. Details are sketched in localities where tracing points are nearly coincident with photo images.

The principle involved in transferring the photo features to the map is simple. It consists in reducing any geometric figure and its contained elements or points on the photo to the corresponding figure, drawn to correct scale and shape on the map. In the case of a square section the method is as follows.

Figure 50 shows the photo outline of a section placed *(A)* so that the northwest corner coincides with the corresponding corner on the transparent base map. While in this position, details in the immediate vicinity, as within the dashed line, are traced. Next, the base map is shifted to B, so that the northeast corners are coincident, and features in this area are traced. The southeast and southwest corners are treated similarly. Finally, the tracing is adjusted so that the centers of the section coincide and this portion is traced. Usually, a small amount of intermediate shifting is desirable if the difference in scale is large. This may be done either by inspection and estimation or by subdividing the section into smaller areas. In the absence of section lines, triangles, quadrilaterals, or polygons formed by located points are adjusted in a similar fashion.

The method for adjusting the position of one point with reference to only two established points is somewhat different from that previously described.

In Fig. 51A, the problem is to locate point x accurately on the base map. On the photo the apparent (scaled) distance from a to b is 1650 feet. These points have been located on the map (Fig. 51B) and the distance between them is 1480. This is a scale ratio of 1480/1650 or .89. On the photo, draw a line from x perpendicular to ab, to locate intersection c. Scale distance ac, in this case 630 feet (on the photo scale). Point

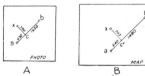

Fig. 51. Locating points by similar figures and proportional scales.

c on the map is distant from a in the amount $1480/1650 \times 630 = 540$ feet, as determined from the photo. Plot this point and erect a perpendicular. The distance xc on the photo is 790 feet. The corresponding distance on the map is $790 \times .89 = 703$ feet. Plot point x 703 feet from c' on the map. If the points involved lie at appreciably different elevations, the location of x will not be precisely correct.

Proportional dividers aid greatly in transferring photo data.

This instrument has an adjustable axis which permits setting the two pairs of points in any ratio to each other. One pair is set to the photo scale and the other to the map scale. Similarly, any of several types of circular ratio computers can be used for scale reduction.

88. Photo Overlay Sheets

A sheet of thin, frosted acetate may be taped on each photo print before it is fastened to the plane table sheet. Fine inked lines should be drawn along the edge collimation marks and a cross at the principal point. These lines serve to register the acetate over the print. The frosted surface is excellent for fine pencil sketching and definite points can be pricked with a plotting needle. The acetate provides a means of preserving the photo for future use without inhibiting its usefulness on the plane table. Another advantage of the transparent overlay is that direct prints, such as Ozalid, can be made directly from the original field work.

89. Interpretation of Air Photos and Mapping Methods

The methods and procedures which enable the field man to use air photos as a mapping device are different from, though related to, the interpretation of the photos. When photos are used in the field, interpretation is largely a matter of correlation by direct observation. Features appearing on the photos are examined on the ground and correlations between the image and the actual object are made for future reference. In a short time the field man will be able to identify the great majority of photo features. This manual is not concerned with photo interpretation beyond the stage of *field recognition*. Several good books treat the broader subject in detail.

The principal problem of the field man is two-fold: first, to identify and accurately locate *on the ground* such features as are needed in the construction of the map; and, second, to map these features in the correct relationship to other details appearing on the map. The first is a matter of careful observation; for example, in sparsely wooded regions, the individual trees apparently photograph as dark gray to nearly black spots or short lines (depending on the type of tree). However, upon careful examination in the field or under a stereoscope, it will be seen that it is the *shadow* of the tree that photographs as a sharply defined detail, the tree itself being rather obscure. When a stereoscope is not available, the field man spots the photo position of a tree at the south, southeast, or southwest end of the dark shadow. Similarly, the position of the channel of a stream or ravine may be difficult to locate where heavy shadows result from steep or sheer walls. The field man must constantly be aware of the dangers of erroneous physical interpretations.

After correctly identifying and pricking a location on the photo, there still remains the problem of correctly locating the point on a map. Some of the field procedures discussed show how to avoid or minimize discrepancies in scale and location caused by topographic relief. These methods produce only approximate results, for no field method will yield precisely accurate locations. A drafting room method by which accurate locations can be made is briefly described in the following article.

90. Radial Line Triangulation

Radial line triangulation differs from the well-known radial line intersection and radial line plot methods in two respects: (1) each photo print is placed and oriented under a base map acetate tracing independently of other prints, and (2) a larger number of points located by surveying methods is required for the triangulation method. The radial line triangulation method is especially adaptable for use in combination with plane table triangulation.

GROUND CONTROL

Although any surveying method may be used in establishing ground control, triangulation has distinct advantages and, therefore, this type of control will be assumed in discussions that follow. The photos should be carried in the field so that points located by the survey can be identified, marked on the photos, and numbered on the photos as well as the plane table sheets. Since the overlap on the photos is somewhat over 60 percent, every point located on the ground will appear on three photos, with, possibly, the exception of a very narrow strip on one of three overlapping prints. Before a *photo control point* is tied into the survey, the identity of the point should be checked on the three overlapping prints (called, collectively, a stereo-triplet). In setting up the ground control, it must be kept in mind that a minimum of three locations arranged in the form of a triangle are to appear on each print. Much time and effort in the field can be saved if the work is carefully laid out to gain the maximum of control with the smallest number of stations.

91. Transposition of Centers

Because of the two-thirds overlap, the ground location of the principal point of an air photo appears near the margins of the

two adjacent prints. The process of identifying, by picture detail, the positions of principal points and relocating them on the adjacent prints is called *transposition* of principal points. When two adjacent photos are arranged so that the two centers and the two *transposed* centers lie on the same straight line, the photos are correctly oriented with reference to each other, as shown in Fig. 52. If a series (flight) of photos is so aligned that all centers and transposed centers lie on mutual straight lines, then the entire series is correctly oriented, each photo with reference to the others. Although the photos are correctly oriented by this procedure, the spacing between principal points and orientation of the series with reference to map bearings are dependent on fixed ground positions to which photo points have been tied.

Fig. 52. Orientation of two successive photos along flight line. Centers and transposed centers lie on same straight line.

92. Orientation by Three Points

It will be recalled that the relative directions of radial lines to photo points are unaffected by parallactic displacements of the points. This principle makes it possible to orient and locate the center of a single vertical photo on the base map.

Figure 53A represents a photo marked for radial line orientation. Points *a*, *b*, and *c* have been surveyed on the ground and identified and pricked on the photo. From the principal point short radial lines are drawn through the control points, as shown, by means of a straight edge and a soft pencil or fine pen. In B of the figure, the acetate base map is placed over the photo and adjusted until the three located points (on the acetate) are cut by the radial lines through corresponding images on the photo. When this relationship has been achieved, the photo is correctly located and oriented on the map. The picture center is now pricked through the map and numbered the same as the photo.

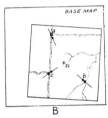

FIG. 53. Radial line triangulation: A. Photo marked for orientation. B. Photo correctly oriented under the base tracing.

93. Orientation by Fixed Centers

In the preceding article it is evident that the *location* of the principal point on the map is dependent on exact adjustment of points on the radial lines. An alternative method reduces or eliminates this source of error.

If principal points are identified by photo detail on the ground and then tied into the plane table survey, these locations become fixed axes about which the photos are rotated for orientation. Furthermore, the lines connecting these stations are fixed directional lines, established by surveying methods, along which an entire flight of photos may be oriented and accurately placed with reference to ground positions. Thus, each photo, when oriented on the flight line, under the base acetate, is exactly analogous to a plane table instrument station in a backsight traverse, provided, of course, the photos are essentially free from tilt. Likewise, a photo oriented by three points, as in the preceding topic, is analogous to a plane table oriented and located by the three-point method. A further comparison may be made in that the position and orientation by three points is strongest when the principal point lies *within* a triangle formed by the three ground control points, just as the three-point plane table location is strongest when the station is within the great triangle.

94. Marking Photos for Secondary Control

When photos are located and oriented by either of the two methods discussed, the number of additional points that can be

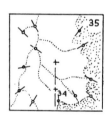

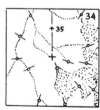

FIG. 54. Adjacent overlapping photos marked for radial line intersection.

accurately located by photos alone is dependent only on the clarity and profusion of photo details, such as trail and stream intersections, isolated trees, rocks, buildings, road corners, small patches of barren ground, grass-covered seeps and springs, or large ant hills and rodent mounds. Any point whatsoever may be located if it can positively be identified on at least two, but preferably three, overlapping photos. The process of radial marking is as follows.

Identify the same point on three prints. Draw a short radial through the point on each photo, extending about one-half inch on both sides. Select another required location and mark the three photos. If desired, these points may be numbered on each print, though usually this is not necessary, for later identification. Continue this rou-

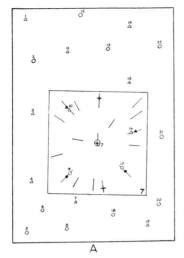

A

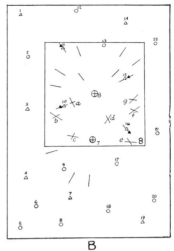

B

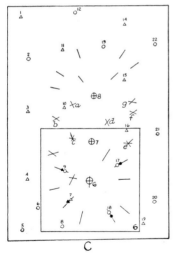

C

Fig. 55. Steps in radial line triangulation. Photos 7, 8 and 6
are placed under the control tracing, oriented, and radial lines are
drawn successively, as in A, B,
and C. (From Julian W. Low,
Plane Table Mapping, Harper &
Brothers, 1952.)

tine until all the required locations are marked. Now take the fourth (adjacent) photo in the flight and mark the previously selected points from the end region overlapping this print. Proceed in like fashion to each succeeding print in the flight. Figure 54 represents a pair of photos marked for intersection.

95. Intersecting the Secondary Control

Place a marked photo under the base sheet and orient it by methods described earlier. Now trace the radial lines through all points marked for secondary control, as in Fig. 55A, photo number 7. Remove this photo and treat the adjacent photo, number 8, in the same manner. This operation results in two-ray intersections lettered from *a* to *g* in B of the figure. These intersections are the true map positions of the marked points, provided there are no errors in placing and orienting the photos or drawing the rays. However, the locations are checked by drawing rays from photo number 6 in C of the figure. It can be seen in the figure that three-ray intersections occur only in the region where the *three* photos overlap, as at *c* and *e,* and single rays appear at the south and north ends of the stereo-triplet. These rays would be intersected if additional photos in the series were introduced.

When a flight strip is completed, an adjacent strip is processed in the same manner. Rays along the side (east and west) margins are intersected to furnish map control in these regions. A few points such as *e,* are already located by three-ray intersections; therefore, the rays to these points from adjacent flight strips serve as checks on the accuracy of the intersection network.

96. Relations of Scale and Bearings

When the radial line triangulation method is used the scale of the resulting map is determined solely by the scale on which the primary ground control is plotted on the acetate base sheet. The method is subject to the same rules as ground triangulation, whose scale is determined by the plotted length of the base line. The base line in photo work is the map distance between plotted principal points. Basically, the photos provide only horizontal angles originating at the principal points; hence, the amount of separation of these points of origin (picture centers) within reasonable limits has no bearing on the accuracy of the map. Photos of considerably different scales can be used without difficulty. However, scales greatly exceeding those of the photos should be avoided, because of drafting errors introduced by projecting radial lines beyond the marked photo points.

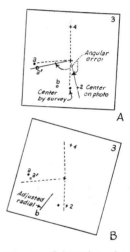

The methods described in preceding articles apply only to vertical photos. If a photo is badly tilted, the horizontal angles originating at the principal point are distorted; therefore, intersected locations will be in error. When the method of "fixed centers" is used, the effect of distorted central angles can be partially or wholly removed.

Figure 56A shows tilted photo 3 oriented on the flight line toward the surveyed position of the center of photo 4. In this orientation, the line to the transposed center of photo 2 does not coincide with the surveyed line; also a surveyed point at a does not coincide with the radial line through a'. It is now necessary to locate a point b by intersection. This point is situated about $\frac{2}{3}$ of the angular distance from a to the principal point at photo 2. Photo 3 is rotated about its fixed principal point until the

Fig. 56. Orientation of a photo on a fixed principal point located by surveying methods. Horizontal angles are corrected by rotating the photo about the principal point.

angular error between a and photo 3 center is adjusted in proportion to the central angle relationship between a, b, and the line to photo center 2. The radial line to b is now drawn on the base tracing as in B of the figure. All other points on this tilted photo are treated in a similar fashion. This method is an approximation; but experience has shown that it produces surprisingly good results.

97. Auxiliary Mapping Methods

The field geologist usually employs a number of instruments and methods which supplement those treated in the foregoing portion of this chapter. These methods are an important part of the field geologist's "tool kit," and a knowledge of their applications and limitations is essential to efficient field operations.

98. Pacing

Measuring distance by pacing consists in counting the number of steps while walking from one point to another and then multiplying by the average length of the step. This is, perhaps, the oldest method of measuring distance, yet it is often used today in connection with field mapping. Remarkably accurate reconnaissance maps have been made by using only pacing for distances and magnetic compass for bearings; but a relatively high order of accuracy is attained only by recognizing the main sources of error and then taking certain precautionary action to avoid them.

Length of Pace

When pacing distances, one should use a natural stride for the reason that it is most likely to be uniform and is less tiring than attempting to step according to some predetermined length. The "natural" pace length varies for most persons in several ways: the length of stride varies for level, uphill, and downhill walking; therefore, the average normal pace length should be determined for different field conditions. The results of these measurements can be recorded in the field book for future reference. It has been observed that the "normal" pace length may gradually change over a period of time, especially if one works in the field only a portion of the year. The pace length should be checked from time to time.

To determine the average pace length, measure a distance of

several hundred feet, by stadia or tape, then count the steps over the same course. The length of pace is the measured distance divided by the number of steps.

When field work is done on horses or mules, their steps may be counted and the distances traversed are computed in the same way as just discussed.

99. Time-Distance Measurements

For rough reconnaissance work on water, the time of travel from one point to another can be converted to approximate distance. This method is reasonably accurate for small-scale maps where (1) there is little, or no, perceptible current, (2) the boat is allowed to drift with a current whose speed is known, (3) an average known rate of rowing or paddling is maintained, and (4) a motor set at a given throttle position is used. Wind, unknown currents, inaccurate bearings, and poorly established time-distance relationships are the principal sources of error.

The time-distance method is frequently used in primitive country where travel is mainly by canoe or small boat, as in the Tropics or the Northwest Territories of Canada. Early explorers of western North America depended largely on travel time on horses for the measurement of long distances, and later measurements by direct surveying have proved the value of the method, although travel time on land is ordinarily less reliable than on water.

100. The Brunton Pocket Transit

The Brunton Pocket Transit, usually called simply "Brunton," has for many years been so essential to the field geologist that it is generally thought of as a symbol of the profession. Details of the construction of the instrument are shown in Fig. 57.

The Brunton is used as a surveyor's compass, hand level, clinometer, and hand transit. It may be mounted on a special plastic base for use as an alidade on a traverse (plane) table, or on a tripod as a universally movable sighting device. The manipulations of the Brunton are described in the following paragraphs.

BEARINGS AND AZIMUTHS

Around the periphery of the compass case is a graduated circle. Those made for military uses are graduated in mills; this type is not practical for geologic work. The geologist's Brunton is graduated from 0 to 90 degrees in each of four quadrants. Readings of bearings are referenced to the north or south points, and the amount of magnetic declination is adjusted by a screw (Fig. 57) so that true north (or south) bearings are read directly.

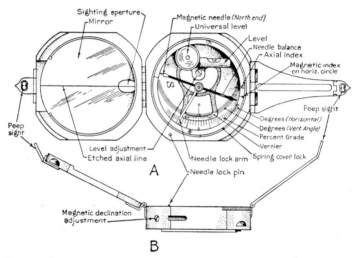

FIG. 57.   Parts of the Brunton pocket transit. (From Julian W. Low, *Plane Table Mapping,* Harper & Brothers, 1952.)

Bearings with the Brunton are determined in two ways. In Fig. 58 the Brunton is held at waist level with the mirror tilted so that it reflects the sighting arm and the point to which the bearing is being determined. The circular (universal) level must be centered. Align the collimation line of the mirror with the peep sight on the arm and the point ahead. Let the needle come to rest and read the bearing. In Fig. 59 the Brunton is held at eye level. The

mirror is turned back toward the observer. The point is sighted
directly from the rear peep sight to the collimation line appearing
in the mirror aperture (Fig. 57A). The level, needle, and arc are

FIG. 58. Sighting a bearing with the
Brunton held at waist level.

FIG. 59. Sighting a bearing with the
Brunton at eye level.

observed in the mirror. Bearings taken by this method should
be checked, for readings are reversed in the mirror and errors are
easily made.

THE BRUNTON AS A HAND LEVEL

When the vertical arc is set at zero the line of sight through the
peep sight and the mirror aperture is level when the level bubble
is centered. The instrument is held
as in Fig. 60. The process of hand
leveling is described in Article 102.

INCLINED SIGHTS

When determining a vertical angle
the Brunton is held as in Fig. 61. The
point is sighted in the same manner
as for hand leveling, and the vertical
arc level bubble is centered by means
of the level arm on the right side of
the compass case. The vertical angle
is then read on the arc. The vertical

FIG. 60. Sighting the Brunton
as a hand level.

arc vernier is graduated to 10 minutes of arc.

The inclination of any real plane, such as an exposed stratum, can be determined by placing the compass case on the plane surface, oriented parallel to the dip, and centering the level as in the preceding paragraph. Also, the Brunton may be held as in

Fig. 61 and aligned by inspection along an inclined surface while setting the vertical arc to center the bubble of the arc level.

101. Adjusting the Brunton

REMOVAL OF THE GLASS COVER

The glass cover must be removed for making all adjustments of the Brunton. The glass is held in place by a spring wire seated in a bezel in the periphery of the compass case. Insert the tip of a small knife or thin screw driver behind the wire and pry upward and inward toward the center of the case. Start at one end of the wire ring and work toward the other end. Take care not to distort the circular curve of the wire.

FIG. 61. Reading a vertical angle by sighting along the edge of the Brunton while the bubble is centered.

ADJUSTING THE NEEDLE

After removing the glass cover, carefully lift the needle and bushings off the pivot. Dust the jewel socket in the needle with a soft dry brush or feather. Wipe the steel-pointed pivot with a *slightly* oiled cloth. Examine the pivot under a magnifying glass. If it is rough or blunt, hone lightly with a fine Arkansas or novaculite hone. Hold the case flat on a level surface, such as the center of a leveled plane table and center the circular level. Replace the needle on the pivot. If one end dips lower than the other, slide the wire wrapping on the needle shaft until the needle is perfectly balanced. The intensity of the vertical component of magnetic attraction varies from one region to another; so the balance of the needle must be adjusted from time to time.

UNIVERSAL LEVEL

Carefully level a plane table. Place the Brunton in the center of the table, and hold firmly in this position. The bubble should be centered. If not, spring the soft metal frame with a knife blade until properly adjusted.

VERTICAL ARC LEVEL

The simplest way to adjust the vertical arc level utilizes the plane table.

With the alidade striding level centered, select some object 200 to 500 feet distant that is cut by the middle wire. The object must be small, but visible to the unaided eye. Carefully zero the vertical arc on the Brunton. Place the Brunton on the plane table and sight the distant object in the peep sights. If the bubble is off

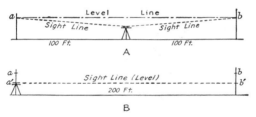

Fig. 62. Establishing a level line with a bubble out of adjustment, and then (in B) using this line to adjust the level.

center, it requires adjustment. Loosen the central adjustment screw (Fig. 57A) very slightly and slip the frame holding the level tube. Reset the arc and sight the object again. Continue this procedure until the bubble is centered, then tighten the adjustment screw.

The "two-peg" method, commonly used for adjusting all types of surveying instruments, is applicable to the Brunton when the plane table is not available. The principle of this method is as follows.

In Fig. 62, a and b are two poles, situated a few hundred feet apart, and A is a point from which Brunton readings are taken, *exactly* midway between the poles. Aa and Ab are lines of sight on the poles with the vertical arc level set at zero. If the level is out of adjustment the sight lines will be inclined, as shown in the figure; however, the errors to a and b are equal, so these two points have the *same* elevation though different from the elevation at A. Once the level line from a to b has been established by the foregoing procedure, the Brunton is sighted from one of these points to the other and the level is adjusted by the method described earlier.

102. Hand Leveling

Hand leveling consists in measuring the difference in elevation between two points by means of an instrument held in the hands.

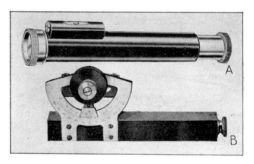

Fig. 63.   A. The Locke hand level. B. The Abney hand level or clinometer.

Several types of instruments may be used for this purpose, but the methods are basically the same for all.

The *Locke* hand level is shown in Fig. 63A. Some prefer to hold the level in one hand, but this is difficult if a relatively high order of accuracy is required or if a strong wind is blowing. The Locke hand level contains a small bubble tube, a horizontal sighting line, and a prism which permits simultaneous view of the bubble, the horizontal line, and the mark or object target.

The *Abney* hand level, or clinometer (Fig. 63B) is equipped with a vertical angle arc and arc level. When used for direct leveling, the arc is set at zero, as with the Brunton.

The *telescopic* (*stadia*) hand level contains a low-precision level, a set of stadia wires as in the alidade, a system of lenses with magnifications ranging up to about 10 diameters, and prisms which provide a view of the bubble adjacent to the cross wires.

In Fig. 64 it is apparent that the difference in elevation between A and B is the sum of the steps 1, 2, and 3. If one stands erect at a and sights a level line to a point on the ground at b, the difference in elevation is equal to the height from the ground to the observer's eyes. Now, if he stands at b and sights to c, the difference in elevation between a and c, is the observer's height $\times$ 2. This

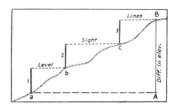

FIG. 64. Process of hand leveling. The sum of heights 1, 2, and 3 equals the difference in elevation AB.

procedure may be extended for any number of steps, but it is essential to keep an accurate count of the number of steps taken. The horizontal distance from one point to another has no bearing on the process if the level is in adjustment.

A *Jacob's staff* is a light wooden pole, such as a curtain rod, which may be painted in graduations of feet and tenths of feet. The exact length is a matter of choice and circumstances, but generally it is such that a hand level placed on the top is at a comfortable reading height. The Jacob's staff is used when the accuracy demanded in hand leveling is somewhat higher than can be attained by the more usual methods. The staff provides a means for accurately measuring fractions of steps and also a steady rest for the hand level. Some sort of rest is almost essential for the telescopic hand level. The Jacob's staff has special application in the measurement of stratigraphic sections, as discussed in the chapter dealing with that subject.

103. Indirect Determinations

It is sometimes necessary to determine the difference in elevation between points on the two sides of a valley, or, perhaps, on the opposite side of a rugged canyon. Much needless effort can be avoided by employing an indirect procedure.

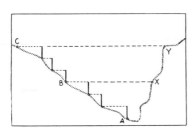

In Fig. 65, the geologist is at A. The difference in elevation between X and Y, on the opposite side of the canyon, is required, as is the difference in elevation between A and X.

FIG. 65. Indirect hand leveling. Obtaining difference in elevation between X and Y by hand leveling from B to C.

Hand level up to a point B, which, by sighting across the canyon, is known to be at the same elevation as X; therefore the difference in elevation between A and B is the same as between A and X. Now hand level from B to C and by sighting across to Y establish this level line. The difference in elevation between B and C is the same as between X and Y.

104. Stadia Interval Steps

The effective spacing of stadia wires in the telescopic hand level is the same as in the alidade or transit; i.e., the relation between interval and distance is 1:100. At a distance of, say, 500 feet the intercept between the upper and lower wires is 5 feet. This relationship permits the determination of difference in elevation or grade of slope from the point of observation.

GRADE OF SLOPE

Percent grade is the number of feet difference in elevation per 100 feet of distance; thus, an elevation difference of 5 feet between two points situated 250 feet apart is a grade of 5/250, or 2 percent. When the telescopic hand level is held in a level position the sight line on the middle wire is a level line. The sight line on either the upper or lower wire departs from the level line at the rate of 0.5 foot ($\frac{1}{2}$ interval) per 100 feet of distance, or 0.50 percent.

In Fig. 66 the instrument is leveled. The problem is to determine the grade to a point below the level line and out of the field of the telescope. While the bubble is centered, select some small object on the landscape that is cut by the lower wire, such as a in the figure. Next, move the upper wire into this position, whereupon the objective, or target point x comes into view. But the wires have not yet been brought to the target, so the upper wire is lowered to b. Now the target point x is midway between the middle and upper wires, and it is evident that the middle (level reference) wire has crossed the point. The level has been moved through two full intervals and it is therefore inclined on a grade of two percent. However, the middle wire passed the point an estimated $\frac{1}{4}$ interval, and the grade from the instrument station to point x is $2 - \frac{1}{4} = 1.75$ percent.

Fig. 66. Determining difference in elevation with the stadia hand level by the interval step method.

When the middle wire is read *short* of the target point, the fractional step is added.

Difference in Elevation

When the grade is known, the difference in elevation can be computed provided the distance to the point also is known. The distance may be measured by stadia, tape, or pacing, or it may be scaled from a map or air photograph. For example, if the distance is 1150 feet and the grade is 3.5 percent, the difference in elevation is $1150/100 \times 3.5 = 40.25$ feet.

105. Hand Leveling from Preëstablished Elevations

Hand leveling does not require the aid of an assistant, so it is an especially useful method for the geologist working alone. Nevertheless there are inherent errors in the method and if carried too far the hand level traverse may become grossly in error. Potential cumulative errors can sometimes be reduced by taking advantage of earlier level work in the area. Moderately accurate levels are usually run on state and federal roads, railroads, and large ditches or canals. The gradients of large streams are in some places determined for power, navigation, or irrigation purposes. Where such surveys exist they may be used as the main lines of control for reconnaissance mapping wherein the hand level is employed for establishing elevations.

CHAPTER V

Topography and Areal Geology

106. General Remarks

The surface distribution and areal patterns of rock formations are governed by the thickness or bulk of the rocks, structure, and topography. A variation in any one of these factors affects the pattern of the areal geology. Thus, a thin formation may occupy a large area if the dip is conformable with surface slope; and a relatively thick formation may occupy a narrow outcrop band under certain conditions of topography and structure. Just as a triangle problem may be solved if one angle and the length of one side are known, any one of the three factors controlling areal geology can be determined approximately if the other two are known. A few simple examples given further on illustrate this principle.

Problems and methods concerning stratigraphy and structure are treated in chapters devoted to these subjects; and although they constitute an important aspect of topography and areal geology, they are brought into following discussions only where essential to specific examples.

Because of the interrelationships of topography and areal geology, this manual departs from the general practice of treating the two subjects as if they were unrelated. Perhaps the presentation under one title will in itself emphasize the close pictorial and genetic relationship as both are strictly aspects of the *surface* of the earth.

PART I. TOPOGRAPHY

107. Geological Relations

Topography is the physical configuration of the surface of the earth. From a purely physical viewpoint it is a subject dealing with surface forms, elevations, stream patterns, and the like; but most of the causes for development of topographic features are geological, and for this reason, the topography of a region may reveal much of significance to the field geologist. When one has correctly interpreted and analyzed regional and local topography, he may have taken a significant step in the analysis of the surface geology. This is an important phase of field geology that is frequently ignored.

The topographer whose training does not include geology is likely to overlook certain relationships of forms, stream anomalies, and areal geology and therefore fail to capture on his maps the characters which find expression in the sensitive sketching of contours within the framework of control points. The geologist, on the other hand, is peculiarly equipped to produce a map that is somewhat better than an engineering generalization.

108. Basic Map Control

Inasmuch as topography is three-dimensional, the vertical (elevation), and the horizontal (planimetric) control are of equal importance. The primary control for both may consist of a triangulation net, which can be set up by plane table or transit-theodolite methods. This type of dual control is most applicable where reconnaissance work in unsurveyed regions is undertaken and where the character of the terrain is favorable for the unobstructed visibility required for triangulation. The basic control for some topographic surveys consists of transit traverse and moderately precise level lines, or these methods together with triangulation.

In general, the methods used in establishing the primary control for topographic mapping are the same as for geologic or any other type. The U.S. Geological Survey has standardized all operations for their topographic surveys. The primary control is generally triangulation of a high order of precision. The triangulation points are plotted on the plane table sheet according to the longitude and latitude on the polyconic projection system. The objective in the sheet layout is to have not less than three intervisible primary triangulation stations on each sheet, from which a plane table triangulation net can be developed. Elevations are carried in the triangulation, but level lines are also run for further elevation control.

The field geologist may have occasion to do the topography prior to geologic mapping, or, perhaps, simultaneously. It may not be necessary in many types of projects to meet the high standards of accuracy required by the Topographic Division of the U.S. Geological Survey. Carefully plotted section and township lines, whose bearings and lengths can be obtained from the U. S. General Land Office, may be sufficient. Air photos aid greatly in recovering land corners on the ground. These corners are marked with signals (flags or cairns) from which spur traverse or resection work can be done.

Plane table triangulation in relatively open country is the best method for establishing accurate control at small cost in time. A few well-placed points can be established by this method and secondary control may be filled in by plane table traverse or resection. (See Chapter IV.)

109. Control for Topographic Detail

The basic control for topographic mapping is established without special regard to topographic features; it is the skeleton of the map, and the overall (rather than local) accuracy is dependent on the accuracy of the basic control. The detail or sketching control is the means of measuring and locating topographic features and fixing the positions of contours. Many devices and "tricks" are employed in obtaining this sketching control, and the expected precision of the different methods varies greatly.

Generally speaking, if the density of elevation points or stations on the map is extremely high, anyone knowing the basic principles of contouring can draw accurate contours. However, the proficiency of a topographer is not determined solely on the basis of accuracy of the map, but also on *how* he goes about making the map in the field. An experienced topographer will make an accurate map with only a small fraction of the elevation points required by the novice, and consequently will be able to map a much larger area in a day's time.

Control for sketching may be considered as all surveyed (located) points, whose elevations are known, together with approximate positions, bearings, or elevations, derived by any means whatsoever that confine the sketching of contours and planimetric features within certain space limitations.

110. "Side Shot" Sketching Control

Plane table triangulation and traversing are discussed in Chapter IV. These methods are used for the basic control. Side shots are stations not in the traverse line or tied directly into triangulation. The position and elevation of a side shot may be no less accurate than a traverse station, but there is no *check* on its accuracy. The primary control for topographic sketching consists of these side shots, which are determined by stadia methods. The progress attained in topographic mapping is determined to a very large extent by the judicious use of side shots. Wherever possible, make one station do the work of two.

The necessary accuracy in position and elevation of side shots is dependent on the scale of the map, the contour interval, and the character of the topography. It is quite important for the topographer to know how precisely the stadia rod need be read in order to give the required accuracy in distance. On a scale of 1:48,000 (4000 feet = 1 inch), 0.01 inch = 40 feet. The average plane table man cannot consistently plot distances closer than about 0.02 inch, or 80 feet on this scale. It would be absurd to strive for stadia distance determinations within say, 10 feet (0.1 foot on the rod) except when the stadia distance is used in the computation of difference in elevation. For a scale of 1:48,000, distances should be read and plotted to the nearest 50 feet. To require more accurate readings does not improve the quality of the map; it *does* place a meaningless limitation on the instrument-man.

The man in the field must determine where the larger discrepancies in the positions of side shots can or cannot be tolerated. On very steep slopes where contours are closely spaced, a relatively small error in the location of a control point may have a significant effect on the character and accuracy of the map.

The preceding discussion applies only to side shots located for the purpose of controlling contours. Definite map points such as stream confluences, land corners, and other planimetric features should be located as accurately as possible. Usually side shots or traverse stations will be located at these points, but other methods, discussed later, are also acceptable.

The elevation of side shots may be determined by whatever method is fastest, yet sufficiently reliable to meet accuracy requirements. The Beaman Arc is faster than vertical angles. The step and gradienter methods are fast and accurate if differences in elevation are small, but too large for level wire readings.

111. Supplemental Sketching Control

Much of the progress of a topographic survey rests on the judgment and training of the rodmen. In rough or wooded country critical features of the terrain may be just out of the range of visibility from the instrument station. Often the rodman can give a shot nearby and with a hand level and pocket compass determine the position and elevation of the obscure point. He should carry a notebook to record such observations and for sketches that may help the topographer when a round of shots has been completed.

Rodmen should be instructed in the use of hand instruments and in estimating or pacing short distances.

Either the Abney hand level or Brunton is a very useful instrument for the topographer. Local detail can be filled in by means of these hand instruments together with paced or estimated distances. From the angle of inclination on a slope, as determined by sighting with a Brunton, the spacing of contours is readily determined by a simple calculation using the formula

Spacing = contour interval × cotangent of slope angle

EXAMPLE:

Slope angle, 12°
Contour interval, 50 feet
Distance between contours is 4.7 (= cot) × 50 = 235 feet

This relationship enables the topographer to extend the contouring beyond the last elevation point, or to space contours where a break in slope occurs between two elevation points. This method is very useful in densely wooded country where it is difficult to place rod stations in the desired locations. The Brunton arc is graduated in percent grade as well as degrees. If the grade scale is used, there is no need for trigonometric tables.

EXAMPLE:

Slope grade, 20%
Contour interval, 50 feet
Distance between contours is $\dfrac{50}{20} \times 100 = 250$ feet

By utilizing the relationships of the components of a slope angle, not only the spacing, but also the bearings of contours can be determined from a single point of observation. In Fig. 67, the topographer is at the foot of a slope at A from which he can see the surface of the ground through corridors in the trees to points B and C. Bearings and slope grades are determined along these lines, as follows:

AB : Bearing N 30° E, slope grade, 9%; Contour interval, 50 feet

AC : Bearing N 5° W, slope grade 18%

From point A on the plane table, whose location has been determined, lightly sketch these bearings. Compute the contour spacing ($AB = 555$ feet) and ($AC = 277$ feet), and plot these distances from A along the respective lines. Contours pass through corresponding points on the two components, as shown in the drawing. Obviously the point A must be at the ground position of a contour, which can easily be determined by hand level from any point nearby whose elevation has been established. This method applies only where A and the two components are essentially in the same plane. It would not be used where elevations and locations could be determined directly by

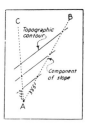

Fig. 67. Determining the direction and spacing of contours from two components of the slope angle.

stadia, but it is a useful and time-saving method under some circumstances.

The topographer should take advantage of the many opportunities to use the intersection method of locating easily identifiable objects on the landscape to augment the stadia sketching control. This method is especially applicable in rugged country where it is difficult for the rodman to reach locations where elevations are needed. If the object sighted upon is an appreciable height above the ground, the vertical angle should be read at ground level, as for example, at the base of a tree.

112. Linear Features

Straight linear features, such as fences, may not be required on the map in its final form, yet they are quite helpful to the topographer in furnishing control for contour sketching. Figure 68 is a traverse along a main highway. Instrument station 4 is carefully selected to lie on the range line of a fence. The alidade is aligned on the fence and a line is drawn on the sheet. At stations 8 and 10, farther along the traverse, a number of posts are intersected and vertical angles are determined to each, thus providing a series of contouring control points without the assistance of a rodman or additional traverse. A transmission line drawn at station 8 will serve a similar purpose when a point is reached where cuts will intersect the line with sufficiently wide angles to yield accurate locations.

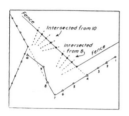

Fig. 68. Utilizing straight linear features as supplemental sketching control.

There are many ways in which the instrumentman can save time and effort by planning instrument locations that are aligned with features on the ground. Courses of streams, cliffs, ridges, terraces, and escarpments are but a few of the many topographic forms whose map positions can be accurately established by sighting from a well-located instrument station.

113. Topographic Accuracy

Topographic maps must be accurate in an engineering sense; i.e., the elevations of the ground surface as shown by contours should be consistent with actual elevations within the limits of scale and contour interval. But the topographer needs some standard that he can apply during the course of field work. The U.S. Geological Survey conducts its work according to such a standard or rule, which is that *the error in elevation as shown by contours should not exceed a certain fraction of the contour interval.* This "rule" applies only to specified categories of maps, but it nevertheless is an example of a workable standard. The fraction 1/5 might well be changed to ½ for less precise mapping. In application, the rule means this: if any point at random is accurately located on a topographic map the elevation as deduced from the contours should agree with the surveyed elevation within 1/5, ½, etc., the amount of the contour interval. For 1/5 interval on a map having a 20-foot interval, the check should be under four feet, for a 100-foot interval, 20 feet, and so on. Only the very best of topographic maps are within this high standard.

Errors in the planimetry of a map also affect the contour accuracy, for the determination of contour accuracy is also based on accurate location. The two are inseparable values.

Particular attention must be given to the extremes of elevation and to the elevations of isolated features. Side shots should be placed on the *highest* part of a ridge and the *lowest* part of a valley. These are the most definite points on a map and will be selected by those using the map for the estimation of elevations. More will be given on this subject in relation to field procedures.

114. Topographic Expression

A topographer should attempt to portray the character of terrain within the limitation imposed by elevation control. Often the difference between a map displaying distinctive character or topographic "texture" and one which is equally accurate in contouring, but lacking character, is simply the shaping of contours between points of control. The topographer should study, in different lights, the country being mapped. When the sun's rays are low, minor irregularities which are obscure at midday, become quite distinct. Oblique views of hillsides often show surface texture better than frontal views.

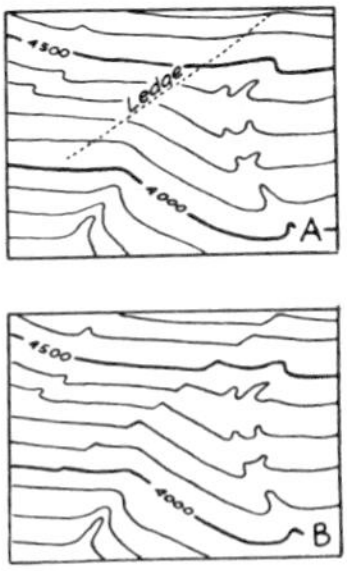

FIG. 69. Topographic expression of geologic features. A. A prominent low ledge is not suggested. B. The ledge is indicated by a sharp break in the contours.

Figure 69A is a slope on which a steeply dipping sandstone forms a low but visibly prominent ledge. The contouring does not indicate the nature of this feature. In Fig. 69B, the alignment of the outcrop is lightly sketched first, and then contours are "broken" along this line so that the peculiarity of the slope is suggested.

Figure 70A shows a broad river terrace which is represented by the pairing of only two contours. Elevations at the points of control show that the higher contour is out of place, but only two

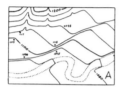

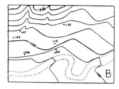

Fig. 70. Topographic license. A. The contouring expresses the bank of the river terrace and the flatness of the ground surface. B. A literal contouring of the control.

contours do not clearly show the 40-foot height of the terrace slope, and the topographer has deliberately drawn contours out of position in order to show this feature. Figure 70B is contoured strictly according to the control points and therefore all engineering requirements are satisfied. The deviation from technological precision displayed in A of the figure is called *topographic license*. Topographic license is a subject of much controversy—and disagreement—among professional topographers. The license to sketch contours above or below the confining elevations of control points should not be abused by indiscriminate practice. Generally the best guide is the sketching limitation mentioned earlier; i.e., if the limit is ½ the contour interval, topographic license should not exceed this amount. In defense of this license, it should be pointed out that a contour sketched in contradiction to the control might result in more accurate interpretation by the map user.

The specific cases where topographic license need be invoked are rare. Usually a few points at which the actual elevations are printed will suffice to clarify ambiguous contouring. Certainly, one must weigh consequences very critically before erroneously contouring a control point.

115. Preliminary Considerations

The mapping of topography involves a multitude of details that require attention, if only to be eliminated from further consideration. The specifications of the proposed map should carefully be reviewed before field work begins, for there may be certain incongruities in the original plans that would need to be alleviated in order to have a well-organized field program. Every item in the operational plans should be examined with reference to actual conditions such as surface relief, visibility, climate, equipment, and personnel. One might set up a sound plan for conducting a detailed or precise survey, but find the equipment and training of field personnel quite inadequate to carrying out the plan. The map specifications and expected progress must be geared to available resources. In other words, an *ideal* plan may be entirely unrealistic in relation to existing conditions if all factors are not taken into account.

In the vital matter of primary control, three factors are paramount—quality of instruments, character of terrain, and experience or general level of ability of the instrumentmen. High precision work cannot be done with mediocre instruments except by men having unusual ability and experience, and then only at high cost in time. Set accuracy limitations within reasonable expectations of the instruments to be used. As stated earlier, triangulation is the most reliable type of primary control, but if the terrain is unsuitable because of poor visibility, triangulation may not be feasible, and methods for high order traversing would have to be explored. Perhaps a combination of triangulation and primary traverse would be best under certain circumstances.

Men can be trained and will gain experience while working on a project. That is the only way that training and experience are attained. But if inexperienced men must do a large part of the work, they should always be placed where technical errors least affect the basic structure of the map, where the errors will most easily be detected, and where they may be localized. In other words, the best men and equipment should be used in establishing the primary control. In the meantime, less proficient personnel and poorer instruments can be employed in running secondary control or detailing traverses within a framework of preëstablished control points.

116. Reconnaissance

Reconnaissance is the part of field work which can contribute most to the smooth operation of any field project, yet this phase of work is frequently done in a most casual manner, sometimes being placed in the hands of those least capable of getting the information required. Topographic reconnaissance should be directed toward very specific objectives and although the nature of the country and project have some bearing on the problems, the following suggestions will pertain to most cases.

ACCESSIBILITY

Generally the most important consideration in the first reconnaissance of a region is accessibility. It should be foremost in mind that the topographic map covers the entire surface; hence, the topographer must have access to every locality in order to correctly control and sketch the topographic forms. The reconnaissance man should have considerable knowledge of techniques and methods of mapping and familiarity with outdoor work and various means of travel, such as boats, horses, motor transport, or back-packing afoot. Areas where different modes of travel are indicated should be sketched and annotated on a map or air photograph.

DETAILING CONTROL

The detailing of topography is usually done from plane table traverses which may be tied into primary lines, triangulation, or short spur lines originating at three-point resected instrument stations. These traverses may be along ridges, stream courses, roads, trails, or railroads, depending on local conditions. Sketch the courses of proposed traverses on the map or photo and indicate preferable routes. This procedure will save much time later when detailing parties enter the area.

DIVISION OF REGION

When several parties work in the same region it is important that their areas be properly joined and adjusted by the close of the field season. Gaps between these operational areas postpone final drafting in ink, for errors in matching cannot be adjusted in the office. It is a responsibility of the reconnaissance man to indicate where matching of sheets can be done most easily.

Areas of low relief are more easily and rapidly mapped than rugged high-relief terrain. This fact should be kept in mind when sketching plans for sheet layout. The aptitudes or experience of men in mapping different types of topography will vary. This factor should be considered, and assignments made accordingly, when subdividing the region on the general map.

LIVING ACCOMMODATIONS

A detailing party may consist of two, three, or four men. It is sometimes difficult to find living accommodations for so many. The reconnaissance man should make all possible arrangements for these parties so there will be a minimum of time lost when the parties move from one location to the next. Agreements on costs for meals and lodging may avoid embarrassment and delay later.

SUPPLEMENTAL TRANSPORTATION

In swamp country, jungles, deserts and mountains the modes of travel are different, and the survey parties may not be equipped to detail such regions. The usual practice is to obtain the necessary aid locally. The availability of boats, horses, etc., as well as rental costs should be determined so that the survey parties will lose no time in continuing their work when they arrive in a new locality.

TRIANGULATION POINTS

High intervisible points that would serve as primary triangulation stations should be located roughly on the regional reconnaissance map or photos. This is quite important, for even from the approximate plot, the distribution and density of primary control can be laid out. If the country is heavily wooded it may be necessary to clear away brush or trees from station locations, and prior knowledge of this necessity would aid in arranging for help or estimating progress in setting up the triangulation net.

There are different categories of field reconnaissance. The foregoing remarks refer to regional work concerned with organizing a season's work for a number of survey parties. The plane table party should reconnoiter every locality in more detail before doing instrumental work or contouring. It is good practice to "scout" each day's work in the morning so that traversing and rodding can be undertaken more effectively. During these short trips in limited areas select the best points for instrument stations and turning points. Instrument stations should be selected with particular emphasis on an advantageous view of the topography which will be contoured, as this is more important than visibility for a distant turning point. If necessary, an extra leg of traverse can be incorporated in the line with but little additional time. Other things being more or less equal, there are distinct advantages in doing first the most distant localities from the base of operations, because a familiarity with details is attained by passing over the same ground day after day. When the time comes to map it, the reconnaissance is already done and at no extra cost in time.

117. Detail Along Traverses

There are two accepted procedures that relate to the secondary or detailing traverses: (1) The traverse is run either as a closed loop or circuit or from one located point to another, without locating or sketching any map features that lie on or near the traverse line. All instrument stations are marked so that they may be reoccupied at a later date. The advantage in this method is that, should an error in elevation occur, it will be found and corrected before any topographic sketching is done. (2) All features crossing or situated near the traverse line are mapped in detail as the traverse progresses. This method eliminates the necessity for setting up on the stations a second time, but it also embodies certain hazards. It is well to explore this method further, for it is the one generally used.

If an error in either location or elevation occurs in the traverse, all following topographic and planimetric mapping will likewise be in error. It is not difficult to correct a plotted traverse line when the exact nature of the error has been determined, but it may be exceedingly difficult or impossible to truly *correct* topographic contours sketched from erroneous control. It is evident that every precaution against traverse errors must be taken. Every instrumental observation, calculation, and plotted distance must be carefully checked before any side shots are taken. Whenever practicable the position and elevation of the instrument station should be checked by resecting from previously established points. At every opportunity the traverse should be tied into established marks or elevations.

As a rule the best route for a traverse is along a road, as lines of sight are unobstructed and the road itself is controlled on the sheet by the traverse stations. Similarly, railroads provide clear sights, and when grades are known, a rough check on elevation can be calculated. However, the plane table must be oriented by the backsight method because of the magnetic interference set up by the steel rails.

The amount of mapping that should be done along a control traverse will vary according to local conditions and the overall plan of the survey. All contours, stream crossings, bridges, cuts and fills, nearby buildings, and the like can be mapped from each station. Either *all* details required on the finished map or none should be delineated. If only a portion of the detailing is done, there is danger of later failing to remember that the apparently finished area is actually incompletely mapped.

118. Ridge and Valley Delineation

The crests of ridges or divides and the stream courses in valleys mark the extremes of relief in nearly all types of terrain, the only notable exceptions being the low points in sink holes of karst

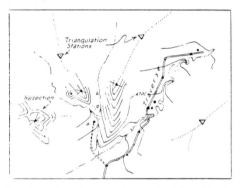

Fig. 71. Preliminary skeleton sketching. Particular attention is given to ridges and stream courses.

topography. When these features are correctly delineated, secondary details are easily mapped with a minimum of elevation control. Field procedures for mapping these primary features vary according to the type of topography and vegetation cover, the specifications of the survey, and personal preference. Traverses may be run both along ridges and in valleys if they are not so closely spaced as to burden the field party with unnecessary traversing. In open country, it is simpler to run main traverses in the valleys and sketch the ridges from below, though this procedure is not necessarily best—much depends on the character of the slopes along the sides of the valley. In some circumstances, traverses are run in the valleys and three-point locations are made on the ridges, from which triangulation points and the previously established traverse stations are visible. Regardless of the *method* by which side shot sketching control is located, the distribution of these points should be such that sketching is adequately controlled.

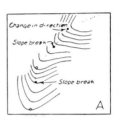

Figure 71 shows the initial work on a plane table sheet. In this example, control traverses are run in the valleys and three-point instrument stations are established on the ridges. The combs of the ridges are indicated by dotted lines, but in actual plane table work these lines are very lightly sketched with a pencil so that they can easily be erased when the contours are drawn. Although the figure indicates an extensive area covered by skeleton sketching, in actual practice the skeleton of ridge and valley control may be kept only slightly in advance of the fill-in detail.

Fig. 72. Contouring ridges. A. Control points are placed at bends in the axis and at breaks in slope. B. Axial control is sufficient for contouring because of the even grade.

119. Slope Break or Gradient

Rod stations along ridges are placed not only at critical points at the bends in sinuous crest lines, but also at all significant changes in slope, which are commonly called slope "breaks," as shown in Fig. 72A. The flattening or steepening of the comb of a ridge is indicated by the spacing of contours; i.e., alternate bands of wide- and close-spaced contours. If the plunge of the ridge is even, or gradually increasing, as in Fig. 72B, control on the alignment is normally sufficient for contouring.

Control points should be located at all major bends and confluences of streams, for these are definite map locations convenient for the map user to find on the ground. Changes in gradient are easily recognized by alternate stretches of ripples and relatively still or smooth water. Places where one type of flow gives way to the other are the correct locations for rod shots. Control points should always be placed at water level in order to show the gradient accurately.

120. Contour Definition of Topographic Features

The accuracy of a topographic map cannot be measured entirely by the positions of contours relative to corresponding elevations on the ground. Such a relationship is a working guide or engineering limitation imposed to maintain a predetermined precision at all levels of control and in the density and distribution of sketching control. However, the topographer's responsibility extends somewhat beyond these engineering limitations, for he should also direct his attention and skills toward definition of minor contour control which gives character to the map.

Fig. 73. Contouring of an alluvial fan. The dotted line represents a light pencil line sketch of the ground plan to aid in drawing the contours.

Figure 73 is an example of contouring which clearly shows an alluvial fan at the toe of a steep slope. This feature stands out sharply on the map because the topographer first sketched the *ground plan* before drawing the contours, as indicated by the dotted line on the right side of the figure. Both sides are sketched lightly on the field sheet to show *precisely* where the contours "break." Such a feature loses all character and identity if contours are carelessly drawn.

Figure 74 shows by *contour symbol* an area in which intricately dissected remnants of a lava flow lie in irregular patches on a relatively smooth sandy terrain. The jagged contour symbol clearly defines these patches of rock that stand somewhat above the general level of the slopes.

Topographic maps drawn in the foregoing manner are especially valuable to the geologist, because these minor deviations from engineering exactness reveal significant geologic phenomena.

121. Cultural Features

The artificiality of man-made features generally contrasts sharply with the natural surface peculiarities of an area. The geometric exactness of curves and tangents of railroad and highway embankments are quite different from the curves and approximately straight lines of streams or terraces. Mine dumps and cuts and fills are not similar to natural landslides. Topographic contours are drawn freehand and the result of minor deviations from exact spacing and configuration results in a naturalness of appearance that simulates the actual topography. When drawing contours of a surface that has been produced by engineering construction, mechanical drawing instruments, such as triangles and French curves, may be used. Contours produced in this manner suggest a rigidity of form similar to the actual feature. Within the permissible license, contouring should distinguish between the natural and cultural features.

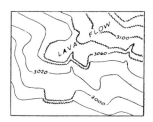

Fig. 74. Use of a contour symbol. Zigzag contours represent intricately dissected lava flows.

122. Contour Conformity

Most professional topographers are critical of "individualistic" contours (i.e., contours which appear to wander aimlessly between points of control). Maps drawn in such a fashion are difficult to read or interpret and have an amateurish appearance which suggests to the map user a lack of professional skill that may extend into the basic accuracy of the map structure. As a rule, the clearest expression of a minor topographic form usually involves more than one contour, even though only one is strongly affected. In those occasions where, technically, only one contour is "caught" by a topographic detail, for the sake of avoiding an appearance of

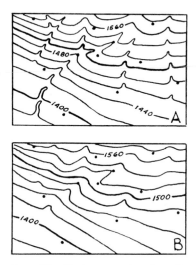

Fig. 75. Contour conformity. By means of the same control points, the contours in A show close conformity to one another; in B, the elevations are honored, but the contouring lacks conformity.

discontinuity it might be better to invoke "topographic license" to the extent of indicating a form relationship in the adjacent contours.

In Fig. 75A, the minor surface irregularities have been contoured with respect to the overall appearance of the slope. Figure 75B shows a ribbed slope contoured correctly insofar as the control in concerned. The lack of conformity in the spacing and the shaping of contours is not so great as to seriously affect the elevation accuracy of the map, yet the character of the terrain is poorly expressed. A comparison of the sketches will show that the two sets of contours do not depart from one another more than the acceptable 1/5 contour interval, but one embodies the distinctiveness of the topography and the other does not.

123. Density of Control

It has been demonstrated by field tests that the number of control points required to control contour sketching is a function of scale and contour interval when the contour interval is used as a measure of the accuracy of the map (e.g., 1/5 or ½ contour interval). This principle can best be explained by an example.

For a specific area it is found that the topography is adequately controlled with 50 points per square mile on a scale of 1:24,000 (1 inch = 2000 feet) and a contour interval of 50 feet. The scale and contour interval are in correct balance for the type of topography to be mapped. If the scale is increased to 1:12,000 (1 inch = 1000 feet) it is necessary to reduce the contour interval to 25 feet if a commensurate balance is to be attained. The spacing of contours on the sheet will then be the same in the two maps. However, the *area* of the map is quadrupled; and in order to properly control the sketching of the 25-foot contours, approximately 200 points are required. This demonstrates the fact that the areal density of control points *on the map* should be constant for maintaining equally accurate control of topographic sketching at different scales and appropriate contour intervals.

124. Standard Practices of Presentation

The U.S. Geological Survey issues a sheet of standard symbols for topographic and other types of maps. These symbols are recognized by most persons who use topographic maps, and therefore should be employed by institutions or companies in order to avoid erroneous interpretations. The Survey has had more experience in the construction and presentation of topographic maps than any other organization, and for this reason, it is wise to study the standard quadrangle sheets in detail to learn the correct uses of symbols. If it is necessary to devise a new symbol for some feature, the sheet of standard symbols should be carefully reviewed to avoid incorrect use of a standard symbol or to invent one closely similar to others already in use.

Heavy, or *index*, contours are used for the purpose of making a contour map easier to read. It is not an uncommon belief that the heavy contours are more accurate than the intervening light ones. This is an erroneous concept, as no distinction between them is made in the control or field sketching.

It is general practice to show every *fifth* contour as a heavy line; therefore, a 20-foot contour interval is better than a 25-foot interval, which would result in 4 out of 5 hundred-foot contours being a light line, and thereby defeat the purpose of index contours.

The elevation numbers of contours should be evenly distributed over the sheet so that wherever the eye falls the direction of slope is immediately realized. It has been statistically demonstrated that about five times as many numbers in rows or columns are needed to adequately label a sheet as would be required by a dispersed distribution. Where map space permits, the highest and lowest closed contours should be numbered.

The lettering of Geological Survey topographic maps conforms to a rigid system from which no deviation is tolerated, and this attitude has resulted in a uniform legibility imitated by other countries but surpassed by none. All land features are designated by vertical lettering of Gothic and Roman styles. The size and weights of lines are selected according to the relative importance of the features.

Water features of all kinds are shown in slanting (italic) letters. Cultural features are shown in vertical letters, excepting certain engineering or industrial constructions, which commonly use the Reinhardt or Gothic italic alphabets. It would be difficult to im-

prove upon this system, and there is no better way to learn the
applications of different alphabets than by studying a few standard
quadrangle sheets.

125. Match Lines

Extensive surveys employ several field parties which are
charged with the mapping of different sections of the map area.
Because of the fact that no man's work is exactly correct, minor
variations usually occur along the margins of sheets where one
party's work joins another. These discrepancies should be adjusted
in the field so that the draftsman has no problems of matching.

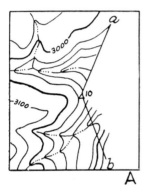 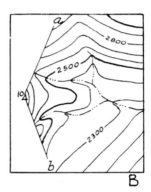

Fig. 76. Dovetailing match lines along adjacent map areas.

It is common practice to overlap along these boundary regions,
but overlapping does not entirely solve the problems of matching,
as differences in the forms of contours and positions of other map
features may still remain, and it may be difficult for the draftsman to reconcile the differences. A method for eliminating all
drafting problems in matching is outlined in following paragraphs.

Figure 76A represents a portion of a plane table sheet. From
instrument station 10 a distant point *a* (out of the map area) is
sighted in the alidade and a line is drawn across the sheet. Now

the alidade is rotated about station 10 and brought to bear on a distant point at *b*. The points should be selected so that *a*, 10, and *b* do *not* lie in a straight line. Points *a* and *b* should be thoroughly described in the notebook and the instrument station must be described and marked on the ground so that it may be recovered and occupied by the topographer mapping the adjacent area. Contours outside the match line need not be erased, as along 10-*b*, or they may be removed to a *neat line*, as along 10-*a*.

When the topographer of the contiguous area matches the completed sheet, he first sets up and carefully orients the plane table on station 10 and duplicates the match lines on this sheet by sighting points *a* and *b*. Next, the detail along the match lines is transferred from the completed sheet to the new sheet by means of tracing paper and carbon paper, and the work is carried on to the east on the new sheet, as shown in Fig. 76B.

Especial care must be taken that the bearings of contours and linear features, such as roads, are maintained across the match lines; otherwise the map will appear to be "broken" along the line. If there are minor differences in orientation or position between the two sheets, they should be adjusted within the bodies of the maps so that no break occurs where they join, for the draftsman must ink the sheets as they are presented.

It is evident that by this method of matching sheets it is impossible for the draftsman to make an error of translation as might occur if the sheets were joined along one continuously straight line. The sheets dovetail into each other in these V-shaped match lines.

126. Applications of Air Photographs

Regardless of the methods employed in topographic mapping, air photographs are extremely useful. If the plane table method is to be used to the exclusion of others, photos viewed under the stereoscope provide a means of studying topography from above, as it is shown by contours on the plane table sheet. In very rugged country, it is the rodman, not the topographer, who sees all the features near at hand, and the rod stations alone are sometimes insufficient for accurate contour sketching. The topographer can observe the photos under a pocket type stereoscope while sketching contours within the control points obtained by stadia observations.

As mentioned earlier in this chapter, it is much easier to contour terrain whose peculiarities are known from repeated observations. Photos offer an excellent means of becoming familiar with the topography before the problems of mapping are encountered. In heavily wooded country the only comprehensive view possible may be through the stereoscope.

127. Photo-Topographic Sheets

Photographs enlarged or reduced to the desired average scale are an excellent base for sketching topographic contours, provided (1) the relief on any one print is not too great, (2) dark shadows do not obscure local detail, and (3) only the central portions of the prints are utilized.

Distortions caused by topographic relief are accentuated near the margins and are small near the centers of photos; so if only the central parts of prints are used, later corrections for horizontal position are reduced. Very high, rugged terrain may be difficult to contour even in the central regions, for dense shadows may blank out the detail needed for accurate sketching.

The photos are used on the plane table in place of the usual drawing paper. If contours are to be sketched in pencil directly on the photos, then the prints should be made on a matte finish paper. A better method is to use gloss finish prints and an overlay sheet of thin-frosted acetate. Preparations for this procedure are as follows.

(1) With a fine pen, ink the center (principal) point as a cross and also the four marginal collimation marks on the photo. Ink any points that have been located accurately by ground methods.

(2) Cut a sheet of acetate or similar translucent material to the size of the photo. Fasten this overlay securely to the photo with Scotch drafting tape.

(3) Trace in ink all the register marks and control points from the photo and ink the number of the photo print in the corner of the overlay sheet.

128. Elevation Control

The three principal advantages of air photos in topographic mapping are: (1) the topographer is afforded a better appraisal of regional topography before detailed work is undertaken, (2) the courses that contours must follow are evident on the photo, and (3) there is no need for determining and plotting distances in areas where photo details are abundant.

Contours are drawn to coincide with the forms as they appear on the photos, even though they may be out of position or distorted due to relief. For this reason it is not essential to operate on a system of triangulation or traverses for horizontal control. The photos themselves contain most of the horizontal control needed and it is the responsibility of the topographer to make the greatest use of the details exhibited on the photos.

Elevation control may be level lines, vertical angle traverses (not plotted), or barometric traverses. It is good practice to number all stations on the ground even when they are not plotted on a sheet. The station numbers, corresponding to those carried in the notebook, should be marked with wax-base crayon or pencil, which resists repeated soaking by rains and the bleaching effects of sunlight. The stations can be numbered on small flat stakes, stones, or strong paper. The writer has recovered station numbers on paper after two years of exposure to the elements. They were preserved as follows:

First, a flat stone was laid on the ground at the station location. Next, the station number and elevation were marked on a piece of notebook paper which was folded to protect the numbers. Finally the folded paper was laid on the flat stone, and another stone was placed on the paper. Additional stones were heaped on to form a mark that could be recognized from some distance away.

129. Delineating Stream Courses

Drainage patterns are the framework for topographic contouring, and air photos afford the best possible means of quickly and easily placing the complete drainage systems on the field sheets. The common practice is to trace stream courses directly on the photo prints, either with a fine pen and ink or with a soft, sharp pencil. The latter is better in that it may be erased after serving its purpose, thus restoring the photo for future use. Although opinions differ as to when and how drainage patterns should be traced, there is much in favor of doing this portion of the work in the office. In other words, the drainage is already traced (in ink) on the acetate overlays before they are taken out into the field.

Except where stream beds are indicated by vegetation, white sands, or steep banks, they may not be distinct on single prints. However, they will be evident under the stereoscope when the relief of the ground becomes apparent. Therefore, drainages should be lined while viewed stereoscopically.

When the positions of a stereopair are reversed from the normal sequential order and viewed under a stereoscope, the relief of the terrain is inverted; i.e., hills become depressions and valleys become ridges. This condition is called *pseudoscopic effect*. It is easier to trace sharp ridges than deep valleys; so when tracing drainages, it may be found better to place the photos in reverse order under the stereoscope. When the stream systems are defined on the photos, the overlay is exactly registered on the print and the lines are carefully inked on the acetate.

130. Linear Features

The inclination to trace all prominent photo features must be tempered with judgment when transferring photo detail to the overlay sheets. Main roads, electric transmission and main telephone lines, and the like are desirable on the topographic map, and may, therefore, be traced before the sheets are taken into the field. However, lesser features may be more conspicuous on the photos, as, for example, beaten cattle trails along fence lines, or barren wagon trails across grasslands. This type of thing should not be traced, for it exerts no control on the topography, is not needed on the final map, and therefore only contributes to cluttering the field sheet with useless and confusing lines. Trace only the lines that will appear on the finished map.

131. Sketching Contours on the Photo Base

The field topographer should carry the air photos that overlap the one fastened to the plane table and a folding pocket stereoscope such as is used by the Army. The exact nature of topographic relief is not always evident either by scanning a single print or viewing the terrain from some distance. But relief is exaggerated in the stereo-model and occasional reference to the stereoscopic view is helpful to the correct interpretation of elevation control points.

Sketching control consists of elevations on visible details on the photos that can also be identified on the ground. It does not matter what the detail may be—an ant hill, barren spot, trail intersection, bush, tree, or rock. The photo is scanned for details that appear to fall about where elevations are needed, then the corresponding points are sought on the ground where a rod shot or barometer reading is made to determine the elevation. The rodman, as well as the instrumentman, should study the photo minutely so that he will be able to recognize the equivalent ground points when detailing the topography.

The spot locations which show as distinct details on the air photo are often short-lived features of the landscape. Tall grass bent down by the hooves of a dozen cattle walking in single file will appear as a well-beaten trail if the direction of light is favorable. Similarly, a gopher mound in light-colored soil will stand out in a background of green grass. Such features do not persist for long, but instead may be replaced by similar ones nearby, perhaps in a few months or a year or two. For this reason it is important for the topographer to know the date when the photographs were taken so that he will be better able to judge which details might best survive the passing of time.

132. Blank Areas

Photographs of grassy or barren flatlands and rolling topography commonly contain rather large areas where no sharply defined details exist. Here the topographer is confronted with a problem on how best to continue the work. If the scale of the photo is constant in the region, the photosheet may be oriented according to methods described in the chapter titled "Field Mapping"; then spur traverses tied into picture points, together with the necessary side shot control, can be run by regular plane table methods. The scale can be checked by scaling on the photo the distance between discernible details and then determining these distances by stadia or taping. The problem is more complicated if the scale of the photo is distorted; i.e., different scales in various directions. In this case the problem is not only one of scale but also orientation. The simplest solution is illustrated in Fig. 77. In A of the figure are five points which are discernible on both the photo and the ground. These points are marginal to the featureless portion of the photo.

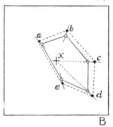

Fig. 77. A. Photo area lacking detail for sketching. B. The photo and surveyed locations are correctly oriented with respect to one another.

The plane table is set up and leveled and a piece of tracing paper is taped to the table. Points a, b, c, d, and e are located by stadia and the topography is contoured by stadia methods. When the detailing is finished, the photo overlay is prepared by plotting the five points and drawing a radial line through each, as shown in B of the figure. The outline of the area on the overlay is shown as the polygon in solid lines. When the tracing paper is placed on the overlay and correctly oriented, the five points will fall on the radials as indicated by the solid dots. This piece of tracing paper may be set aside and incorporated in the final map when radial line adjustments are made. However, it is better to reduce the work to the photo scale so that contours can be adjusted and joined in the field where additional control can be obtained if necessary. The adjustment to the photo scale can be made by sub-dividing the area into triangular segments whose apices are common points on the photo and tracing, such as *c, d,* and *x.* By shift-ing the overlay a little at a time within the triangle boundaries, the contours are adjusted to the scale distortion of the photo; they should then easily be tied into contours controlled directly by photo detail. When photo scale distortion is due primarily to ground relief, adjustments should utilize radial lines to the prin-cipal point.

133. Reducing the Photo Overlays to True Scale

Contours on the overlay sheets are off scale to whatever extent the scale of the individual photos is distorted, and they are cor-rected by any means applicable to air photos.

ADJUSTMENT BY SHIFTING

In the preceding article it was shown how a true-scale segment of a map can be transferred to the scale of a photo. The same process, in reverse, can be employed to reduce a photo overlay to a base map scale. Of course it is essential for this and all other methods to have located on the base map tracing and the photos a sufficient number of points to control the work. When applying this method of adjustment, first place the control point on the base map exactly over the corresponding point on the overlay. Orient the tracing on the radial line toward the principal point. The principal point is located on the tracing by the radial line triangu-lation method described in Chapter IV. When the contours are traced in the immediate vicinity of the located points, shift the tracing slightly to reduce the discrepancies in position, making whatever adjustments are necessary in the contours, drainage lines, and other map details.

ADJUSTMENT BY PROJECTION

Because the overlays are on translucent acetate they can be placed in an ordinary photographic enlarger and projected on to the base map in such a way that most of the control points coincide. A print is then made and used under the base map tracing for compilation of the map data. If it is necessary to reduce the size of the scale of the overlay, this can be done by photographing the overlays to the desired scale.

There are now several projection machines on the market by which very small or very large differences in scale can be adjusted simply by turning a couple of control knobs. The image is projected through a glass table top on which the base map is placed. This is a rapid and accurate method for compiling photo data, or, for that matter, any data from maps of various scales.

In the final analysis of photo-topography, it is the judgment and technical knowledge of the man doing the work that is most important. Methods and equipment are necessary, but they are inexact tools at best, and they are capable of producing satisfactory results only when used intelligently.

PART II. AREAL GEOLOGY

134. Introductory Remarks

When mapping is contemplated for unexplored regions, topography and areal geology come to mind as the information most needed in the early stages of geologic appraisal. Topography (or hydrography) is important because it bears, not only on correct interpretation of the geology, but also on the economic aspects of exploration. Areal geology is essential to even the roughest of geologic and economic evaluations. A longstanding practice for those who first map a region areally is to classify and name the formations that appear on the maps. It is therefore self-evident that recognition of formations in the field and a knowledge of stratigraphic or age sequence in the exposed rock column are prerequisites to mapping. Where the formational sequence is fully exposed in canyons or mountains, or by steeply upturned strata, the characters and stratigraphic relationships can easily be detailed before mapping of areal distribution is begun. The geologist then has the necessary data for identifying the rocks that occur in small isolated outcrops. But, unfortunately, such ideal situations are not common, and the mapping of areal geology cannot be reduced to simple cut-and-dried procedures.

The field geologist is commonly faced with the problem of working structure, stratigraphy, topography, and areal geology simultaneously, even though areal geology is the principal objective of the field work. If the rocks crop out only in small scattered areas, the stratigraphic column cannot be compiled without considerable knowledge of regional and local structure. Dips and strikes must be determined and plotted on a suitable base map in order to chart the figure that a formation band would make at the surface. Similarly, the course of a formation band at the surface may be controlled primarily by topography, and where rather pronounced structural deformation is combined with strong topographic relief, the problem of mapping poorly exposed rocks becomes quite complicated.

Of all the factors influencing the patterns of areal geology, topography is the only one which can be treated entirely independent of the others. This is the reason that, whenever it can be so arranged, topographic mapping precedes geologic mapping. This is also the reason that topographic expression of minor geologic features was discussed in Part I of this chapter. In short, topographic contours should be drawn with a geologic connotation to provide the field geologist with the kind of base needed.

135. Interpretation of Areal Patterns

Space does not permit a complete discussion of the interpretation of geologic maps; however, a few facts need be reviewed because of their importance in the analysis of geologic field observations.

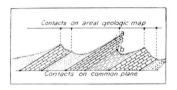

Perhaps the most important fact to keep in mind is that an areal geologic map is a picture such as would be obtained by a photograph from a plane at an exceedingly great height—so high that the slightly converging rays into the camera can be considered parallel. In this kind of projection the positions of geologic contacts are not necessarily referred to a common plane. Figure 78 is a cross section showing the positions of formations as they would appear along a straight line on an areal geologic

Fig. 78. Geologic cross section showing the relationships between boundaries on an areal geologic map and those reduced to a common plane.

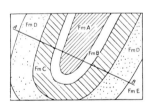

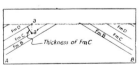

Fig. 79. Areal geologic map of an anticline where the ground is essentially level.

map and on a level plane cutting all boundaries. It is possible in this kind of projection for an apparent formational contact, as mapped on the areal map, to overlap the actual contact, as *a* and *b* in the figure.

Where the terrain is nearly level, a geologic boundary is also a structural contour at that particular stratigraphic horizon. If the thicknesses of all the formations are known, an accurate structural contour map can be made from the areal geologic map simply by reducing all boundary contours to the same stratigraphic horizon. Thus, Fig. 79A is an areal geologic map of essentially level country, and each of the different geologic boundary lines is a structural contour. In the cross section it can be seen that, when the top of Formation B is taken as the structural datum, the stratigraphically higher boundaries are reduced to structural contours by vertical projection downward according to the stratigraphic interval. The value of the reduction (aa' in the figure) is calculated by the formula

Depth = stratigraphic interval × secant of dip angle.

Now if the angle of dip is not known, it may be calculated from the known stratigraphic interval and the width of the outcrop band by the formula

$$\text{Sine of dip angle} = \frac{i}{H},$$

when i is the stratigraphic interval and H is the width of the outcrop. These relations are shown in Fig. 80.

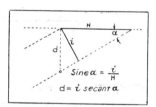

FIG. 80. Calculation of angle of dip and depth to a specific horizon when the width of outcrop and stratigraphic interval are known.

The width of an outcrop band is determined by the thickness of the stratigraphic interval, the rate of dip, and the surface relief, or topography. Consider first the effect of changing dip on the widths of outcrops where ground relief and variation in formation thickness are negligible. Figure 81A shows how the width of outcrop changes in flat terrain as a result of variations in the rate of dip. In Fig. 81B the dip is constant, but widths of outcrop bands are determined by topographic relief. It is obvious that structural interpretation of areal geologic maps is unreliable if the effect of topographic relief is not taken into consideration.

136. Alluvial Cover

A thin mantle of sand, soil, glacial till, and similar materials may conceal the consolidated sediments. Practice in mapping formational boundaries concealed by alluvium is by no means uniform. The U.S. Geological Survey shows these hidden boundaries as dashed or dotted lines where the approximate locations of formational contacts are supported by nearby outcrops of bedrock. Where the unconsolidated surface material is thick and outcrops are sparse, no attempt is made to show the boundaries of the formations beneath. The greater part of the Prairie Provinces of western Canada is covered with glacial till ranging in thickness from five to 200 feet. If only exposed bedrock were shown on areal geologic maps there would be no continuity of outcrop patterns. The Government surveys trace the formations by means of outcrops along streams, and wells that penetrate the drift. From this information the distribution of formations under the drift is inferred and sketched on the maps. Areas where bedrock crops through the drift are indicated by symbol so that the reliability of interpretations can readily be evaluated.

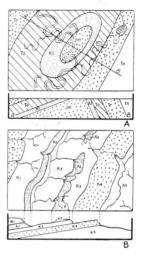

Fig. 81. Widths in outcrop bands vary with the rate of dip (A), and according to topographic relief (B).

137. Observations on Isolated Outcrops

The mapping of areal geology where outcrops are continuous or nearly so is a very simple matter, for it differs from planimetric mapping of roads, fields, and the like only in the necessity of recognizing formations and formational contacts. The task becomes increasingly difficult as the areas of bedrock exposure are reduced. In regions where much of the bedrock is covered by unconsolidated material, it is extremely important that all outcrops be found and thoroughly examined for whatever information they might yield.

Carefully determine the dip and strike and plot the location on the map. If the stratification is poorly developed, try to determine the approximate attitude of the beds—a general strike or a dip component. This information will be needed later. If the formation is not recognized, describe the rocks in detail in the notebook; for as knowledge of the stratigraphy develops during progress of the field work, there may come a time when the outcrop can be placed in its proper position in the stratigraphic column. If the outcrop is large enough to show on the scale of the map, sketch the ground plan as accurately as possible. Measure or estimate the stratigraphic thickness of beds exposed.

Before leaving the locality, study the surrounding topography carefully for tell-tale irregularities that may reveal obscure outcrops or bedrock near the surface. Notice if there is any distinctive vegetal association with the outcrop or soil characteristics that might aid in finding the same sequence near the surface in other localities.

138. Significance of Outcrops

Patches of protruding bedrock do not occur in alluvium for no reason at all. It is not a matter of pure chance that a hard sandstone makes an impressive outcrop at one place, and fails to extend above the surface under apparently similar conditions elsewhere. The field geologist should attempt to determine the reasons for scattered outcrops. In doing so he will not only increase the likelihood of finding others, but he might also learn more about the basic geologic conditions of the region.

In hilly country the most promising places to examine are stream channels, or their banks, and the combs of ridges, for in general these are the places where rapid erosion is most likely to take place. By studying topographic maps or air photographs determine, and mark for investigation, the most favorable places along the streams. Pay particular attention to the following features.

HIGH GRADIENT

Where the gradient of a stream is high, unconsolidated materials are more likely to be removed. Bedrock may be exposed very near the bottom of the valley.

STEEP SLOPES

The mantle is probably thin or absent where slopes are quite steep.

ANOMALOUS TOPOGRAPHY

Variations in the regular forms of contours should be marked for field checking. Small isolated closed contours, sharp noses and reëntrants involving only one or two contours may have geological significance.

STREAM ANOMALIES

The downstream banks of sharp bends in the courses of streams are excellent localities for outcrops, for at these places the streams tend to undercut the banks in periods of high water.

BARREN SLOPES

In northern dry climates the south and west slopes of hills are generally more barren of vegetation than the north and east; therefore, the mantle is usually thinner because of excessive erosion. The probability for outcrops is much better on the barren slopes.

HIGHWAYS, RAILROADS, AND CANALS

In some regions the only existing exposures of bedrock are along man-made cuts. Where highways, railroads, canals, and ditches cross small hills or ridges without change in direction, deep cuts must be made in order to maintain a constant grade. Such engineering works should be investigated. Likewise, mines, prospect holes, cellars, basement excavations, and terrace grading may uncover bedrock.

139. Areal Patterns in Relation to Dip and Slope

Perfectly level parallel strata form an outcrop pattern that is exactly coincident with topographic contours; the surface trace of every geologic boundary is in fact a topographic contour. The surface pattern or bearing of vertical strata or dikes is not affected by topographic relief. Where dips between horizontal and vertical occur the boundaries tend to conform to, or oppose, the topography, depending on the steepness and direction of dip relative to the steepness and direction of the surface slopes.

Where streams cut downward through the strata the outcrop pattern migrates in the direction of the dip, or dip component. The V-shaped salients or reëntrants of areal patterns in valleys demonstrate this tendency. The apex of the V-shaped figure may point either upstream or downstream. If the strata dip downstream at a steeper angle than the gradient of the stream bed, the salient of the outcrop pattern is opposite the reëntrant of the topographic contours (see Fig. 81).

140. Projection of Structural Plane on to a Topographic Surface

As mentioned in an earlier article, the mapping of areal geology generally precedes the construction of structural as well as various types of stratigraphic and facies maps; however, in some circumstances this procedure is difficult to follow. In areas largely covered by soil and alluvium, data obtained from wells may be sufficient to control accurate structural maps. By combining structural contour maps and topographic maps, the areal geology can be drawn quite accurately. It is assumed that the soil and alluvium mantle is not so thick as to materially affect the accuracy of the constructions.

Figure 82A shows the topography of an area in which the dip and strike of the underlying strata is constant. The plane of one stratigraphic horizon is indicated by the straight structural contours in B of the figure. This map should be drawn on translucent material. In C the structural tracing is correctly registered over the topographic map for the purpose of delineating the surface trace of the structural datum on the topographic surface. The contours on both A and B are based on the same (sea level) elevation datum. Wherever topographic and structural contours of the *same elevation* intersect is a point where the structural plane and the topographic surface intersect; therefore, a line connecting a series of such intersections is the surface trace of this particular horizon—an areal geologic boundary as indicated by the dashed line in the figure (Datum 1). It is evident that a series of structural maps whose datums are the tops (or bases) of formations will constitute all the information needed for drawing the boundaries of an areal geologic map.

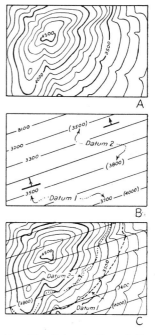

If the strata in a stratigraphic sequence are essentially parallel and the rate of dip is low, the structural contour on one horizon can be converted to another structural datum stratigraphically higher or lower simply by raising or lowering the numbers of the contours by an

FIG. 82. Determination of the trace of a geologic boundary. A. From a topographic map. B. From structure maps. C. The traces of two boundaries.

amount equal to the stratigraphic separation between the two structural datums. Thus, in Fig. 82C a formation top occurs 300 feet higher in the section than Datum 1. In order to convert the structural map of Datum 1 to Datum 2, it is necessary only to raise the contour values 300 feet. Now the second boundary

(Datum 2) can be sketched on the areal map, as shown by the dotted line. Numbers in parentheses indicate the higher elevations.

141. Projection of Undulating Structure on to Topography

The principle discussed in the preceding article applies, not only to a structural plane, but also to any structural form. Figure 83A is a contour map of an anticlinal fold. The two sets of numbers indicate elevations on two horizons, the higher being at the top of the formation *K,* and the lower at the base of the same formation. The structure superimposed on the topography is shown in Fig. 83B. The area of Formation *K* at the surface is stippled. In a very general way the geologic boundaries conform with the topographic contour pattern. It is apparent that the closest conformity occurs where the structural strike is generally parallel to the topographic contours, and the greatest deviation occurs where topographic and structural contours cross at angles approaching 90 degrees. There is little in the areal geologic pattern to suggest the anticline; and for this reason, one

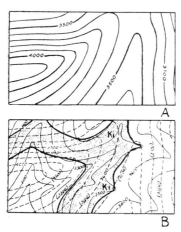

Fig. 83. Areal pattern of a formation determined from the structure map (A) and the topography shown in B. The formation is 500 feet thick, indicated by the two elevation numbers on the structure contours.

should beware of hasty conclusions regarding the patterns of areal geology in country of moderate to high topographic relief, even though the structure is well known. The courses of boundaries must be carefully worked out as in this example.

142. Projections of Planes in the Field

Detailed structural maps are sometimes not available to the geologist mapping areal geology; therefore, it is necessary for him to observe and measure structural effects piecemeal as the map progresses. It has been shown how a structural plane can be accurately projected on to a topographic surface. This can also be done directly in the field without either a topographic or a structural map. The method assumes that the dip and strike of the strata are moderately constant within the locality being mapped, and that some scattered outcrops are present.

The simplest means of projecting the plane of an exposed stratum to surrounding hills utilizes the plane table. First, the dip and strike of the bed are determined with a Brunton. Next, the plane table is set up and the thumb screws of the tripod head are released. Then, place the Brunton alongside the table and orient it in the direction of strike while tilting the table to the approximate angle of dip. Set the Brunton arc at the correct angle of dip and adjust the tilt of the table the necessary amount. Check the strike on the top of the table and adjust if necessary.

By sighting along the surface of the table *in any direction,* the trace of this plane can be located on the ground. An assistant may be signaled to the correct positions, which are temporarily marked, and then these localities are examined in detail for evidences of the projected bed. The alidade, with the arcs set at zero, may be *held* on the plane table and rotated from point to point along the suspected trace of the bed on the landscape. The telescope may reveal sufficient details to identify the bed from a distance, and thus avoid the delay of "walking out" the imaginary trace.

A modification of this method consists in setting the plane table in the same plane as a stratum by direct observation. This procedure requires an exposure at about the same height as the tripod head above the general ground level. With a few trial settings and sightings across the table and the bed, the table can be placed in the same plane. The tripod thumb screws are locked and then the table is used as a sighting plane in the manner just discussed.

Any component of dip can quickly be determined on an exposed stratum and then be projected. After carefully uncovering a bedding plane, lay a flat board, hard-covered notebook, or similar flat surface on the bed. Align the Brunton in the *direction* toward which it is desired to locate the bed and draw a pencil line along the edge of the Brunton. Now determine the bearing of this line. Next, place the Brunton upright on the line, center the arc level, and read this *component* of the dip. You can now use the Brunton for sighting across a valley or up on a hillside to a point on the same bearing and dip angle as determined on the surface of the bed.

A Brunton tripod with a universal head on which the Brunton is clamped may be purchased for a few dollars. This device may be used in much the same way as previously outlined for the plane table, except that sights on the exposed stratum and to more distant points are made by rotating the Brunton in the plane of the bed.

As mentioned earlier in this article, these methods assume moderate constancy of dip and strike, a supposition which may or may not be valid. The localities to which sights are made should be carefully examined for any direct evidence of the projected bed. Perhaps the greatest advantage of the method is that it will usually place one in the immediate vicinity of the stratum, and thereby narrow the area of search.

143. Evidences of Concealed Bedrock on Air Photos

Except in regions that are heavily forested, air photographs commonly reveal lineation which represents changes in lithology beneath the mantle. The subtle variations in the gray tones of the photos may be caused by differences in soil derived from under-lying rocks or from water productive or retentive properties of certain types of soils, which in turn exert considerable influence on the types and color values of vegetation. The lithologic bound-aries suggested on the photos can be checked in the field by examination of the subsoil and bedrock on the two sides of the photo boundaries. Sampling by auger holes or shallow pits will verify any lithologic differences that may exist. Even though the lines or bands do not correspond precisely with the formational boundaries being mapped, the banding serves as a guide for sketching the desired lines.

144. Printing and Coloring Geologic Maps

Black-line patterns or color and color patterns are generally used to differentiate stratigraphic units on areal geologic maps. If the map is to be reproduced by Ozalid or blueprint methods it should be drawn on vellum, acetate, or tracing linen and the contrasting patterns must be in black lines. Drawing the black-line patterns is a slow, tedious task. A wide variety of reproducible black-line patterns on cellophane or acetate can be purchased under several different trade names. This transparent material is trimmed to match the geologic boundaries and is then buffed sufficiently to form a strong bond to the map surface. The adhesive hard wax on some of these transfers softens in the heat of printing machines. If the map is to be reproduced by Ozalid or similar machines ascertain that the transfer patterns will resist high temperatures.

Colors may be applied to prints in the following ways.

WAX-BASE COLORED PENCIL OR CRAYON

Spread one color evenly over the appropriate area. Dip a paper (charcoal) blending stump in benzene and rub on the colored area. The benzene dissolves the wax of the crayon and spreads the color to an even tone. The color is resistant to water. Apply only one color at a time and spread with the blender before applying the next; otherwise the colors along boundaries may be mixed when the blender is used.

INDELIBLE (WATER COLOR) PENCILS

Spread the color evenly on the paper, then sprinkle lightly with drafting pounce or any very fine white abrasive. Rub to a smooth tone with a blending stump, pieces of blotting paper, or cleansing tissues. Be very careful that no water comes in contact with the indelible colors, for they turn to deep-hued dyes which cannot be removed from the paper. After all colors have been applied the map may be waterproofed by brushing on clear lacquer or by spraying with Krylon, a liquid plastic which can be purchased in a pressurized container at artists' supplies stores.

Printers Inks and Mineral Spirits

A superior method for hand coloring maps, developed by "Geophoto," consists of the following procedure. Thoroughly mix mineral spirits in ordinary colored printers ink until it has the consistency of thin cream. With a red sable artist's brush cover an area on the map not larger than six inches in diameter. Next, place a sheet of facial cleansing tissue over the fresh color and pat down to absorb the excess mixture on the paper. Now rub to apparent dryness with a wad of the tissue. Repeat the process, allowing the second application to overlap the first. When this is rubbed off the overlap will completely disappear.

The *first* color applied to the paper will fill the pores so that additional applications are not absorbed. For this reason, when following a boundary with the second color, there is no need for avoiding overlapping the first color; however, the darkest shades should be used first, as the lighter colors will wipe off the dark without leaving a trace. Printers inks are quite waterproof, so maps colored by this method may safely be mounted on cloth by wet methods.

CHAPTER VI

Structural Field Work

145. Introductory Remarks

Geologists are sometimes prone to speak of "structural work," "stratigraphic projects," "areal geologic investigations," and the like as if each were an independent aspect of the science of geology. Although such terminology is useful and necessary for emphasizing certain departments of investigation, it is unfortunate that it also tends to isolate these subdivisions in actual conduct of the work. Practicing geologists in the fields of education and commercial applications of the science are fully aware of the interdependencies of the various branches of geology; but the common habit of unqualified reference to "structural projects" and "stratigraphic projects" as if they were completely independent of one another often leads to the practice of treating them independently. There are indeed few times in a geologist's career when he can devote his entire time to the pursuit of any one branch of geology to the exclusion of inquiry into other related subfields. Thus, terms such as the title of this chapter (as well as the titles of other chapters in this book), carry no implication of exclusiveness; it is merely simpler to discuss (and to understand) methods and procedures according to some systematic plan whereby the interrelationships of the methods are made clear.

A "structural geologist" must also be a stratigrapher. The great Goethe said (in free translation): "He who knows only his own language, knows not even that." The structural geologist cannot possibly understand geologic structure unless he also possesses a fundamental knowledge of stratigraphy and sedimentation and an intimate knowledge of the stratigraphy within the area in which the structure is being analyzed. The overall thickness of the sedimentary column, wedging of stratal units, and the relative competency of beds wield great influence on the types and magnitudes of structures. Similarly, the determination of stratigraphic thicknesses is dependent on analysis of the structure.

As a prelude to discussion of field methods and procedures employed in the solutions of structural problems, it might be well to scrutinize a few examples of the role played by stratigraphy. The illustrations given have been selected because they represent actual cases of structural misinterpretations made by supposedly competent geologists who were so engrossed in the structural phase of field work they neglected to give proper attention to the stratigraphy. These errors could have been avoided had the stratigraphic relationships been examined in detail. The mistakes in structural interpretation were later brought to light in the course of stratigraphic studies.

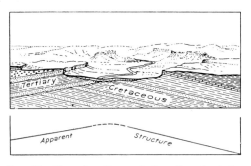

Fig. 84.   Unconformity producing dips simulating an anticline.

Figure 84 illustrates an area in northwestern Nebraska. Throughout this region the Cretaceous and Tertiary rocks are separated by an angular unconformity. Locally the angularity amounts to several degrees and strikes are widely divergent in the two systems of rocks. In the area shown in the cross section, the contact between Tertiary and Cretaceous formations is concealed beneath Quaternary sands and gravels; so the presence of the unconformity is obscure. However, in nearby areas the discordance is obvious, and no doubt the erroneous interpretation of

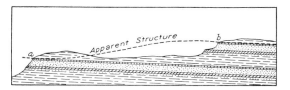

FIG. 85. Repetition of similar sequences of beds erroneously correlated, thus giving a false impression of the structure.

structure would not have been made if the field geologist had seen the angular relationships in other portions of the region.

Figure 85 shows an error in the interpretation of regional structure in southern Saskatchewan. Regional dips are very low, outcrops are sparse, and large-scale slumping adds to the difficulties of determining accurate local dips and strikes. Cyclothemic

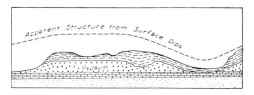

FIG. 86. False dips caused by the solution of near-surface gypsum.

sedimentation in the Upper Cretaceous formations involves shales, soft sandstones, bentonite beds, and a few species of Ostrea, which are associated with the sandstones. Only very careful stratigraphic work disclosed the fact that identical sequences of lithologies and fossils recurred at a number of stratigraphic positions. It was supposed by early structural workers that only one such sequence existed; hence, elevations were established on what was thought to be the same horizon throughout the region (points *a* and *b* in the figure) and structural contours were drawn accordingly.

Figure 86 represents an area in south-central Kansas where thick beds of gypsum in the Permian occur near the surface over most of the region and crop out at a few localities. Shallow wells have shown conclusively the nature of the subsurface structure. Although surface dips and strikes are at wide variance with the shallow subsurface dips, the discrepancy should have been suspected if outcrops had been critically examined. The anomalous surface dips are caused by solution of the underlying gypsum and consequent sagging of the surface strata into the near-surface caverns.

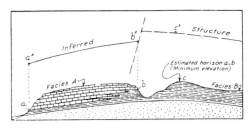

Fig. 87.   Abrupt changes in facies suggesting the presence of a fault.

Figure 87 shows the erroneous structural interpretation of an area in southern California where profound facies changes take place within very short distances. Exposures of the sedimentary rocks are sparse, and differential erosion in the various facies produces an effect of faulting at the surface. Early workers in the region were not aware of the extreme changes in facies; therefore, when contacts between unlike lithologic units were observed at a number of localities, they were assumed to be at the same stratigraphic horizon (*a* and *b*). Likewise, where dissimilar lithologies were seen in lateral juxtaposition, it was assumed that the relationship indicated a fault (*b* and *c*). These facies changes can be determined at the surface by meticulous stratigraphic work. In some areas it is possible to "walk out" the passage from one facies into another, despite the scarcity of outcrops.

In addition to the examples cited, there are many other stratigraphic pitfalls awaiting the "structural" geologist who attempts to confine his observations exclusively to structural phenomena. The persistent cross-bedding of sandstones has resulted in many serious errors in the interpretation of structure. In small outcrops it is difficult to distinguish between planes of cross-bedding and "true" bedding, especially where the cross-laminations are essentially parallel throughout a considerable thickness of beds. Slumping produces false dips and strikes, which in no way reflect true structural conditions. Slumping may occur where there is very low dip and low-relief, rolling topography, such as the plains of Alberta. Surface carbonate rocks often erode along planes in such a manner as to simulate dip slopes, or parallel jointing may be mistaken for bedding planes.

Faunas tend to migrate with the transgression or regression of favorable environments, as for example, oysters living on sandy shoals. As the shoals shift with the changing of currents in the seas, the associated faunas shift with them. Therefore, the association of lithologies with certain fossil forms sometimes gives a false assurance as to the identification of a stratigraphic horizon. The recurrence of complex lithologic and faunal characteristics in a stratigraphic sequence is not uncommon, yet such relations are a constant hazard in structural work in some regions.

From the foregoing it is clear that structural geology must depend upon stratigraphy. Consequently, the structural geologist must have a sound working knowledge of stratigraphy and other allied subjects in order to carry out structural field assignments. Certain aspects of procedures dealing with this subject will be discussed in detail later.

146. Types of Investigations

Structural field projects may be classified in a number of ways, some of which are referred to methods of measurement, the required degree of accuracy, the amount of detail to be shown on maps, and the size of the area to be surveyed. Several purposes are served in classifying projects—placing a project in a certain category aids in the selection of appropriate methods, the planning of field work, choice of personnel, and critical evaluation of results of the survey. At best, the various categories are only relative; for instance, the term "regional" may imply quite different quantities in different localities. A regional survey in the Midcontinent or California might encompass a few counties, but a regional investigation in the Northwest Territories of Canada or in the Southwest of the United States would be more likely to refer to thousands of square miles. A reconnaissance survey of structure where the "regional" dips are in the order of 15 feet per mile might require an accuracy of three or four feet in the determination of structural elevations, whereas errors of 10 to 25 feet would be permissible in regions of strong dips and high structural relief. Conversely, the horizontal control should be more precise where folding and faulting are intense. It is apparent that terms signifying the type of survey mean little unless fully qualified with regard to the area or the general characteristics of the problems involved. Speaking relatively, the "reconnaissance" work in an area of complex geology might employ the same methods and density of control that would constitute a detailed survey where conditions are appreciably simpler.

147. Explanation of Dip and Strike

The concept of dip and strike is fundamental to structural geology. Therefore, the geologist must know precisely what is meant by these terms.

The *strike* of a stratum or succession of strata is the direction, or bearing, of a *level line* on one of the bedding planes. The bearing of the strike should be recorded as read on the compass dial— north 30° east, when facing in a northeasterly direction; or south 30° west, when facing in a southwesterly direction. The practice of recording bearings in this manner reduces the possibility of error that might result in mentally converting the bearing from one quadrant to another. Furthermore, it is easier for the geologist to recall the exact conditions under which the observation was made.

The *true dip* of a stratum is the *degree of inclination* or angular departure from a level plane in a *direction perpendicular to the strike*. The amount of dip may be stated in degrees and minutes of arc, feet per mile, or percent of grade. The *grade* of an inclined surface is the number of feet rise or fall in one hundred feet of horizontal distance. Thus, if the horizontal distance normal to the strike is 150 feet and the difference in elevation at the same stratigraphic horizon is 25 feet, the dip expressed in grade is $25/150 = .166$, or 16.6 percent. An angle of 45 degrees is a grade of 100 percent. For certain methods described later, dips expressed in percent of grade are more convenient than the conventional degrees. The Brunton pocket transit has arcs in both grades and degrees.

A *dip component* is the rate of dip along any line *not* perpendicular to the strike. The *direction* of the component must always be given in order that it may be utilized in structural work. The inclination along a component is always a lesser angle than the true dip.

The *surface trace* of a bed is coincident with the strike only under three conditions: (1) where the surface of the ground is level, (2) where strata dip at 90 degrees, and (3) where the strike parallels a slope.

Figure 88 illustrates the definitions given above. The surface of a lake is shown as the level plane of reference. It is evident that the surface trace of a bed (where the dip and strike are constant) diverges from the bearing of the strike according to the amount of topographic relief.

148. Methods for Determining Dip and Strike

The field geologist should be able to determine accurate dips and strikes by many different methods. One method may be quite applicable in one circumstance, but unsuited to another. Some methods are more precise than others; a fact that should be kept in mind in order to maintain a proper balance in the various phases of structural work.

Within the areal limits where dip and strike are constant, the

Strike N40°W, Dip 30°SW

Fig. 88.   Diagram illustrating the relationships of dip, strike, and the surface trace of strata.

longer the lines of measurement, the greater will be the accuracy of determinations. Small irregularities in bedding cause serious errors in strike if the line of measurement is short, but are practically eliminated in long lines. Such discrepancies are most apparent where the rate of dip is very low. If dips are very steep—upwards of 30 degrees—strikes are not likely to be appreciably in error even though comparatively large errors occur in establishing the level line.

"Contact" Method with the Brunton

This method is the simplest, but also one of the least accurate because of extremely short lines along which measurements are made. It is most adaptable where bedding planes are even and easily separated, such as laminated shales or siltstones. It is the only method that can be used in small pits or bore holes. The procedure is described below and illustrated in Fig. 89.

Select a spot, preferably on a slope, where surface drainage is good and the strata are dry. Remove all weathered materials from an area two to four feet wide. With a hand pick, carefully

Fig. 89. Dip and strike. A. A bed is carefully exposed and the strike is drawn along the edge of the Brunton. B. The dip is determined perpendicular to the strike.

uncover any distinctive bed, such as a lamina of iron oxide, carbonaceous matter, or bentonite. When the overburden has been removed to within an inch of the selected bed, be very careful not to disturb the underlying strata. The final layers may be plucked away with a pocket knife and then lightly brushed with the hand to rid the surface of any small lumps projecting above the general plane of the bed. When about a square foot has thus been prepared, lay on the bedding surface any flat, board-like object, as for example, a stiff-covered field notebook. Make certain that it is everywhere in contact with the bedding plane and that the upper surface is parallel to that plane. Now set the vertical arc of the Brunton on zero, and place the instrument on the notebook as shown in Fig. 89A. Rotate the Brunton until the arc level is centered. The base of the Brunton is now oriented along the strike. With a soft pencil (Number 2) draw a line along the base. Be *very careful* that the notebook is not shifted until the readings are completed. Turn the Brunton to a horizontal position with the edge aligned on the pencil line and level it by means of the universal circular level. When the magnetic needle has come to rest, read the bearing of the strike. *Do not move the notebook.* Place the Brunton in the position shown in Fig. 89B, at right angles to the line on the notebook. Bring the bubble to center by

Fig. 90. A. Section of board leveled with Brunton. B. Bearing of strike read with Brunton alongside. C. Dip is determined with board at right angles to the strike.

adjusting the control lever on the back of the instrument and then read on the arc the degree, or grade, of the dip.

As a check on the determination, dig to a stratigraphically lower stratum and repeat the entire process. If there is a marked difference in the two sets of readings, check further by digging a new pit a few feet away from the first and making a third set of determinations. Where bedding can be discerned at the surface, step back from the pit and compare the attitude of the exposed plane in the pit with nearby stratification. If they are not in harmony, determine a number of dips and strikes over a wider area and average the strikes and the dips.

A variation of the contact method just described is applicable where hard, resistant strata preclude the digging of pits. Dip slopes or "steps" in outcrops often expose bedding planes that are somewhat pitted or rough and, therefore, are not suitable for determining dip and strike within the small area of a notebook. The length of line along which measurements are made can be increased, thereby reducing the error caused by minor irregularities, by using a straight board, such as a section of a stadia rod, as shown in Fig. 90. The vertical arc is set at zero, as before, and the Brunton is placed on the edge of the board as shown in A.

The board and Brunton are now rotated as a unit along the bedding surface until the level is brought to center. The Brunton is next placed against the side of the board and leveled for reading the bearing, as in B. Now the board is turned at right angles to the strike, with the Brunton again on the upper edge, and the angle of dip is determined, as indicated in C. This method is considerably more accurate than the one first described because the lines of measurement are several times longer. However, on dip slopes or any other surfaces long exposed to erosion one must be particularly observant that the plane being measured is a true bedding plane. When using this method be certain that points of contact with the rock are near the ends of the board.

FIG. 91. A. Sighting a strike line from a position in the same plane as a stratum. B. The dip is read while holding the Brunton at right angles to the strike and in apparent coincidence with the bed.

"Indirect," or Sighting Methods

There are several ways in which the dip and strike may be obtained by sighting with the Brunton in the manner of a hand level or a hand transit. The conditions and procedures are described in following paragraphs.

Bedding planes are sometimes exposed in places difficult to reach for determining dip and strike by methods discussed; however, if one can stand in a position where the eyes are in a *projection* of the plane, quite accurate readings can be made. Likewise, if the planes are irregular and a board is not available to aid in establishing the average plane in the manner described previously, a sighting method will most likely produce the best results.

FIG. 92. Sighting a dip and strike across a valley.

In Fig. 91A, the geologist stands in a position where his eyes are exactly in the plane of the bed cropping out at some distance away. From this position he can sight a level (strike) line along the plane, and at the same time select a point on the line of sight to which the bearing is determined. He then turns the Brunton in the position shown in B, with the upper straight edge aligned on the distant bedding surface. While the Brunton is held in this position, the bubble is brought to center, thus indicating on the arcs the rate of dip. Care must be taken that the eyes are kept in the plane of

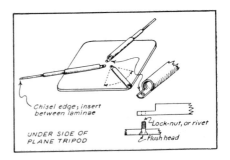

FIG. 93. Construction of the plane tripod.

the bed and that the Brunton is oriented at right angles to the line of sight.

A common sighting method of obtaining dip and strike is illustrated in Fig. 92. The observer stands near a prominent bed or ledge that can also be seen across a valley at elevations both above and below that at the point of observation. The exact position is found by hand leveling to the "marker" bed near at hand, as at point *a* in the sketch. Next, the level point on the same bed across the valley is sighted and the bearing of this line (the strike) is determined by compass, as at *b*. While holding the Brunton as in Fig. 91B, normal to the line of strike, read the dip along the bed from *b* to *c*. When making readings on distant points, hold the Brunton at arm's length in order to avoid parallax and indistinct eye focus on the Brunton.

DIP AND STRIKE IN BORE HOLES

In regions where bedrock is covered by several feet of soil, alluvium, or drift, a boring machine is sometimes employed as a means of obtaining the dip and strike of strata. These machines are similar to powered post-hole diggers used by telephone companies. They consist of an auger-like rotating digger mounted at the rear of a heavy truck. They can bore holes up to 30 inches in diameter and 15 to 20 feet deep. When stratified rocks are encoun-

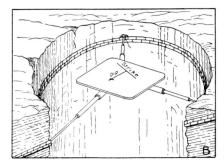

FIG. 94. Plane tripod set on a stratum in a pit. Dip and strike are determined with a Brunton on the aluminum table.

tered in the bore hole, the geololist must descend by ladder or rope and make the necessary observations. It is difficult to determine the dip and strike in a round hole. To do so, a special device can be constructed as shown in Fig. 93. As can be seen in the figure, the legs of the plane tripod are telescopic and can be rotated in the plane of the aluminum table so that the ends of the legs can be set in any horizontal position in the bore hole. Figure 94 is a cut-away view of a bore hole with the plane tripod in position for determining the dip and strike. The tripod legs are made from brass tubing and are attached to the aluminum table with brass or aluminum rivets—all nonmagnetic materials; therefore, the readings of dip and strike are made directly on the table.

A somewhat cumbersome but effective means of getting the dip and strike in a bore hole utilizes only materials that are usually available. This method may sometimes be used to advantage in pits that expose only soft clays in which it is difficult to uncover bedding planes although the laminations can be traced along the walls of the pit. The materials needed are three medium-sized eye-screws; three light rubber bands; and a piece of light, strong cotton cord, such as is used for tying packages. Figure 95 shows how these materials are assembled for use in a bore hole or pit. When using this cord assembly, first set one of the eye-screws in the wall at the selected horizon. By trial and error find a point on the opposite wall that is level. In determining this point, hold the Brunton in one hand while moving the end of the string in the other until the right position is found. To read the bearing of the strike, place the Brunton under the cord and align the axis of the instrument with the taut cord. Place the third eye-screw at right angles to the strike, as in the figure, and read the dip angle.

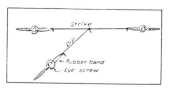

FIG. 95. Dip and strike device constructed from easily obtainable materials.

DIRECT DIP AND STRIKE BY PLANE TABLE

On surveys employing the plane table, it is sometimes convenient to plot a very accurate dip and strike on the plane table sheet by direct observation with the alidade. In order to do this it is necessary to set up the plane table on a bed that can be seen at a number of places from the instrument station. A dip slope is ideal for the purpose. The procedure is as follows.

With the stadia rod, measure the exact height of the center of the alidade telescope above the ground. Assume this height to be 4.3 feet for the purpose of illustration. Now send the rodman out from 50 to 100 feet on the same horizon occupied by the plane table and by signalling up or down along the dip, determine the level line, which in this case will be where the level (middle) cross wire reads 4.3 feet. Draw the strike line along the edge of the alidade. With a triangle, lay off a perpendicular to this line at the map position of the instrument station, and lay the fiducial edge of the alidade along this line, pointed either up or down

FIG. 96. Dip and strike by plane table. A. The rod is held at a point level with the instrument station and the strike is drawn. B. The rod is placed at right angles and the dip is read on the vertical angle arc.

the slope, depending on where the best exposures occur. Signal the rodman into this line of sight and read the vertical angle to the 4.3-point on the rod. This is the angle of dip. Figure 96 illustrates the procedure just described.

The Three-Point Method

Dip and strike can be determined accurately from the plotted positions and elevations of three points situated on the same stratigraphic plane, provided the points are located in the form of a triangle (i.e., not in the same straight line).

Figure 97A is a portion of a plane table sheet which shows the trace of a key bed on which points *a*, *b*, and *c* have been located by stadia. The determination of strike and dip (illustrated in Fig. 97B) is performed according to the following principles.

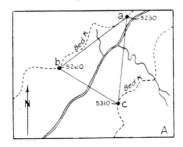

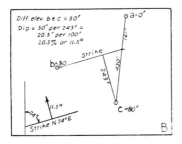

FIG. 97. Three-point dip and strike. A. A plot of three stations on the same bed. B. The graphic solution to the problem.

(1) Let the elevation of the lowest point, *a*, equal zero. The elevations of the other two points, *b* and *c*, are then only the differences in elevation between these points and the point *a*. This simple relationship is quickly determined by subtracting the actual elevation of the lowest point from the elevations of the higher points. Thus, if the actual elevations are $a = 5230'$, $b = 5260'$ and $c = 5310'$, the relative elevations are $0'$, $30'$, and $80'$.

(2) On the line connecting the *highest* and *lowest* points, *a* and *c*, find the elevation of point *b*, (the intermediate elevation). The difference in elevation between *a* and *c* is 80 feet. The elevation of *b* is 30 feet; therefore, the elevation of *b* is found along the plane between *a* and *c* at a distance from *a* according to the proportion

$$\frac{30}{80} \times 430 = 161 \text{ feet.}$$

Scale 161 feet from *a* and draw a straight line to *b*. This is the direction of strike.

(3) The dip is determined from a perpendicular to the strike

passing through either *a* or *c*; but it is best to use the perpendicular to the more distant point, in this case, to *c*. The distance scaled from the construction is 243 feet. The difference in elevation between *b* and *c* is 50 feet. The rate of dip is, therefore, 50 feet in 243 feet of distance, or 20.5 feet per 100. The grade is 20.5 percent. The tangent of the angle of dip is $50/243 = .205$, and (from tables of natural tangents) the angle of dip is approximately 11.5 degrees.

When the plane table map is on a small or intermediate scale and the distances between points used in the determination of dip and strike are relatively short, the scale employed in the solution of the problem must be enlarged. A separate sheet of paper may be taped to the table for this purpose. Either the north line or the magnetic meridian must be drawn on this sheet so the bearing of the strike can be laid off correctly for plotting at the proper location on the map. The scale selected and the precision in measuring distances and elevations are determined by the size (on the ground) of the triangle defined by the three points (Fig. 97). No rule can be stated for fixing the permissible error; because an error in position or elevation affects the direction of strike and the calculation of dip by amounts that vary according to the shape of the triangle, the relation of strike to the triangle, and the rate of dip. The best policy is to study the relationships critically before making a decision in regard to these matters. In order to become familiar with the effect of various errors on the ultimate determination of dip and strike, practice on a few hypothetical relationships. First set up and solve a three-point dip problem. Next introduce an error in distance between two of the points, and redetermine the dip and strike, noting the effect on the bearing of strike and the amount of dip. Repeat the process with an error in elevation. The field procedures and size of scale necessary to achieve the desired results are made obvious by this trial-and-error method. If the outcrop area is very small, perhaps in the order of 50 feet from side to side, and the dip is moderately steep, distances should be measured to the nearest foot, and the scale employed in plotting these distances should provide the same order of accuracy.

THREE-POINT DIPS FROM BORE HOLES

The principles described in the preceding topic are applicable to shallow borings, provided a recognizable stratum occurs at known depths in at least three holes situated in the form of a triangle. If the stratified rocks are soft and the unconsolidated soil or alluvium is but a few feet thick, the holes may be bored with an ordinary rotary post hole digger (see Chapter VII). By employing such simple devices, reliable dips may be obtained in strategically situated localities where bedrock is entirely concealed beneath the mantle. The usual procedure is as follows.

After the loose surface materials are penetrated, save representative samples of cuttings from each six-inch interval. If a distinctive change in lithology or color is encountered, do not bore deeper. Bore the second hole in the same manner and closely watch the cuttings for the appearance of the "marker" found in the first hole. Note any other changes in the appearance of the beds penetrated. If the marker is found, proceed to the third hole. In the event that the first-selected marker is not recognized in the second or third holes, return to the first hole and drill deeper in search of any distinctive bed that may have appeared in the other two holes.

It is necessary to record the depth (at the time of boring) to any change in lithology so that the elevation of the horizon can be computed by subtracting the depth from the elevation at the top of the hole. The alidade may be used to establish the relative surface elevations. When the holes are bottomed at the key bed, the stadia rod is simply lowered to the bottom of the hole and the elevation is determined directly from the portion extending above the ground.

Shallow hand-dug or drilled water wells may furnish valuable dip and strike control near the surface if the aquifer is known to be within a stratified sequence rather than the unconsolidated mantle materials. One can generally learn by inquiring at precisely what depth the water-bearing bed was encountered in the wells. The dip and strike are determined in the same manner as described in the preceding paragraphs. The depth to the surface of the water standing in wells is of no value in structural work; if the water in several wells stems from the same continuous stratum, the static elevation of the water surface will be approximately equal regardless of the elevation at which the stratum occurs.

STADIA (TELESCOPIC) HAND LEVEL METHOD

The stadia hand level, as mentioned elsewhere, is similar to the telescope of the alidade in that the stadia wires are spaced to give the relationship of 1 foot intercept equals 100 feet distance. It is clear that this relationship (1 foot per 100 feet) is the same as percent of grade; therefore, the rate of dip can be established with this instrument without any knowledge of ground distances. For this reason, the stadia hand level is especially suited to types of work where the geologist has no assistant.

The strike, or level line, is established by centering the bubble on the middle wire while sighting the same wire on the object whose elevation is desired. The bearing to this object (some point on the key bed) is then determined by Brunton or other types of compass. When the bearing of the strike is found, the compass is used to predetermine the direction in which the hand level is directed to read the dip. The procedure now employed is identical to the "step method" with the alidade.

(1) Get into a position such that the eye level is at the same elevation as the key bed at the point from which observations are made. It is necessary to rest the level or the arms on some stable support, such as the key bed itself.

(2) While sighting in the bearing of the true dip, bring the bubble to center (bisected by the middle wire), select a point cut by the lower wire (when facing down the dip) or the upper wire

(when facing up the dip). Keep this object in sight until the next step is completed.

(3) Move the level down until the upper wire cuts the object identified in step 2, and while holding the upper wire in this position, select some new point intersected by the lower wire. Continue this interval stepping until the key bed is bracketed by the stadia wires.

(4) It would be fortunate if on the last step the middle wire should intersect the key stratigraphic horizon; more frequently this objective point will fall somewhere between the middle and upper, or the middle and lower wires. In either event, the fractional interval must be estimated. Remember that the *middle wire* is the index on which the dip is based, even though the upper and lower wires are utilized in the stepping process.

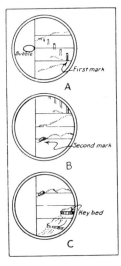

FIG. 98. Determination of dip with a stadia hand level.

EXAMPLE:

Figure 98A represents the first (level) position of the hand level. The lower wire cuts the base of a fence post, though any other distinct object would do. In B, the telescope is stepped down one interval so that the upper wire cuts the base of the post. In this position the lower wire bisects a rock in the lower left portion of the field. The upper wire is again stepped down into this position, as in C. The key bed is now bracketed between the middle and lower wires. It is estimated that this intercept is 0.4 interval below the middle wire; therefore, this amount must be added to the full steps. The telescope has been moved down 2.4 intervals to bring the middle wire from the level position to the key bed. Therefore, the dip is 2.4 percent. The angle of dip can be computed in two ways: The tangent of the angle of dip is 2.4/100=.024, and the angle is 1° 22′. The upper and lower stadia wire subtend an angle of approximately 34 minutes; hence, the angle represented by 2.4 intervals is approximately 83 minutes, or 1° 23'. The discrepancy of 1' is negligible, and it is much easier to convert the values to degrees and minutes or decimals of a degree by the latter method.

In the example it is assumed that outcrops of the same stratum are continuous or sufficiently numerous to permit all readings on the "key" bed. Such conditions are fulfilled on dip slopes and where bedrock is dissected by surface drainage. Where outcrops consist of small, widely scattered patches protruding through the mantle, one should examine the local area in detail for the most advantageous position for instrumental work.

Although it is advisable to determine both the dip and the strike on the same bed, it is not essential to do so, nor is it necessary to read both dip and strike from the same point of observation. Figure 99 shows small outcrops of a formation on which the determinations of dip and strike are made independently of each other. This is done in order to

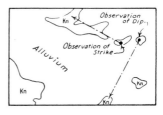

Fig. 99. Determination of strike from one point and dip from another.

obtain longer lines of sight. Two outcrops lying at about the same elevation are first selected for the determination of the strike bearing. From this, the bearing of the true dip is established. Two nearby outcrops aligned with the dip bearing are now selected, and the rate of dip is read along this line. Inasmuch as elevations do not enter into the calculations of dip, the strike may be read on one bed and the dip on another, so long as the two beds are parallel.

DIP COMPONENTS DETERMINED BY HAND LEVEL

The preceding examples deal with areas where outcrops permit selection of sight lines for finding the true dip and strike. Frequently it is impossible to get the dip and strike by conventional methods; i.e., by direct sighting for these values. The pattern of

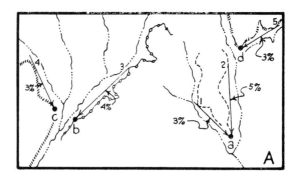

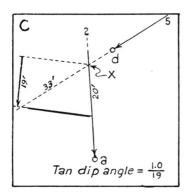

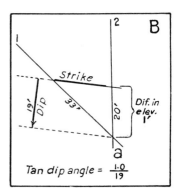

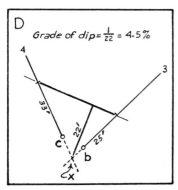

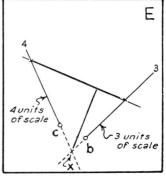

Fig. 100. Determining the strike and dip from two components of dip.

minor stream systems commonly controls the orientation of out-crops. If there are distinctive beds in the exposed rocks, the methods described earlier should be applied. However, it is not unusual to find excellent exposures of repetitious sediments which contain no such marker, or key, beds. In these circumstances it might be quite difficult to trace any single bed from one side of a valley to the other so that a direct determination of strike and dip can be made. Nevertheless, individual beds may be distinctly traceable along one side of a drainage, though not correlatable to the opposite side. In this case the dip components on different beds are determined, and from these components the true dip and strike are established.

Refer to Fig. 100A, which shows the traces of a number of different beds along which the bearings and rates of dip are determined with the stadia hand level and a compass. The small letters represent the positions of the geologist when making the readings. First, consider point a, from which two components on the same bed are read. Figure 100B shows the large-scale plot of these components and the rate of dip on each. The grade (obtained with the hand level) of component $a1$ is three percent; the grade of component $a2$ is five percent. It is evident that the change in elevation from point a along the components is three and five feet per 100 feet, respectively. The distance along component $a1$ in which the elevation changes one foot is $100/3 = 33$ feet; along component $a2$ it is $100/5 = 20$ feet. Therefore, at a point 33 feet from a along component $a1$ the elevation is the same as at a point 20 feet from a along $a2$. It is clear that a straight line connecting these points is the strike of the bed. The true dip, of course, is perpendicular to this line, and the amount of dip, in grade, is

$$\frac{\text{difference in elevation}}{\text{horizontal distance}}.$$

Greater accuracy is attained in the graphic solution of dip and strike if the angle between the components is near 90 degrees.

The solution becomes quite weak if the angle is appreciably less than 30 degrees.

The dip and strike obtained from the components in Fig. 100B are checked by using a third component, as d5 in C. In this construction, components a2 and d5 produce the same dip and strike as those derived from a1 and a2. This also indicates that there is no change in the dip or strike within the area in which these components occur.

In Fig. 100D, the dip and strike are determined from components observed on two different beds from two points of observation. Point x is the intersection of projections of the observed components at c and b. It will be seen later that this point may fall far from the area where the outcrops occur, but this fact has no bearing on the solution of the problem.

A rapid method of determining the strike from components is illustrated in Fig. 100E. The data are the same as those used in D. On any convenient scale, let one scale unit equal one percent of grade. From point x, along component c4, plot the rate of dip from b3 (4% = 4 scale units); on b3, plot the dip from c4 (3% = 3 scale units). The line connecting these points is the strike. (Compare the results with D.) This is a very convenient field method in that no computations whatever are necessary. However, it does not provide an equally simple solution to the rate of true dip; the dip must be determined according to the method described earlier. If the dips are low (5 degrees or less), the procedure given above may be applied without appreciable error simply by letting a scale unit equal one degree or one minute of arc.

The stadia hand level is especially applicable where the dips are quite gentle—from a few feet per mile up to about 4 degrees—and where long sight lines are possible. The telescope, normally X4 or X5, aids in identifying and reading exactly to a key bed at considerable distances. If angles of dip exceed 4 or 5 degrees, significant errors may occur. These errors result from two sources: (1) There are approximately two interval steps per degree of dip.

Each step in the process given earlier constitutes a potential source of error in that the step markers may not be distinct or small enough for precise settings of the stadia wires. (2) The stadia intercept (interval) is a correct measurement only on a vertical plane with the telescope in a level position. A progressively larger error is introduced as the telescope departs from the horizontal position. This error is very small in the first few degrees, but becomes a measurable quantity on moderately steep angles. It might also be mentioned that the method is slow and tedious when many steps are to be taken for a single dip.

DIP COMPONENTS DETERMINED BY BRUNTON

As stated before, the Brunton contains a vertical arc graduated in percent grade. When the component method is employed, this arc should be used instead of the one graduated in degrees. If dips have already been recorded in degrees and minutes they may be quite easily converted to percent grade by resetting the Brunton arcs to the recorded angles and then reading the percent grade on the lower scale. The methods of solving the dip and strike problems from components of dip apply to the Brunton as well as to the telescopic hand level.

FIELD SELECTION OF COMPONENTS

Where field conditions permit reading both dip and strike on the same stratigraphic horizon it would not be wise or practicable to employ any of the component methods. Likewise, if the component method is indicated, considerable care and judgment should be exercised in the manner in which it is used. The component methods are subject to certain inaccuracies, some of which have been mentioned or should be apparent from preceding discussions. The shape of the triangle formed by the components and the strike has been intimated as an important factor in the accuracy of the dips and strikes obtained by this method. Outcrops in many regions tend to parallel the drainage patterns. This being the case, it is often possible to choose one of several directions in which the component of dip can be established. Wherever this is possible, pairs of components should be selected to intersect as near at right angles as possible, thus providing a strong figure for the solution of the problem. It should be clear that components approaching parallelism are of little value in the solution of dip and strike problems. Since the best exposures of bedrock commonly occur along the sides of main drainages, one is likely to spend more time and make more observations in these places. Unfortunately, the traces of beds along main valleys tend to be nearly parallel. Hence, it is better to make a number of dip observations in the lesser valleys where the orientation of outcrops is favorable, even though the outcrops themselves are less impressive. Air photographs may be of great assistance in the selection of intersecting components. Base maps of the U.S. Forest Service and other organizations usually show rather complete drainage patterns that have been compiled from air photos. U.S. Geological Survey topographic sheets are excellent field guides in respect to low-order drainages. The field man should take advantage of these available maps. It is a good practice to plot the components on a base map as they are determined in the field so that favorable directional relationships are currently evident.

149. Dips and Dip Components from Geologic Maps

If geologic boundaries from areal geologic maps are carefully superimposed on a topographic contour map, dips, strikes, and dip components can be determined from the relationships thus shown. The accuracy of dips derived in this manner is dependent on (1) the accuracy of topographic contours and geologic boundaries on the maps, (2) the precision with which one is traced on to the other, (3) the scale of the map (i. e., the accuracy of scaled distances), and (4) the relationship of degree of dip and the topographic contour interval. All these factors must be considered in evaluating results of this method. As might be expected, the method might be quite satisfactory in one part of a map area and relatively ineffective in another, for the relationships mentioned above will vary from one place to another.

When areal geology has been transferred to the topographic sheet, the entire map should be carefully studied for the purpose of selecting the best localities for resolving the dip and strike. Particular attention should be given to "known" and "inferred" boundaries. Inferred boundaries are often shown as dotted or dashed lines and "mapped" boundaries as solid lines. Dips obtained from inferred boundaries are unreliable. Similarly, topographic contours are generally more reliable along roads, railroads, canals, and main stream courses. The most reliable dips may be found where a geologic boundary crosses the largest number of contours in the shortest space, for in such places there is evidence of strong dips and large differences in elevation on the same stratigraphic horizon, both being favorable circumstances for accurate determinations.

The principle of the method may be explained simply as follows. The boundary line on a geologic map is the surface trace of a continuous stratigraphic horizon. The configuration of this line is controlled by undulations (structure) in the strata and the form of the surface (topographic) which the strata intersect. It is evident that where a boundary line is crossed by a topographic contour, the elevation of that stratigraphic horizon must be identical to the contour; therefore, in areas where a number of contours cross the same geologic boundary a dip of the stratigraphic unit is indicated. It follows that where the same topographic contour recrosses the same geologic boundary these points of intersection have the *same* elevation; and, by definition, a line connecting these points is a strike line at that horizon. Where the boundary is parallel to straight topographic contours the boundary line is also a strike line, If, on the other hand, the boundary remains parallel to *meandering* topographic contours, the strata are level, or dip at an extremely low angle.

It is common practice in the U.S. Geological Survey to sketch areal geology on a base map having topographic contours. Although now out of print, many of the Survey's Geologic Folios contained sheets that had both geology and topography. (Very recent maps issued indicate a return to this presentation in published works.) Topographic maps provide the base upon which the geology is sketched in England and elsewhere. Often the surveys that are concerned with topography and areal geology do not treat structure in detail, but data are given from which structure may be determined.

Figure 101 is a topographic map on which have been traced

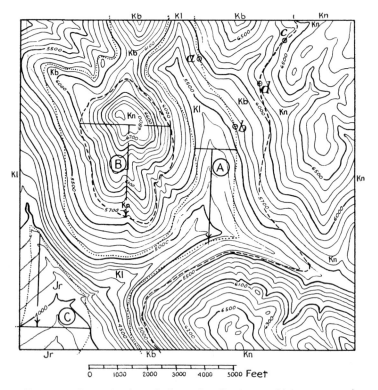

FIG. 101. Determination of dip and strike by combining topography and areal geology.

geologic boundaries from the map shown in Fig. 102A. In Fig. 101 the boundaries are indicated by dashed and dotted lines for the purpose of distinguishing them from the contours—here, the type of line has no reference to the accuracy of the boundary, as

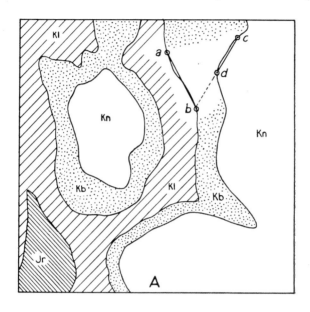

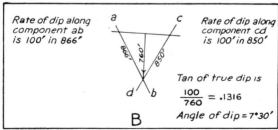

FIG. 102. A. Areal geologic map from which boundaries are transferred to the topographic map shown in Figure 101. B. The method of computing dip and strike from two map-derived components.

suggested earlier. Dips and strikes have been determined at localities *A, B,* and *C.* At locality *A,* the lower boundary of Unit *Kb*
intersects the 5500-foot contour on the two sides of a valley. The
straight line connecting these points is the strike of the strata.
This boundary cuts across successively lower contours in a south-
erly direction. A point is selected where the boundary intersects the
5100-foot contour and a line is drawn from this location to intersect the strike at right angles. This is the direction of true dip.
It is evident that the difference in elevation between this point
and the strike line is 400 feet. The scaled distance is 3125 feet.
The tangent of the angle of dip is $400/3125 = .128$, and from
tables of natural functions the angle of dip is shown to be approximately $7° 20'$.

At locality *B,* the dip and strike are determined at the base of
Unit *Kn.* In this case the formation caps an isolated knob, but it
is apparent that the procedure in obtaining the dip and strike is
exactly as described above.

At locality *C,* the procedure is the same, but ground conditions
are somewhat different. The strike is determined in the lower
portion of the valley because of the greater distance that can be
spanned at this position. The perpendicular line is drawn up-dip to
a point where the boundary crosses a higher contour.

If it is necessary to determine a dip and strike in the north-
eastern part of the map area, a component method must be employed, for there is no place where one of the geologic boundaries
recrosses the same contour; hence, the strike cannot be resolved
by direct methods. Along the lower boundary of *Kb* a component
of dip from *a* to *b* is seen to be 300 feet. On the base of *Kn* from *c*
to *d* the difference in elevation is 200 feet. These points are shown
in Fig. 102A, and the solution of the problem is illustrated in
Fig. 102B. By scaling distances off the map it will be seen that the
rate of dip on the two components is 100 feet in 866 feet and
100 feet in 850 feet, respectively. The method for determining
dip and strike from components has already been discussed, and
these methods apply to the solution of the problem regardless of
the source of data. The strike obtained by components diverges

slightly from those at localities *A, B,* and *C.* This may be the result of small errors in drafting, some stratigraphic convergence between the two formations involved in the construction, or an actual swing in the strike. However, errors or variations of such small magnitudes may be neglected in most structural problems.

In areas where small-scale folding is present, the methods described must be used with some caution. It is better when using these methods to restrict the area within which the determination of dip and strike is made so that the dips obtained more truly represent the local attitude of the strata. Although these methods apply more to the drafting room than the field, they are of importance to the field man as a type of reconnaissance whereby he may chart the course of day-to-day field procedures, and perhaps point up areas of special interest.

150. Datum Surfaces

In ordinary surveying, a *datum "plane,"* or more specifically, a *datum surface,* is a real or imaginary level surface to which the measurements to points in space are referred. Thus, *sea level datum* simply means the projection of the sea level surface, which is spheroidal, across the area of the survey. In geology the term *datum* has a quite different connotation. In stratigraphy, a datum is any designated stratigraphic horizon to which measurements of thickness or depth are referred. A *structural datum* is a selected stratigraphic horizon whose space position is designated by elevation above or below sea level or any other level surface. It is the stratigraphic surface on which structural contours are drawn. Both the elevation datum and the structural datum are involved in a structural contour map. If the elevation of the level surface has been given an arbitrary value, then the resulting structural map is said to be on an "assumed datum."

151. Structural Elevations and Key Beds

A *structural elevation* is an elevation on any known or identifiable stratigraphic unit or horizon whose footage position above or below the selected datum has been determined. Where dips are quite gentle, the datum elevation is computed simply by adding or subtracting the stratigraphic separation between the structural elevation and the datum. Where beds dip steeply this reduction to datum elevation employs a trigonometric calculation which is discussed later.

A *key bed* or "marker bed" is any distinctive stratum whose stratigraphic position relative to the datum is known or can be computed. A key bed is not necessarily an important stratigraphic boundary. Structural field surveys often make use of many key beds in areas where different parts of the geologic section are exposed in various localities.

Key groups or sequences refer to any distinctive sequence of beds occupying a small stratigraphic interval at a known stratigraphic position above or below the datum. Such a "group" may be distinctive because of lithologic individuality, fossil content, or the relative stratigraphic intervals separating beds within the group. For example, in a thick section of characterless gray shales containing occasional beds of bentonite, a rapidly alternating sequence as listed below might be unique within the map area, and would thus constitute a key group useful in structural mapping.

Rock Type	Description	Thickness	
Shale	gray, fissile	100 feet	
Bentonite	gray-white	3 inches	
Shale	gray, lumpy	2 feet	Key Group
Bentonite	gray-white	4 inches	Total thickness
Shale	gray, lumpy	5 feet	8 feet 3 inches
Bentonite	white, green cast	8 inches	
Shale	gray	45 feet	

The structural elevations may be established at either the top or the bottom of the key group so long as the stratigraphic position of the elevation point is clearly indicated.

152. Structural Contouring from Datum Elevations

Although structure may be indicated by various symbols, the only manner of showing continuously and quantitatively the configuration of warped strata is by means of contours. The preparatory work consists in plotting on the map the locations of points together with their structural elevations. In order to differentiate between elevations determined directly on the datum and those established on a key bed and reduced to the datum level, it is common practice to letter the key bed elevation above a line and the computed datum elevation below. Some geologists prefer to write all computed datum elevations in parentheses. The reason for making such a distinction is that the "converted" elevations are more likely to be in error because of certain variables which are discussed later.

Before contouring the map it is sometimes helpful to assemble or review available structural data on the region of the map area in order to gain an impression of the types of folding or faulting that might be expected, the regional trends or grain of the structure, and similar information. Usually the points of control for contouring are not distributed in a manner that precludes erroneous interpretation of structure; therefore, any data that will provide clues as to the nature of structure should be employed in addition to the elevations.

The principles of contouring are exceedingly simple; so are the principles of freehand drawing, yet knowing the principles of drawing does not make one an artist. Contouring is a means of expressing in two dimensions the three-dimensional structural forms visualized in the mind's eye. Unless the structural geologist has the faculty of three-dimensional visualization, he is seriously handicapped in the solution of most structural problems. But in addition to the imaginative side of contouring there are certain rules that govern the technical procedure. These rules must be satisfied in all contouring.

(1) A structural contour is a line of equal elevation (a level line) on a continuous or restored stratigraphic surface (the structural datum).

(2) A reversal in slope must always be shown by a repetition

of the highest contour (on anticlines) or the lowest contour (in synclines). A single contour should never mark the axis of reversal of slope.

(3) A contour must never cross over itself or any other contour.

(4) Two or more contours merge into a single line only where the datum surface is vertical for a height exceeding the contour interval. Where two or more contours do merge to show a vertical surface, the line should be somewhat heavier than the ordinary contours. In topography, this is called a "cliff line."

(5) The under side of an overturned fold cannot be shown satisfactorily by contours. A heavy (cliff) line may be drawn at the place where the strata are vertical. An overturn dip and strike symbol or supplementary cross section will indicate the true nature of the fold.

(6) Contours must always be correctly placed with reference to the elevation control points, even when broad generalization is desired. For example, a 550-foot contour in normal sequence with 500-foot and 600-foot contours could not pass between two points having elevations of 560 and 590 feet; it would be located below both points.

(7) Exact interpolation for position between two control points is required only where it is desired to show a constant rate of dip. Wide spacing indicates a low rate of dip, close spacing, a high rate, and gradational spacing, a gradual change in the rate of dip. One should be careful that the contours and contour spacing truly represent the known or inferred dips.

(8) The ground plan of a meandering contour may closely approximate a section profile of the feature depicted, though the vertical scale of the profile may have to be exaggerated in order to bring out the similarity. Figure 103 shows a portion of a map and a profile along the line of section. Compare this profile with the heavy contour on the map. It is clear that if the recurves of contours are broadly rounded on, say, plunging anticlines, they represent rounded surfaces in profile; if they are sharply recurved,

the cross section of the feature will be sharp. This principle aids in contouring "character" into a map.

(9) The locations of control points are usually determined by the distribution of outcrops, rather than by design of the field geologist. Therefore, the elevations may not be favorably situated with reference to positive control for the contouring of structure. The assumption that the highest *observed* elevations are on the highest parts of the structure, and that the lowest observed elevations are at the lowest structural positions is often fallacious, yet it is not uncommon for maps to reveal such assumptions. Similarly, it would be exceptionally fortuitous if contours recurved precisely at the locations of control points, as at the axes of anticlines and synclines. Of course, where the critical features of structure can be seen in the field, the elevations would properly be determined at such locations; but field conditions rarely permit observation and map delineation of the criti-

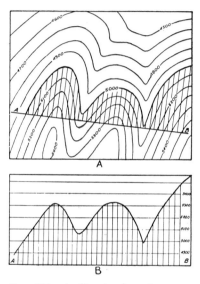

Fig. 103. A. Structural contour map on which a transverse section is shown, and the area to the 5000-foot contour is shaded. B. A true profile along line *AB*. Notice the similarity of the two shaded areas.

cal points and lines of structure to the extent that contouring is reduced to a mere mechanical operation. The geologist is more likely to *depend* upon contouring as a means of defining indefinite axes, high and low points, structural fabric, and various other aspects of structure.

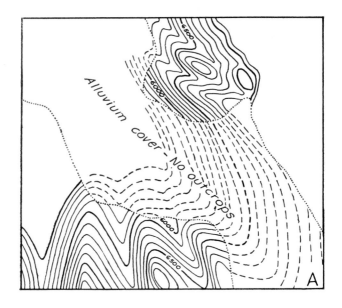

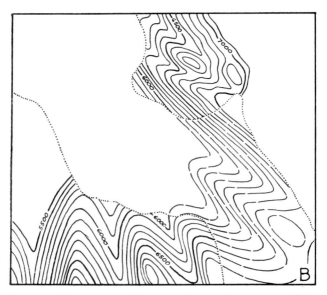

FIG. 104. Two structural interpretations of the same area. In B a fold is sketched in the covered area on the basis of rhythmic occurrence, as suggested by the three noses to the southwest.

153. Contouring License

Within the framework of control points it is permissible, or often desirable, to shape the contours and space them in a manner that best expresses the geologist's concept of the structure. As stated in the preceding article, contouring must adhere to certain principles, but so long as technical restrictions are satisfied the geologist should bring all his knowledge to bear on the picture presented. The key to good contouring is imagination and visualization. Where control is sparse one must fall back on "geologic probabilities" to guide the way. Many structural features have been "discovered" with only a few points of control plus the sound reasoning of a geologist who saw beyond the few solid facts available. *Contouring license* refers to the latitude in drawing contours which permits imaginative expression. Geologic data are usually fragmentary and reveal only a fraction of the whole picture. One who can interpret only what is obvious in the geologic record, is not yet a fully capable geologist, nor will he be until he can project his reasoning into the realm of the obscure with some assurance that his predictions will be essentially correct in a large percentage of cases.

Figure 104 illustrates an area where the imaginative contouring of a geologist resulted in the discovery of a large oil field in the midst of a series of plunging anticlines, some of which produced large quantities of oil from small closures developed along the axes of the folds. Alluvium covers the central portion of the area, and for various reasons geophysical techniques were ineffective. In A, of the figure cited, solid contours are controlled by numerous outcrops, and dashed lines represent the structure as commonly inferred by geologists for a number of years. In B, the interpretation is quite different. The evidence for this interpretation is intangible; it consists simply in projecting into the concealed area the rhythmic occurrence of folds observed where the formations are exposed. But the importance of this imaginative contouring became evident when a test well resulted in the dis-

covery of a large oil field, and, incidentally, confirmed the existence of the inferred anticline.

154. Preparation for Field Work

The effectiveness of the field parties may be appreciably increased if major aspects of the project are examined critically
before the field work is undertaken. In some regions, because of
widespread alluvium, drift, or vegetation cover, the geologic data
that can be obtained by surface methods are scarcely worth the
necessary expenditure in time and money. It would be a mistake
to organize and equip field parties if such conditions were suspected. Before doing so, it would be more economical to exhaust
every source of information in the literature and by direct inquiry
of those who might have knowledge of the region. A reconnaissance
flight over the area in a chartered plane might provide a great deal
of information regarding the feasibility of the projected ground
survey.

In contrast to the conditions mentioned above are those regions
where high topographic relief combined with nearly complete
exposure of bedrock and structural and stratigraphic variation
provide almost limitless opportunity for any type of field investigation. Where conditions similar to these are prevalent, the
tendency of the field geologist is to exceed the requirements of
the project and thus increase the cost of the survey. One can easily
be overwhelmed with the abundance of data in arid canyon regions
and for this reason it may be difficult to discriminate wisely between what is *essential* to the objectives of the survey and the
interesting but relatively unimportant details.

The planning of a field project must be based on some general
knowledge of the country and the various problems involved.
Likewise, the detail in which a survey can be planned and organized is dependent on the extent of knowledge of the region. Sometimes planning and organization are carried to a point exceeding
this knowledge with the result that the prescribed methods and
procedures are more confusing than helpful to the men in the

field. Much has been written on the subject of organization and planning; but it would be presumptive and impractical to attempt to provide a formula whereby the solutions to such problems would be forthcoming simply by inserting known values into the formula. When contemplating the structural investigation of a region, it might be to one's advantage to write down a number of pertinent questions and then proceed to answer them by whatever means are available. As a model from which to work, a few such questions are given below. Obviously, the type of query will depend largely on the particular project being considered.

(1) What are the reasons for this project being undertaken?

(2) What geologic objectives are to be sought?

(3) Does present knowledge of the region indicate that these objectives can be attained by a surface investigation?

(4) What economic advantages are gained if the geologic objectives are fulfilled?

(5) How much time and money and how many men are available to complete the project?

(6) Are sufficient supplies and equipment on hand or readily available to outfit the field parties?

(7) What categories of field data are essential to the principal objectives of the survey? (Such as dips and strikes, elevations, topographic or hydrographic features.)

(8) What methods are to be used in the field, and are the available men trained and experienced in these methods? If not trained, has provision been made for their training?

(9) After careful consideration of the preceding topics, is this project well-conceived and feasible, geologically and economically?

Although these questions do not purport to touch upon the main problems of many structural surveys, they illustrate one means of analysis which may be applied in most cases. The "question" approach is preferred by many engaged in this type of work because it is brief, self-critical, and direct; furthermore, it tends to stimulate overall appraisal of the contemplated project. Regardless of the method of planning employed, every project should be planned carefully, for this preliminary work is often the most important of the entire undertaking.

155. Field Reconnaissance

Structural reconnaissance cannot be defined in terms of the kind or amount of work to be done because of the variations in terrain, geology, and travel conditions in different regions and the objectives toward which different surveys are directed. Generally speaking, structural reconnaissance of a map area should attempt to establish the regional grain or fabric, determine what formations are at the surface and approximately where they crop out, the direction of regional dip, and types of local individual "structures," such as faults and anticlines. In addition to observation of broad geologic features, some consideration should be given to accessibility of outcrops, roads, living accommodations, and other factors that may have an important bearing on the operation of field parties.

Reconnaissance work should not become involved with detail, except as detail is *essential* to an understanding of generalized features. All direct observations and measurements should be recorded in one form or another. Whenever practicable the observations should be plotted on a suitable base or road map, or shown as sketches and diagrams. A good camera, with either color or black and white film is one of the best reconnaissance tools, provided the exposed film can be processed in time for use by the detail parties. Documentary photos must be annotated in order to be fully effective.

One should not be overly cautious in the matter of tentative impressions or concepts of the regional geology. It should be kept in mind that reconnaissance work is not final, and the geologist will not be held to account for errors in detail, though he might be criticized for withholding ideas gained during the traversing of an area, even if the ideas are somewhat vague. The geologist undertaking detailed work may have seen but a small portion of the region, and any light that can be thrown on the overall aspects of the geology will make the way easier for him. Certain suspected features may well fail to materialize when the area is examined in detail, but this is in no sense a disparaging reflection on the reconnaissance geologist, for if he were precisely correct in all observations and conclusions there would be no need for detailing. Quite frequently reconnaissance work done under the pressure of very limited time is exceptionally good *because* of this limitation. The apparent reason is that only major features are observed and these are seen in rapid succession. The interrelationships of structural phenomena are sometimes easier to comprehend when they are visited one after the other within a short period of time. The geologist does not have time to tarry long at any one outcrop and still cover the necessary amount of ground—he is forced by circumstances to observe *selectively,* giving little heed to unimportant details.

Where structure and stratigraphy are relatively simple, there may be little or no need for reconnaissance of the area. On the other hand, however, where opposite conditions obtain, reconnaissance work may properly constitute as much as 25 percent of the total time spent in the field. Among those who have had little field experience two fallacies are often expressed: (1) When time is short, reconnaissance work can be omitted, and (2) the relatively inexperienced man should do the reconnaissance work while those with more experience work on detail. When time is stringently limited, the work must be planned so that none is wasted. Effective planning is dependent on good reconnaissance. As mentioned earlier, reconnaissance consists in selective observation and on-the-spot analysis. Only the *experienced* geologist can be selective without danger of passing up essential data; therefore, the geologist with the broadest experience should ordinarily do the reconnaissance work.

156. Mapping Structure by Elevations

Structural elevations, datum surfaces, key beds, and the principles of contouring have been discussed, and now it is appropriate to see how these concepts are related to field work. It is the primary task of the field geologist to obtain and process data needed for the construction of a contour map, and then to contour the data according to his best interpretation of the structure as observed in the field. Even though the positioning of contours will be determined by structural elevations, direct observation of dips and strikes and various minor irregularities of the structure aid greatly in the sketching of contours between control points. Where bedrock exposures are widely dispersed, topographic forms may furnish clues to local or regional trends. The practiced field geologist makes use of every possible device in the construction of the contour map.

157. Initial Procedure

With few exceptions, regional reconnaissance precedes and guides structural mapping. Within the broad framework of the reconnaissance map or compilation, a somewhat more localized and analytical investigation of various relationships continues during the course of detailing. It matters little if one is determining a dip and strike, collecting fossils and rock samples, or selecting a point for elevation control, the local area should be reconnoitered before the spot of detailed observation or measurement is chosen. Only by following this procedure can one be sure that the control point is representative of the locality or that observations have been made at the most favorable locality.

The selection of each control point should be guided to some extent by the most advantageous distribution of the elevations, which is not necessarily a uniform distribution. The control points should be placed (where field conditions permit) at "break-over" positions on the regional dip, reversals of dip (axes of folds), changes in the directions of strike, or at changes in the directions of fault traces. A structural map can be well controlled by few points, or poorly controlled by many points, depending on the distribution of the control.

Figure 105A shows an area in which structural elevations are

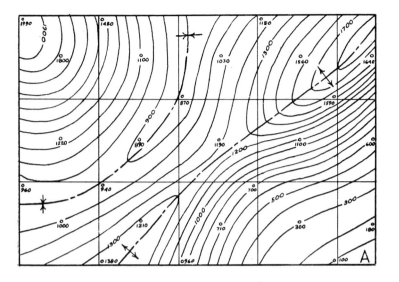

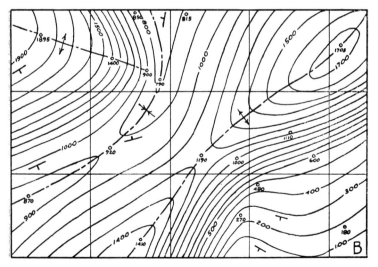

FIG. 105. Density of control. A. Structure is defined by even distribution of 26 points. B. Seventeen points are placed at more definitive locations.

rather evenly distributed. Contouring is controlled entirely by these elevations. There are 26 points of control within the map area. Figure 105B is the same area controlled by 17 points of elevation, but the distribution of these points has been governed by structure rather than density of points. In addition to the elevations, a few dips and strikes have been utilized in sharpening the definition of certain structural features. It is self-evident that this map is better controlled than the one containing a larger number of stations. As in the case of time spent in doing reconnaissance work, the time spent in the careful placement of control points is repaid by reduction of traverse and the number of observations necessary to adequately delineate structural details.

The selection of a datum for contouring should take several factors into account. Perhaps one of the most important is the areal extent of the formation or bed. If a given stratigraphic unit is known to extend far beyond the limits of the map area, it is well to consider such a unit for the datum because at a future time it may be desirable to extend the map, and obviously this would be much easier to do if contouring could be continued on the same datum. If a near-surface (shallow) horizon has been used extensively as a datum in nearby subsurface work, considerable advantage is gained by continuing this horizon in the surface mapping, even though the area of outcrop is small. In regions where the above-mentioned factors do not apply, the datum should be selected on the basis of continuity within the map area, wide distribution in outcrops, ease of identification, nature of the contact with under- or overlying formations, and position in the exposed stratigraphic column. In regard to the latter, it is often better to use as a datum some well-defined bed midway in the exposed section so that key beds can be determined both above and below, thus reducing the magnitude of interval corrections at any one locality. There is greater danger for significant errors in datum elevations where stratigraphic interval corrections are large.

158. The Stratigraphic Section

Except in places where a datum or key bed crops out over the entire map area, a stratigraphic section must be measured for the purpose of establishing the intervals between key beds or groups and the structural datum. Localities for measuring the sections should be carefully selected on the bases of (1) total thickness exposed, (2) completeness of exposure and degree of weathering, (3) location within the map area, and (4) degree of structural complications. These topics are expanded in the following discussion.

(1) It is important to measure the section (or sections) where the largest thickness is exposed continuously, because stratigraphic intervals may change appreciably across the map area. Contacts of units should be examined closely to ascertain that no unconformities are present, or if they do occur, they should be walked out laterally to determine the amount of relief or angularity, as the case might be. If large thickness variations are suspected, an attempt should be made to select an area where the whole section is exposed in the smallest area, as, for example, where dips are steep or topographic relief is great. A section measured in such areas more closely approaches a *point* of control than where the same stratigraphic interval is distributed over a greater horizontal distance.

(2) Structural elevations are specific points of control. When key horizons are to be used, they must be specifically identified in the control sections with respect to other key beds and to the datum bed; otherwise, the reduction of elevations on key beds to datum elevations may introduce serious errors. The necessary detail in sections can be obtained only where bedrock is well exposed and weathering has not appreciably altered the appearance and physical characteristics of the strata. When ground conditions permit a choice of localities, control sections should be measured and described where fresh, unweathered rocks crop out. It should be emphasized, however, that weathering characteristics, topo-

graphic expression, and vegetation affinities should be recorded for future reference, because in different portions of the area it may be expedient to establish elevations where the strata are poorly exposed and stratigraphic relationships are somewhat obscure.

(3) As will be demonstrated later, the locations of sections within the map area may be extremely important. Where stratigraphic units are essentially parallel, the location of a control section has no bearing on the mapping of structure. If, however, the intervals between the datum and key beds vary sufficiently to affect structural measurements, this factor must be considered, because the sections should then be located for the purpose of providing control for isopach maps, which, in turn, will be employed in resolving the structure.

(4) It would be absurd to attempt to assemble a stratigraphic section where complex folding and faulting are prevalent, if a section is exposed where structural relationships are simple. Local reconnaissance will indicate where the most desirable exposures occur. Frequently, the best outcrops are caused by local structural anomalies, so it becomes a matter of careful discrimination in selecting a site for measurement. Each of the four factors discussed are considered separately and then weighed according to the peculiarities of the section or the requirements of the structural work.

In certain types of stratigraphic investigations the lithologic or faunal characteristics of a sequence are of greater importance than the thicknesses of the units. Structural work, however, requires accuracy in the measurements of *thickness,* and the approach to problems and methods is somewhat different. Chapter VII, which deals with stratigraphic field work, as such, should be referred to in preparation for structural field work.

159. Composite Stratigraphic Sections

A simple stratigraphic section is one measured along a line where all the units are in sequential order and more or less continuously exposed from the base to the top. A *composite section* is one *compiled* from segments measured and described in different localities. It is always better, where conditions permit, to use simple sections in structural work, although generally this is impossible, or impractical.

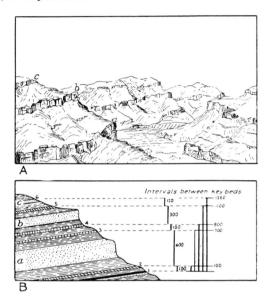

Fig. 106.   Identification of key bed zones by identifying them with prominent, though poorly defined, thick members. A cross section showing stratigraphic positions of the key beds is shown in B.

When doing reconnaissance preparatory to assembling a composite section, one should be especially observant of any units that can be recognized throughout the map area. Commonly, such units are thick, resistant sandstones or limestones. Such beds may not be generally suitable for elevation control because of indefinite or poorly exposed basal and upper contacts. However, they serve as a skeleton of stratigraphic control within which specific horizons may be identified and located. The importance of establishing broad stratigraphic control on the basis of prominent units can hardly be overemphasized. Figure 106 illustrates a typical example of the use of large indefinite units in conjunction with thin key beds. It is clear that the thick resistant units are strongly expressed in the topography, but the intervening key beds provide more exact structural control. The prominent members bracket key beds in such a way that gross errors in identification are unlikely.

Sections may be built up from the large intervals measured at one locality and intervening details from another where gross relationships are not too clear, as shown in Figure 106B. It may also be necessary to resort to the fill-in procedure where formations are erratically exposed. Certain errors may develop in this procedure if the large intervals tend to thicken and thin.

The intervals separating key horizons should be checked wherever two or more occur in the same outcrop area. Changes in intervals are thus brought to light, and at the same time data for the necessary corrections are accumulated.

160. Plotting the Composite Section

Stratigraphic sections in the form of field notes are of little direct use to the structural geologist. The portions of sections measured and described at various localities should be plotted to a definite scale in standard color or black-line symbols and appropriate descriptions. The plotting of sections should begin immediately upon the completion of the first section measured and then be kept strictly up to date as new sections are added. This procedure insures *early* recognition of stratigraphic variations which may require additional field work for clarification. If the drafting of sections is postponed, the field party may have moved out of the locality before the irregularities become evident, thus necessitating a return to the "completed" area. In short, field data should be *continuously* processed. It is common practice to process each day's work in the evening so that the next day's work can be planned more effectively.

The field draft of stratigraphic sections need not be in a "finished" form. The probability is that the final arrangement of sections or partial sections, will be somewhat different from the order in which the sections are measured, and the effort put into drafting niceties may be largely wasted. Geologists sometimes prefer to plot the sections in the field notebook for convenient reference in the field. If the simple section from each locality is plotted on a standard well log strip, preferably in color, correlations of stratigraphic units are greatly facilitated. The strips can be laid out in any desired sequence for direct comparison with each other. A further advantage in this procedure is that the stratigraphic control need not be pursued in any special order in the field and later fill-in or checking work does not nullify earlier drafting work, as would ensue if the early work were done on a composite correlation section.

161. Concurrent Stratigraphic and Structural Work

The order in which structural and supplementary stratigraphic field measurements should be undertaken is dependent on several conditions, such as relative complexity of structure and stratigraphy, amount of formational thinning, size of area, and accessibility of outcrops. Theoretically, it would be distinctly advantageous to complete all stratigraphic work before attacking structural problems. But this procedure necessitates traversing the ground twice; so from the practical standpoint, it is usually better to carry on stratigraphic and structural work more or less concurrently. In a geographic sense, stratigraphic (section) work may slightly precede structural detail without impairing general progress.

If formations are difficult to correlate or facies relationships are complex, it may be necessary to work out the major stratigraphic problems over the entire map area before specific structural mapping is begun, despite the fact that considerable repetitive effort results. This procedure can hardly be avoided if key beds are obscure. It might be pointed out that varying stratigraphic *intervals* do not interfere with structural observations and mapping when the relative positions of key beds are known, for corrections to the datum can be made at any later time. If, however, the identifications or correlations of beds in the sections are not reasonably certain, then these relationships should be determined before extensive structural determinations are made.

162. Definition of Major Features

An area in which the structure is moderately simple can be efficiently mapped according to the most convenient procedure for getting over the ground; i.e., by traversing roads, trails, and stream drainages or ridges. The map may be started at one side of the area and detailed solidly as the work is expanded. However, if the area is structurally complex, it may be better to first define the major features, such as faults and anticlinal and synclinal axes, and then fill in with additional control for detailing the broad characteristics of these features. This procedure will probably necessitate the running of more traverse. If the salient structural alignments are accurately drawn on the map, secondary features of the structure can be established with a minimum of control. Therefore, the additional time spent in delineating the major fabric is regained before the project is completed. One of the main advantages of this procedure is that the geologist attains an early grasp of the entire problem and can therefore direct detailing operations more decisively.

163. Reduction of Key Bed Elevations

If the datum bed is exposed throughout the map area, control for contouring is established simply by determining the elevations and horizontal positions of points on the datum bed. Frequently such favorable conditions do not prevail because the datum bed either lies below the surface in some localities or is eroded away where structural "highs" coincide with topographic "lows." In this event, elevations are determined on *key beds,* which occur at known stratigraphic intervals above or below the datum. Figure 107A is a plane table sheet showing the positions of 11 stadia stations where elevations have been established. Beds A, B, and C lie stratigraphically above the datum, D, and beds E and F are below the datum. The stratigraphic intervals above and below the datum are shown in Fig. 107B. A method of recording the various relationships and computing the datum elevations is illustrated in the following table.

Station Number	Key Bed	Surface Elevation	Difference to Datum	Datum Elevation
1	A	4620	−140	4480
2	B	4440	−90	4350
3	C	4950	−50	4900
4	C	4650	−50	4600
5	D	4900	00	4900
6	D	4600	00	4600
7	E	5070	+30	5100
8	E	5150	+30	5180
9	F	4830	+60	4890
10	F	5140	+60	5200
11	C	4450	−50	4400

Figure 107C represents a structural contour map based on the elevations in the last column in the table. The locations of the rod stations are accurately plotted on an overlay tracing and the appropriate *datum* elevations are inked as shown in the figure. Contours are then sketched lightly in pencil by interpolating for the map position between the control points. When the sketching is complete, the contours may be inked.

In the example just discussed, it is assumed that the rate of dip is moderately low; hence, no trigonometric correction is necessary; likewise, it is

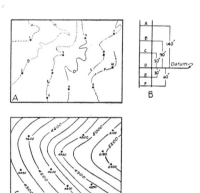

Fig. 107. Reduction of key bed elevations to a structural datum.

assumed that stratigraphic intervals are constant over the map area.

164. Reduction of Elevations in Steep Beds

Where beds are inclined at steep angles, the difference in elevation between the datum and a key bed stratigraphically higher or lower is somewhat greater than the stratigraphic interval separating the two horizons. This discrepancy can be ignored if the dip is moderately low. But inasmuch as the amount of the error increases according to a trigonometric function, it must be taken into account wherever dips are steep. The amount of the error is also a function of the thickness of the interval between the two beds; so where dips are moderately steep and the stratigraphic interval is large, the error may be sufficient to greatly distort the true structure on the contour map. The formula employed in reducing key bed elevations to datum elevations is

secant of dip angle $\times$ stratigraphic interval

Figure 108 illustrates the effect changing dip has on datum elevations, even though the stratigraphic interval is constant. Ob-

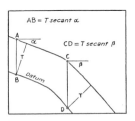

FIG. 108. Trigonometric reduction of key bed elevations to a structural datum according to the angle of dip.

serve the increase in the magnitude of the correction from AB to CD. In the Appendix, natural secants are given in Table 6. If natural secant tables are not available, the elevation correction may be made graphically. Plot the dip and on a perpendicular to this line scale the stratigraphic interval (T in the figure cited). Now draw the vertical line (AB or CD) and scale the difference in elevation.

If only elevations, but not dips, have been determined on the key bed, the amount of dip can be found, provided three elevations in the map arrangement of a triangle have been established. The three-point method of dip and strike determination is discussed in Article 148.

165. Relations of Surface Dips to Datum Dips

It is not uncommon for structural maps to exhibit discrepancies between observed surface dips and the spacing of contours, which, in turn, are controlled principally by elevations. Such discrepancies would not occur in many cases if all adjustments were correctly made. Where steep dips occur at points stratigraphically above or below the datum bed, the position of the dip on the map must

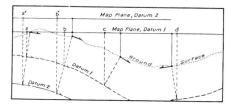

FIG. 109. Lateral migration of dips on to a structural datum.

be adjusted in order to agree with the actual inclination of the strata at the stratigraphic level of the datum. This map position is determined by either a graphic or a mathematical projection normal to the bedding plane at the location where the dip determination was made. Figure 109 is a cross section showing parallel folding and four surface dips and strikes. The following relationships are apparent in the drawing.

Where there is a variation in the rate of dip in parallel folding, the projection of dip must be perpendicular to the bedding planes. Such a projection results in a map displacement of the point of observation. The amount of displacement is a function of the angle of dip and the thickness of the stratigraphic interval between the point of observation and the datum. Two datum surfaces are shown in the figure. The map positions of points on these surfaces are shown at a, b, c, and d on the upper datum, and at a' and b' on the lower. Figure 110A shows the trigonometric relationships between c (the surface position), a (the projected point on the datum), and b (the map position) of the point on the datum. The distance bc is the amount of map displacement. If the point of observation is stratigraphically above the datum, it is migrated up the dip; if below the datum, it is migrated down the dip, as shown in Fig. 110B. The dip is displaced in a line normal to the strike.

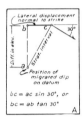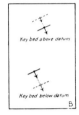

The amount of migration may be determined graphically by laying off the angle of dip, scaling the stratigraphic interval at right angles (ca in the figure cited), and then erecting a vertical line from a to intersect a horizontal through c. The distance bc is scaled and then plotted on the map, as shown in B of the figure.

FIG. 110. A. Trigonometric relations involved in dip migration. B. Relative direction of dip migration from points stratigraphically above or below the structural datum.

Where the terrain is moderately flat, the amount of migration is determined mathematically from the horizontal distance normal to the strike of the beds. In Fig. 111, let H be the horizontal (map) distance between the datum and a key bed, θ the angle of dip, T the stratigraphic interval, and m the amount of migration. By similar triangles, angle θ equals angle α; therefore

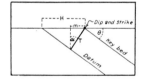

FIG. 111. Relations of horizontal distance parallel to dip, stratigraphic thickness, and dip migration.

$$m = T \text{ sine } \theta$$

If the stratigraphic thickness is not known, it may be computed by the relation

$$T = H \text{ sine } \alpha$$

By substituting this expression for T in the preceding formula, the migration of the dip can be computed from the horizontal distance and the angle of dip, as follows

$$m = (H \text{ sine } \theta) \text{ sine } \theta$$

or

$$m = H \text{ sine}^2 \theta$$

Figure 112A is a map showing the outcrops of the datum and an overlying key bed on which a dip and strike are located. The dip of the bed is 32 degrees and its elevation is 4870 feet. The horizontal distance normal to the strike is 1050 feet. It is desired to reduce both the dip and the elevation to the same point on the datum bed. The computations are as follows.

The stratigraphic thickness (T) is 1050 sine 32°=556 feet
The dip migration (M) is 556 sine 32°=295 feet
The datum elevation, E', is 4870−(556 cos 32°) or
4870−471=4399 feet

By applying the principles and formulas discussed, the dips that are obtained from cores in test wells may be predicted. When a test well is drilled on an asymmetrical anticline, it is necessary to locate the well somewhat off the axis on the low dipping flank in order to penetrate the objective horizon on the crest of the fold. The dips encountered in such a location will gradually diminish with depth until they become essentially level. If the dips in cores

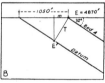

FIG. 112. Reducing both dip and elevation to a point on the structural datum.

then begin to increase after the level point is passed it may be that the drill has penetrated the axial surface and is encountering dips on the opposite flank from where it started at the surface. Other applications of the dip-migration principle are given in a later article.

166. Structural Effects of Stratigraphic Wedging

The thickening and thinning of stratigraphic intervals can cause serious errors in the projection of key bed elevations to the datum bed unless the nature of the convergence is understood and treated in a systematic manner. The isopach (convergence) map is the best means by which to reduce structural elevations through wedging units to the datum. As mentioned earlier, if appreciable variation in thickness is noticed in measured stratigraphic sections, data should be assembled for the purpose of controlling isopach maps. This situation may demand considerably more section work than would be required where intervals are nearly constant. Furthermore, if the changes in thickness are abrupt or erratic, the effects on structure, as interpreted from surface observations, may be very drastic, depending largely on the relationship of the anomalous thickening and the character of the structural element affected by the convergence. In any event, the isopach map should be as well controlled as surface conditions will permit.

Figure 113A is an isopach (thickness) map constructed according to stratigraphic thicknesses measured from the key bed A to the stratigraphically lower structural datum. As can be seen on the map, this interval ranges from 73 feet to 225 feet across the map area. Small x's are points where elevations have been determined on the key bed, and open circles are points of elevation on the datum. By means of thicknesses interpolated between isopachs, key bed elevations are reduced to datum values. Thus, at point a the elevation on bed A is 5490. By interpolation between isopachs 175 and 200, the stratigraphic interval is found to be 185 feet; therefore, the datum elevation at this point is 5305 feet. In B of the figure, all reductions have been made and these derived values are contoured to show the structure on the selected datum. If the dip is quite steep the difference in elevation between the key bed and the datum must be computed by the secant formula discussed earlier.

167. Reduction of Surface Structure to a Lower Datum

The preceding article briefly describes a method of employing isopach maps in the reduction of key bed to datum elevations. Isopach maps are also invaluable for reducing a contoured surface structural map to a deeper horizon. In petroleum ge-

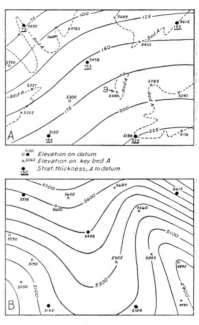

ology the "closed" anti-cline or dome is commonly sought as one of the most favorable types of traps for oil accumulation; therefore, it is a matter of more than passing inter-est to the field geologist to attempt to project the sur-face structure to deeper horizons where effective reservoir rocks exist. If stratigraphic intervals are constant and dips are gen-tle the process consists simply in subtracting the stratigrapihc interval from all points on the upper datum and then recon-touring the sheet. If steep dips occur the lower eleva-tion is obtained by the se-cant formula. However, if there is appreciable thin-

FIG. 113. Reduction of elevations to structural datum by isopachs. A. Loca-tions of measured intervals, key bed ob-servations, and isopachs (thickness con-tours). B. Structure map derived from these data.

ning of the interval between the two datum horizons, an isopach map of this interval must be drawn for the purpose of constructing the lower map.

Figure 114A is a combination surface structural and areal geo--

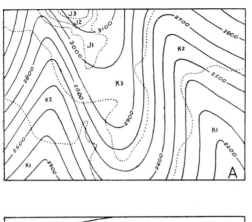

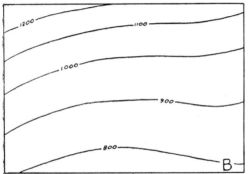

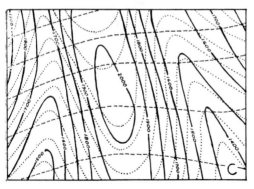

Fig. 114. Reduction of structure near the surface to a lower datum by means of isopachs. A. Structural and areal map. B. Isopach map. C. Relationships of all three maps. Notice the three-point intersections of contours.

logic map. The datum for the structural contours is the top of formation $K3$, which crops out over much of the area. Formation $J3$, which does not crop out within the map area, is a potential oil producer where structural conditions are favorable; therefore, it is imperative to translate the surface manifestations of structure on $K3$ into terms of $J3$. Figure 114B is an isopach map of the interval $K3$ to $J3$. The data used in constructing the isopach map were derived from surface sections and a few wells outside the boundaries of the map area. Inasmuch as all dips are moderately gentle, the differences in elevation between the two horizons are essentially the same as the stratigraphic interval; i.e., there is no need for computing the difference in datum elevations by the secant of the dip angle.

Figure 114C shows the isopach map exactly registered over the surface structural map. In practice, the easiest way to do this is to trace the simpler of the two maps and then adjust the tracing over the other. At any point where a structural contour crosses an isopach the elevation on $J3$ is determined by subtracting the interval (the isopach value) from the contour value on $K3$. It usually is not necessary to reduce all contour-isopach intersections unless either or both maps are quite complex. However, all salient features on *both* maps must be adequately represented. When making such a reduction, a second sheet of tracing paper or linen is laid over the two maps mentioned and securely fastened with drafting tape or thumb tacks. Land lines and other important planimetric features are traced. Selected intersections are marked and the elevations on $J3$ are determined as stated above and lettered on the tracing at the appropriate points.

Figure 114C shows the relationships of the structure on $K3$, the isopachs of the interval between $K3$ and $J3$, and the structure on the top of $J3$, the latter being represented by heavy solid contour lines. The closed area on $J3$ is entirely masked in the surface structure by the wedge of sediments separating the two datum horizons. It is obvious that the thickening and thinning of formations must be handled in a systematic manner in order to reveal well-concealed features that occur at considerable depth. Although the process just described is not primarily a field method, the field geologist should be vigilant in regard to the thickness behavior of formations that crop out in the map area. Where thicknesses vary appreciably, appropriate steps should be taken to obtain sufficient stratigraphic data for constructing the necessary isopach maps.

168. Migration of Fault Traces

A vertical fault surface or "plane" traverses all stratigraphic levels at exactly the same map position. Such a fault projects on to a horizontal plane as a straight line; and it will also be a straight line on a structural contour map, regardless of the complexity of the folding. Figure 115 illustrates this relationship.

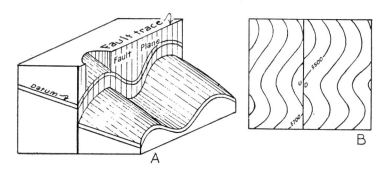

Fig. 115. A. Block diagram showing vertical fault plane cutting folded strata. B. No datum gap or bending of the fault trace.

The trace of an inclined fault plane will be a straight line on any and all stratigraphic horizons provided (1) the dip and strike of the fault plane are constant, and (2) the strata are level or the dip and strike are constant. However, the map position of the fault trace will vary according to the stratigraphic position of the structural datum. Similarly, a sinuous or curved trace will be the same at different stratigraphic levels if the strata are level or have a constant dip and strike, and the strikes and dips of the fault "plane" persist with little variation at depth. The horizontal positions of the trace will vary on structure maps drawn on different stratigraphic horizons, but the meanders caused by undulations in the fault surface do not vary with depth.

Unlike the special cases cited above, the directions, and forms of the traces of most faults, as well as the amounts of throw, are subject to much change depending on stratigraphic intervals involved, amount of displacement on the fault plane, the character of the plane, and a number of other factors. The field man is concerned with the means of coping with the problem of correctly depicting faults on his field structural maps and the data necessary to solve the problem. From the following discussions on the relationships of datum surfaces to fault surfaces, the types of data needed from the field should become apparent.

In an earlier article it was demonstrated how certain mapping values can be obtained by superimposing one contour map upon another and then obtaining the desired quantity at the intersections of the two sets of contours. The same principles may be used in the delineation of faults on maps. The process can best be explained by employing a few illustrations portraying average field conditions and steps in the process of projecting fault data.

Figure 116A represents a plane table sheet with a number of stadia control points on various beds and a few observations on the surface trace of a normal fault. In B, the structure has been contoured where the distribution of data permits, but the sheet is left blank in the vicinity of the fault. This contouring will be completed at a later stage of the work. From the few points on the surface trace of the fault, the fault surface is contoured, as in C. The contouring of the fault surface should be done on tracing paper on which are also located a few points common to the two sheets, such as section corners and other fixed planimetric marks. The contouring of the fault surface in C shows that this surface is slightly warped; therefore, a mathematical solution to the problem would be exceedingly complicated. The fault tracing is carefully registered over the partially contoured structure map and taped securely in this position, as in Fig. 116D. At all points where the elevation of the fault surface is the same as the datum elevation it is evident that a point of intersection exists. Thus, at *a* and *b* the 5500-foot structural contour intersects the 5500-foot

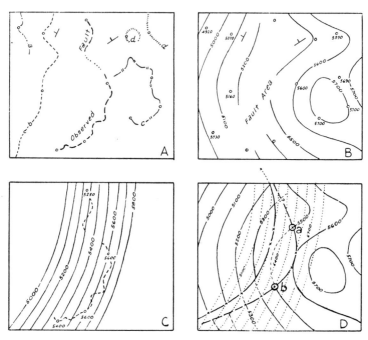

Fig. 116. Defining a datum gap by means of contour intersections.

fault "plane" contour; these points lie on the *trace* of the fault at the datum horizon. It follows that a line connecting a series of these points is the trace of the fault.

It would be an unusually fortunate circumstance if points common to the two surfaces could be determined in sufficient numbers in the field for contouring both the fault surface and the structural datum. In lieu of such control, the datum is tentatively contoured into the region of the fault by extending the trends established by direct ground control. Each side of the fault must be treated separately, for the downthrown block may have a somewhat different configuration from the upthrown. The contours have been extended in D of the figure cited above. Because of the fact that the fault surface is inclined, the datum surface on the downthrown side of the fault not only moves downward, but also *outward* from the upthrown block. The result of this lateral component of displacement is a gap in the datum surface, commonly referred to as a *fault-datum gap,* or simply a *datum gap.* The area and shape of this gap are dependent on the relationships and attitudes of the datum and fault surfaces. In the figure it is crescent-shaped and regular in form, simply because a symmetrical anticlinal nose is cut by an inclined surface which is very slightly warped. The datum gap may be an irregular area, and the only practical means of accurately delineating the datum gap employ the principles just described.

From the foregoing, it is evident that inclined normal (but not vertical) faults should be represented on structural contour maps by two more-or-less parallel lines instead of one. A single line is used where the gap is narrow or the scale of the map will not permit drawing the gap to scale. Inasmuch as the datum is absent in the datum gap, the structural contours do not cross it, as indicated by solid lines in the figure cited. The dashed lines are extensions of the contours used in the determination of the fault trace.

When the method of determining fault-datum relationships is clearly understood, the field man is more cognizant of the need for carefully placed points of control and will therefore direct his efforts toward obtaining the required data. It is important to make certain that points on the *surface trace* of a fault, regardless of the stratigraphic position, are points of control *on* the fault surface and can be used in the contouring of that surface, even though their stratigraphic position is unknown and they will be of no use as control for structural contouring of the datum.

169. Apparent Throw of Surface Faults

The throw (vertical component of the net slip) of a fault may vary from one horizon to another as the inclination of the fault surface varies at different levels. For this reason, the amount of throw observed in surface beds may be confusingly inconsistent until the relationships have been accurately plotted in some sort of three-dimensional drawing, such as contour maps. Although certain types of faults actually die out or increase in magnitude at depth, others only appear to do so because of changing relationships between the dip and strike of the fault surface and the dip and strike of the displaced strata.

Figure 117 is a common type of reverse fault which passes into bedding planes at depth. The total amount of slip is constant;

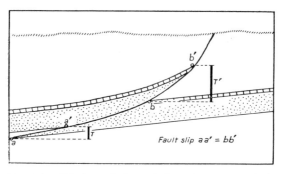

Fault slip a a′ = bb′

FIG. 117. Relations of slip and throw in a reverse fault. Slip *aa′* is equal to slip *bb′*, but the throw *T* is clearly much smaller than *T′*, where dip of the fault surface is steeper.

that is, the slip from *a* to *a′* is equal to *b* to *b′*, but the throw at *a* is nearly zero though it is quite significant at *b′*. Slump or "Gravity" normal fault surfaces sometimes have a similar configuration in that the dip of the surface diminishes with depth. Faults which steepen with depth occur in some places near the margins of deep basins. The variations in the relationships between fault surfaces and strata and between the strata on the two sides of a fault are almost limitless. In fact, there are so many possibilities it would be impractical to attempt to review them here. However, the field geologist should be aware of the relationships shown in the figure: namely, that for any given amount of slip normal to the strike of the fault, the stratigraphic displacement increases as the fault surface approaches a plane normal to the bedding. Thus, the throw, or stratigraphic displacement, of a fault measured on key beds stratigraphically above or below the datum may not be the same as that at the datum horizon. Contouring the fault surface will generally provide the most reliable means of reducing both the trace and the throw to the datum level. The field man should attempt to obtain control, both above and below the datum, for contouring the fault surface.

170. Surface Criteria for Detecting Obscure Faulting

Fault criteria, such as slickensides, offsets in strata, and others, are discussed in detail in many books on geology. The geologist or student of geology should become familiar with these criteria before going into the field, for they are necessary in the analysis of faults and fracture structures. One of the field geologists' most pressing problems is recognition of the existence of concealed faults in the map area. Faults are often quite obscure or entirely hidden at the surface and their presence may be deduced only by indirect evidences.

Faults are easily overlooked if occurring in thick sections of homogeneous shales or sandstones or monotonously repetitious sequences of these lithologies. Frequently, the best evidence is abrupt and local variations in dip or strike, or both. These anomalous dips usually are the result of drag or incipient slicing and are therefore found near the fault itself. Sometimes radically anomalous dips and strikes are dismissed as slump or other surface phenomena—not a good practice unless there is good supporting evidence to corroborate such a conclusion. When anomalous dips are observed the locality should be thoroughly examined and the observed dips should be plotted accurately on the map. As the map develops it may become apparent that the localities of erratic dips fall into some tangible linear pattern suggestive of a fault. In other words, one anomalous locality, alone, can hardly support a fault hypothesis; but a number of such occurrences may constitute strong evidence.

Strata in the immediate vicinity of a fault or fault zone are commonly highly fractured. If the strata are poorly lithified as are some shales, the only visible evidence consists of a profusion of calcite, gypsum, or silicious veins and seams. Mapping unusual occurrences of these mineralized areas is often the most effective means of delineating a zone within which a fault or a fault zone occurs.

Water, gas, or oil seepages are commonly associated with faults, and the geologist should be alert to these phenomena. It would be hazardous to accept such criteria alone as sufficient evidence of faulting; but in combination with other factors they might prove to be valuable. Vegetation patterns have been mentioned in regard to their association with certain strata. Definite offsets in vegetation lineaments or bands of vegetation transecting strata are strong evidences of faulting. Barren bands cutting across verdant areas may be caused by gas seepage along faults.

Discordant topographic alignments are frequently due to faults. The importance of constantly studying the topography during structural work can hardly be overemphasized, not only for faulting, but also for other structural features. Any topographic alignment, ridge or valley, not in harmony with surrounding features should be given special attention in the field to ascertain the reason for its existence. Abrupt changes in the gradient or direction of flow of water courses may denote significant structural control.

Whenever air photographs are available they should be studied in detail for features not apparent on the ground. Such features can be verified by detailed ground methods after they have been "discovered" on photos, though one may have to resort to auger holes or pits for the necessary confirmation. As mentioned earlier, direct observation from aircraft often results in recognition of faults and other structural features that are quite obscure on the ground.

171. Mapping Structure by Dips and Strikes

Thick successions of Cretaceous and Tertiary shales and sandstones are well exposed in many parts of the world, yet within these series are few, or no, distinctive beds that can be used extensively for mapping structure by means of elevations. However, moderately accurate contour maps can be made on the basis of dips and strikes by the following procedure.

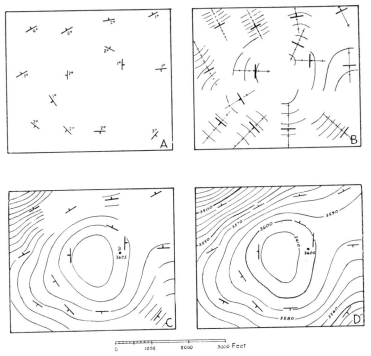

FIG. 118.   Mapping structure by dips and strikes and only one datum elevation.

Inasmuch as both the strike of a bed and a structural contour are level lines, it follows that structural contours *are* strike lines. Therefore, structural contours must always parallel observed strikes accurately plotted on the map. The spacing of contours is determined by the *rate* of dip. This relationship is expressed by the formula

$$S = I \cot \theta$$

when S is the contour spacing, I is the contour interval, and θ is the angle of dip.

Figure 118A is a field map on which are plotted a number of dips and strikes. There are no steep dips; so it is not necessary to migrate the locations according to the principles discussed in a previous article. In B, the dips are extended by light pencil lines. The contour spacing is computed by the cotangent formula, and the spacing for each dip is plotted for several contours along

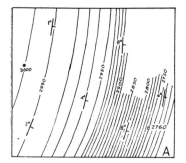 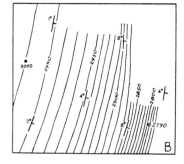

FIG. 119. Discrepancies in contouring from dips and strikes resulting from dip locations not being at points where the rate of dip changes.

the lines. At point *a*, in C of the figure cited, is a bed selected as the datum. The elevation of this point is 3650 feet. The contouring must be started at this point in order to maintain elevations as nearly correct as possible. The point lies midway between the 3600- and the 3610-foot contours. Lightly sketched *tentative* contours are drawn at each of the dips, care being taken to "bend" the bands of contours toward adjacent strikes. This is the skeleton of the contour map. Figure 118D is the finished contour map. The numbering of contours is based on the one elevation point.

172. Inherent Errors of Dip-Strike Contouring

The method just described is moderately accurate if dips and strikes are closely spaced or where axes of folds and breaks in strike or dip are well defined; but if the control is sparse, errors of rather large magnitude may develop. These errors may be either compensating or cumulative, and they may occur for two reasons: (1) an error in the interpretation of changing rate of dip and (2) misjudging the curves in contours from one strike to adjacent strikes. Although experience and good structural interpretation play an important part in attaining accuracy in the contouring, there is also a large element of chance.

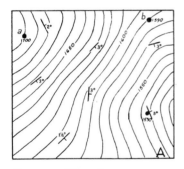 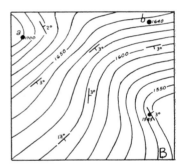

FIG. 120. Dip-strike contouring where both dips and strikes vary over the map area.

Figure 119A illustrates the contouring of a series of changing rates of dip where the strikes are nearly parallel. The points where observed dips begin to increase or decrease are not indicated; so the manner in which the transitions occur is an arbitrary interpretation. The same dips are contoured in B. Superficially, the two segments of structure are alike, but the discrepancy is indicated by a comparison of the difference in elevation shown by the contours on the two drawings.

Figure 120A shows the contouring of changing strikes and variable dips. The same data are again contoured in B. Here the starting elevation at *a* is the same as in the first example, but a discrepancy appears in the elevation at *b,* which is derived from contouring based on dips and strikes.

Where both dips and strikes change, the chances for errors are numerous; but, fortunately, within a large map area, there is considerable tendency for the errors to compensate.

From the foregoing it is apparent that data should be closely spaced if accurate results are to be expected. Furthermore, it is extremely important, whenever field conditions permit, to select points of observation as near as possible to the place where changes in dip or strike occur—not midway between these "breaks."

173. Elevation Correction Sheet

Although a monotonous series of shales and sandstones may not contain a sufficient number of key beds to serve as elevation control for structural mapping, a few elevations at known stratigraphic positions greatly strengthen a dip and strike map. From a few structural elevations, a correction contour sheet is drawn and by means of this sheet, the structural map is adjusted. The procedure is as follows.

Figure 121A is a dip-strike contour map, whose elevations are based on a prominent bed cropping out at point *a*. This bed is the structural datum. In wells at 1, 2, 3, and 4 the same bed is encountered at elevations given at the respective locations. These correct elevations do not agree with the contours; therefore the map is in error in the amounts of the discrepancies. In B the differences between actual elevations of the datum in wells and the elevations derived from contours are plotted on a sheet of tracing paper and then contoured. These contours represent the amount the original contours must be raised or lowered (indicated by plus and minus) in order to make the structural contours agree with the known elevations. This correction sheet is now carefully registered over the structural contour map as shown in C. At points of intersection of the two sets of contours a new set of structural elevations is obtained by adding or subtracting from the structural contour value the amount indicated on the correction sheet. When an adequate density of control points is obtained

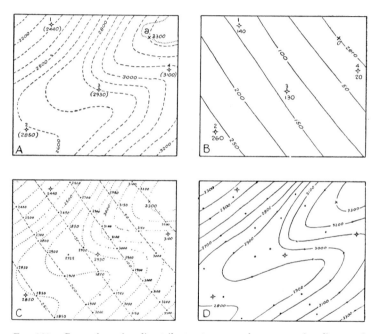

FIG. 121. Correction of a dip-strike contour map by means of well control and a correction "isopach" map (B).

by this process, the sheet is recontoured, as shown in D. This is the corrected structural map. Now compare the corrected map with the original draft in A.

The method just described usually does not eliminate all elevation errors in the original dip-strike map; but the small residual errors are redistributed in such a way that they do not materially affect the structure as a whole.

174. Mapping Structure by Dip Components

Under certain field conditions it is much easier to obtain dip components than dips and strikes. Ledges and other types of exposures commonly occur along the sides of valleys and banks of streams and for this reason, the outcrop pattern may closely resemble the drainage pattern. Under these circumstances it is often possible to obtain long sight lines on a component of dip but difficult to determine comparably long sights for both dip and strike. It is obvious that where field conditions are favorable there is some advantage in a method wherein only components are needed.

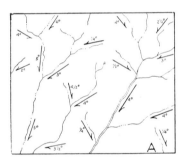 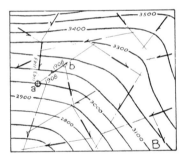

Fig. 122. Construction of a structural contour map from dip components. A. The lengths of sights and rate of apparent dip are shown. B. The framework of components provides the essential information for drawing structural contours.

An earlier article explains a graphic method for determining a dip and strike from two intersecting dip components. The principles given are only slightly modified when applied to mapping structure.

Figure 122A is a field map showing dip components measured by Brunton and plotted on the sheet by means of a protractor.

The approximate length of sight is shown by a heavy line. This line should be inked on the sheet. The light lines in B represent pencil extensions of the components. These lightly drawn extensions form a network of intersections with adjacent components over the entire sheet. This network is the skeleton on which the contoured structure is developed.

The datum is determined by the elevations given to the contours drawn on the first pair of components used in the construction, unless an elevation is obtained on a definite stratigraphic horizon selected as a datum and contouring is adjusted to this point. Sometimes it is not feasible to follow the latter procedure, in which case the stratigraphic horizon of the datum is unknown at the time the contouring is done.

Point *a* of Figure 122B is the intersection of the *initial pair* of components. The *initial contour* will pass through this point and the positions of all succeeding contours will be determined by this point. The contour interval is to be 100 feet. As stated earlier, the spacing of contours is computed by the formula

$$S = I \cot \theta$$

when S is the spacing, I is the contour interval, and θ is the dip (or dip component) angle. Therefore, the spacing of contours on the left component is 100 cot $5° = 1143$ feet (Fig. 122B); the spacing along the right component is 100 cot $3° = 1908$ feet. These spacings are indicated by tic marks (in pencil). Contours starting at *a* will pass through these marks. The right component intersects the extension of a third component at point *b*. The procedure for determining contour *spacing* is the same as from point *a;* but, since the *positions* of contours along the common component have already been established, some adjustment on the third and all succeeding components may be necessary.

When the dip component method is used the field man should pay particular attention to directional relationships. In order to set up a strong network of components it is essential to plot the observations on a map as the data are obtained. The strongest figure is one where the two components intersect at an angle near 90 degrees. Where there are numerous outcrops, the geologist can be critical in selecting components that will provide a strong lattice over the entire map area. The strongest network is attained when one of each pair of components is common to another pair; that is, when three components form two pairs. If this principle is maintained throughout the map there should be no errors which result in pronounced structural anomalies.

175. Discussion of the Dip Component Method

Every geologic field method has certain favorable and un-favorable attributes. An awareness of these attributes is essential to wise application of the method. Inherent errors in the dip-strike method of contouring and a means of adjusting elevation errors have been briefly discussed. The component method is subject to the same errors as well as others. It should be foremost in mind that when two components are used in lieu of an observed and measured dip and strike, it is assumed that they lie in the same or parallel planes. Usually this assumption is valid if the components are not too far apart. But if minor surface warping of the strata exists, then there is danger of the components lying in differently inclined planes, in which case the resultant dip and strike would be in error.

Even though a structural survey is undertaken with the intention of using the component method, *both* dip and strike should be obtained wherever possible, thus avoiding some of the errors peculiar to the component method.

It is well to consider some of the advantages of the component method. As anyone experienced in field work knows, it is often difficult and time-consuming to obtain both the dip and strike on poorly bedded strata, for the exposure is likely to be quite elongate in one direction, thus providing only one long line of sight. The effects of irregular bedding are reduced in proportion to the length of sight; hence, a reliable component may be gotten where a dip and strike would be subject to large errors.

The angle and bearing of a component can be determined in a small fraction of the time required for reading an accurate dip and strike. For this reason, the component method is a good reconnaissance tool. This method is especially amenable for use with air photographs in reconnaissance work. The position of the point of observation is marked on the photo and the bearing and angle of the component are recorded in the field book together with the station number, which is marked on the photo. If the definition of outcrop lines is sharp on the photos, only the angle of the component need be observed in the field, the direction of the component being evident on the photo. However, even in this procedure, the position of the observation point should be marked and numbered on the photo to avoid the possibility of confusion later.

176. Area Controlled by Two Components

The area controlled by two components of dip should be considered as the *minimum area that will contain both components.*

The extensions of components to the point of intersection is necessary for the graphical solution of the problem, but this construction in no wise extends the control beyond the area of observation. Figure 123 is a schematic diagram showing two components on a warped surface. That portion of the surface in which the components are shown may be considered a plane. The point of intersection occurs far above the surface, but this does not interfere with the solution of the problem, for the *area of control* is only that portion of the figure within the dotted boundary.

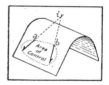

FIG. 123. Area controlled, structurally, by two components. Notice that the intersection at i is a point in space, but this does not affect the dip-strike construction within the area of control.

The area within which two components may be considered reliable control depends on the regularity of dip and strike. If there is appreciable variation in the angle of dip along components having similar bearings, then there is a probability of either changing strike or changing rate of (true) dip. Figure 124 shows how failure in the field to recognize a change in dip may result in serious errors in a map dependent on dip components for control. The true structure is shown by means of contours in A. The

developed contouring based on components *a* and *b* is shown in B. This is a true representation because the area of control is within a "plane" area of the warped surface. Components *a* and *c* give an erroneous picture because the two components are in different planes of the sur-

FIG. 124. Errors caused by pairing two components lying in different planes, such as *a* and *c*. The correct contouring is shown in A.

face. Since components *b* and *c* are parallel, the variation in apparent dip should forewarn the geologist of changing true dip. Obviously, the only safeguard against such hazards is close spacing of components used as a construction pair.

177. Plotting Bearings with the Brunton

When the plane table is used for mapping, a fast method of plotting components or other bearings on the sheet employs the Brunton pocket transit (compass) instead of a protractor. This

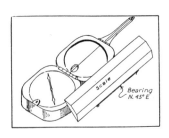

method requires no line of reference on the sheet, which is an advantage when the sheet is already congested by a multitude of details.

Figure 125 illustrates the manner of using a flat plotting scale inclined against the side of the Brunton to bring the lower edge in coincidence with the station location. The Brunton is placed near the location and roughly oriented

FIG. 125. Laying off a bearing through a plotted point by means of a Brunton and a plotting scale.

by the magnetic needle along the bearing observed on the component. Now the scale is placed alongside and the compass is rotated to the exact bearing. Hold the compass firmly in this position and shift the *inclination* of the scale until it coincides with the point, then draw the bearing along the edge. Take care that the plotting scale is pressed against the side of the compass.

178. Definition of Nonconformities by Dip-Strike Contouring

There are many places where regional angular unconformities are known to exist, but the relationships of structure above and below have defied precise definition by conventional mapping methods. One of the principal reasons for this situation is that key beds are lacking in one or both sequences of strata; therefore, structural elevation methods are not applicable. It is of considerable interest to geologists in several fields of investigation to ascertain the relative ages of folding, and the attitudes of strata above and below subtle nonconformities are revealing of the times at which structural disturbances occurred. A good example of such a nonconformity is that which occurs between the Cretaceous and Tertiary in Nebraska, Wyoming, Colorado, Utah, and elsewhere. In general, the angularity is small, except locally, where it may be above 10 degrees. The broad regional relationships have not yet been precisely mapped.

In many places the contact of unconformable series is obscured by surface materials or is lithologically indistinct; hence, the nature of the contact surface is not mappable. However, identification of each series as a whole is not difficult; so by the dip-strike or dip component method, the structure within each series can be determined in the field and then compared by means of contours. The extra field time required to collect dip and strike data for two series of rocks occurring in the same area is not great. Often it is only a matter of a few yards from one to the other, and if the ground is being traversed for the purpose of mapping structure in one series, the additional data can be obtained at small cost.

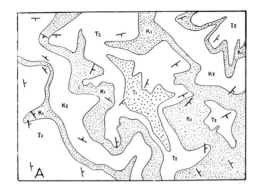

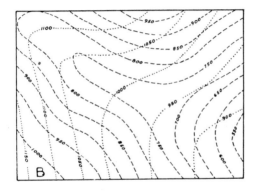

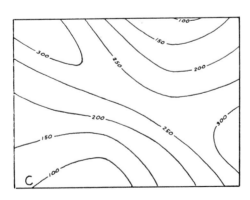

Fig. 126. Determination of the magnitude of a nonconformity by means of two structure maps, shown in B, from data obtained from a geologic map, A. The amount of discordance is shown in C.

Figure 126A is an areal geologic map showing the distribution of Cretaceous and Tertiary beds and dips and strikes in each series. In B, the structure of each is shown on one map by two sets of contours, the dashed lines being on the Cretaceous and the dotted, on the Tertiary. Contour numbers (elevations) are assigned arbitrarily for the purpose of clarifying the direction of dip. The nature of the discordance may be shown as an "isopach" map of the beds between the two datums. The process is similar to others employing two sets of contours. At contour intersections the lower value is subtracted from the higher to provide a control point for the third map, shown in C of the figure. The discordance is greatest where contours are closely spaced, and least where widely spaced.

179. Contour Expression of Geologic Surfaces

Any surface can be contoured provided (1) it is not level and (2) there are at least three control points arranged in the form of a triangle. Consequently any inclined geologic surface, such as a stratum, unconformity, or fault surface can be shown quantitatively as a contour map. Any contoured surface can be tilted or rotated into a predetermined position by constructing a set of "contours" representing the space through which the plane, or surface, is to be rotated and then superimposing this sheet on the contoured map, thereby obtaining new control values by subtraction or addition of contour values. This principle has been demonstrated in preceding topics.

During the course of repeated orogenies a stratigraphic horizon may assume a number of varying attitudes. Sometimes it is highly important to restore an inclined or warped bed to a position occupied earlier in its history. This problem is involved in tilted oil-water interfaces of oil fields, former attitudes of erosion surfaces, and determinations of foci of uplifts.

Figure 127A shows two sets of structural contours drawn on the basis of the indicated dips and strikes. The dashed-line contours are on the higher horizon, and the strike and dip of the beds are N 50° W, 14° SW. The solid-line structural contours are on a datum below a nonconformity. The strike and dip in these beds are N 80° W, 20° S. The problem is to show by means of contours the strike and dip of the strata *below* the unconformity when the datum *above* the unconformity is restored to a level position; i.e., the attitude prior to tilting of the two series of beds.

Fig. 127. Determination of a former dip and strike in beds that have been tilted. The present dips and strikes above and below a nonconformity are shown in A.

The first step in the procedure consists in drawing a map which shows the nature of the *space* between the upper datum and a level plane. This is the space through which the lower datum must be rotated in order to accomplish the requirements of the problem. Inasmuch as the values of structural contours represent the departure of the structural datum from a level (elevation datum) surface, the "space wedge" has exactly the configuration of the structural surface. Therefore it is only necessary to change the *numbering* of the structural contours to convert the map into an isopach map representing this "space wedge." The problem illustrated deals with inclined planes, and consequently, the contours and isopachs are straight lines. Any contour on the higher structure map may be taken as the *axis* of rotation, but the problem is simplified if the highest contour is used (1500 feet in the figure). Along the axis of rotation there is no change in spatial position; so this is designated a zero isopach.

Fasten a sheet of vellum over the upper structure map and trace the contours. Number these contours, from zero, as indicated in the preceding paragraph, according to the difference between the values of the initial contour and each successively lower contour, as, for example, $1500 - 1400 = 100$ and $1500 - 1300 = 200$. These are the "space isopach" values.

Now carefully register this isopach map over the *lower* structure map, as in B. At intersections of these structural contours and the isopachs add the value of the isopach to the elevation of the structure contour. This procedure results in the removal of all postunconformity tilting from the structure below the unconformity.

Solid lines in Figure 127B show the attitude of the lower structural datum prior to the later period of tilting. The direction of strike may be obtained by measurement with a protractor and the rate of dip by scaling the distance between contours and applying the formula

$$\text{Tangent of dip angle} = \frac{\text{Difference in elevation}}{\text{Horizontal distance}}$$

In a case such as the foregoing, where only true planes are involved, the problem can be solved more quickly by descriptive geometry or by use of the stereonet. However, it is seldom that one meets with such ideal conditions in structural geology, and the principles developed in this example are applicable to complex situations, whereas the other two methods are predicated on *planes* in space. The following example illustrates the use of contour maps in solving a somewhat more complicated problem.

Figure 128A is an idealized cross section showing the structural and stratigraphic relations between two datums situated above and below a nonconformity. Contour maps on the two datums are shown in B and C. The problem is to show the structure on the lower datum before the arch was accentuated in the second period of folding. An arbitrary level plane is assumed somewhat higher than the highest contour in B. On the basis of this level plane the contours of the structure map are renumbered to represent the interval *between* the level plane and the structural datum. The map is the same; only the contour numbers are different. This "space isopach" map is then placed over the structure map shown

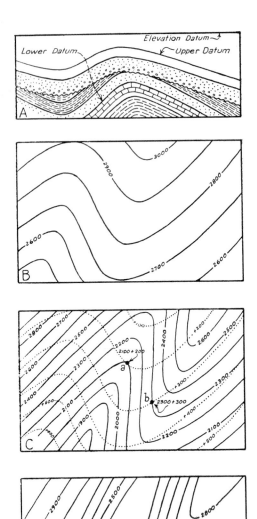

Fig. 128. Method for removing the effects of late folding from a stratum or series that has undergone two or more periods of folding. New control points are computed at contour and "space" isopach intersections, as at *a* and *b* in C.

in C, and the contour intersections are computed as outlined in the preceding example. The structure map shown in D is based on elevations derived in this manner. It is a fair representation of the structure in the pre-unconformity series during the time the post-unconformity beds were being deposited.

180. Remarks on Contour Methods for Solving Problems

Strictly speaking, the two foregoing examples of employing contours in the solutions of three-dimensional problems are not directly concerned with field geology; yet, the field geologist can frequently apply the principles illustrated in the solution or clarification of many perplexing field problems. It has been shown how warped surfaces can be transformed and shifted in space according to rigid contour control. Where structural relationships are complex the man in the field may avoid confusion in securing or interpreting surface data through the use of various contour maps and overlay sheets. For example, intermittent exposures of a single fault may appear to be several faults, or *vice versa*. If the data are sufficient for even approximate contouring of the fault surface, this type of analysis will often illuminate the principal relationships so that additional control can be obtained for defining all features of structure.

Contour maps are three-dimensional. Several planes or surfaces can be shown simultaneously in exact interrelationships. For this reason, the contour method is especially suited to many structural problems.

Adeptness in the applications of contours comes with practice. Block diagrams and isometric projections are useful devices for *demonstrating* geologic relationships, but they have very limited application in the solutions of complex three-dimensional problems. Quite often unsuspected relationships become evident when two or more contour maps are superimposed one on another, and the great advantage in the method is that only one surface is considered at a time.

When problems require contours on several surfaces, it is

generally best to draw each map on a separate sheet of transparent material with common marks, such as land corners, so that they may be correctly registered on each other in any desired order. If more than two maps are to be used together, the contours should be drawn in contrasting colors in order to avoid confusion of lines.

Other applications of contours in geologic work are presented elsewhere in this manual. The student of geology should become thoroughly familiar with this very versatile, yet precise, mode of expression and method of analysis.

CHAPTER VII

Stratigraphic Field Work

181. Introduction

This chapter is concerned with measurements and other operations that pertain to stratigraphic field work. Although accurate
measurements of stratigraphic thicknesses are essential to the
solutions of certain structural problems, the objectives of many
projects do not extend beyond the investigations of stratigraphy
itself. To varying degrees and in differing ways geologic structure
enters into the study of stratigraphy; it is not feasible to treat
either subject with complete disregard for the other. However,
the following discussions apply to projects whose principal aims
are the solution of stratigraphic problems, and structural phases
are introduced only where they bear directly on stratigraphic field
work.

There are numerous approaches to the study of stratigraphy,
as might be deduced from the many books and professional papers
on the subject. Despite the fact that concepts differ fundamentally
and methods of study are at wide variance, the field man's requirements and field procedures need not be greatly affected, for
the main purpose in field work is to observe, measure, and record
stratigraphic relationships. It is hazardous for one to undertake
field investigations for the purpose of assembling data to support
any particular theory on sedimentation, because significant data
not *directly* related to the specific inquiry are thereby likely to be
neglected or ignored. The field geologist must be an impartial
observer of geologic phenomena even though his inclinations are

267

toward specific aspects of stratigraphy. Field observations should be based primarily on descriptive geology. When the information collected in the field is complete it serves the purposes and needs of later research irrespective of the motivating theory. It should be kept in mind that a widely accepted theory of today may be discarded tomorrow. Field work should be placed on more enduring foundations so that it need not be revised or repeated in order to keep pace with changing ideas on sedimentation processes, the development of sedimentary rocks, or their classification. Generally, the field man has fulfilled his obligations when he brings back from the field a complete record (and tentative interpretation) of observable geologic data. The refinement of such records must be determined by conditions under which the work is done. But to classify too strictly the kind of data to be collected, is to invite a costly return to the field at a later date for the purpose of completing the job. Thus, if samples are collected mainly for the purpose of extracting the microfossils, without regard to lithologic changes, in all probability the section will have to be resampled to determine its lithologic characteristics.

One aspect of field geology that is frequently neglected, yet can hardly be overemphasized, is the complete recording of observations. The study of data does not end with the field season, though some field men would appear to believe so. Properly recorded data, whether on maps, in notes, or labeled specimens become an ageless bank of information, not only for the one who performed the field work, but also for those who carry on studies later. The information carried in one's mind is not available to coworkers and is of only temporary use to the possessor.

182. Reconnaissance

Reconnaissance for stratigraphic field work should begin in the office or library. Much field time will be saved if the literature and various files are thoroughly perused and all pertinent data are classified and put into readily usable form prior to going into the field. In some regions little or no reconnaissance is necessary.

Whether reconnaissance is desirable or necessary can be decided by considering the factors that play an important part in planning and conducting field operations. Examine the following questions with regard to the area to be studied. If all the topics can be answered as indicated in parentheses no field reconnaissance would be required. The amount of time and the nature of preliminary work might be estimated by the number of topics that cannot be answered with the information at hand.

(1) Are outcrops extensive? (Yes)
(2) Are exposures badly weathered, locally? (No)
(3) Is the region everywhere accessible by the means of transportation available? (Yes)
(4) Does structure present any special problems? (No)
(5) Does topography materially affect the methods to be used? (No)
(6) Do you have a wide choice of instruments and methods? (Yes)
(7) Does time or expense limit the amount of field work that can be undertaken? (No)
(8) Are lodging accommodations or camp sites adequate? (Yes)
(9) Are essential supplies available? (Yes)

A number of the topics listed can be investigated without going into the field; those which require checking on the ground should be noted for specific examination when the field reconnaissance is undertaken.

As a part of the office preparations, portions of available areal geologic maps may be sketched on to road maps and colored with pencils so that the outcrop bands are distinct but do not obscure the roads and trails. Oil service company road maps, state highway county maps, and U.S. Forest Service maps are very good for such compilations. Formation thicknesses and lithologies, characteristics of geologic boundaries, facies changes, and like data may be found useful in the field.

Field reconnaissance should endeavor to answer the nine questions above, and, perhaps, others that are important to the project.

Its objective is to provide a regional grasp of the geology before detailed work is started and to weigh the various problems that will be encountered so that the course of operations will be charted according to the most productive course of procedure. When the time for a project is quite limited, one's natural inclination is to begin at once on the detailed work and omit much or all of the reconnaissance work. This is usually the wrong thing to do, for when time is short it must not be wasted in too hasty action. Reconnaissance is a means of *saving* time; it is a means of *defining* economical procedures; it should be the preliminary step in nearly all field projects.

183. Types of Projects and Field Methods

The various types of stratigraphic projects may be classified according to the detail required, laboratory work to be done, field methods to be employed, and other considerations related to the subject. When no laboratory work is to be done, it may not be feasible to collect samples, which is ordinarily a time-consuming task. In a case such as this, field descriptions of the rocks must be prepared in greater detail because they cannot be supplemented or amplified later. Studies of formation thicknesses over large areas may be made for the purpose of predicting drilling depths only, and, therefore, do not become involved in lithologic descriptions at all. On the other hand, research in sedimentation processes, geologic history, and the like often requires the utmost detail in recording of field relations and sampling of the sections. Stratigraphic work is sometimes undertaken to provide lithologic characteristics of the formations to aid in recognition of the units penetrated in wells. Sampling of the sections would have to satisfy this requirement.

The foregoing comments might seem to be in contradiction to those made in the introduction to this chapter. In clarification, it should be stated that a distinction is made between *biased* observations, which tend to minimize the importance of phenomena opposing a preconceived idea, and observations which are *restricted* in detail because of various limiting factors, such as time, size of the area, and lack of instrumentation. A project limited by economics or technical necessity is not generally construed as a genuinely scientific investigation, but rather a technical operation, which does not purport to be otherwise.

The following topics describe field procedures employed in stratigraphic work. Various phases of field operations are grouped according to technical similarity, not according to the objectives of field study. The selection of methods described must devolve upon the user of the manual; for it is not practicable to treat every type of investigation in detail.

184. Simple and Composite Stratigraphic Sections

A "simple" stratigraphic section is one that is measured along a continuous straight line. For such a section, outcrops must be quite extensive near the line of the traverse. More commonly, outcrops are scattered so that it is necessary to measure portions of the section in different localities. A section compiled from portions measured at a number of localities is called a *composite section*. If the formations vary in thickness or lithology from one place to another (and they generally do), the composite section

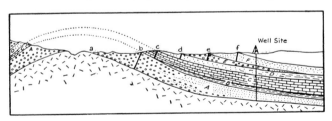

Fig. 129. Cross section illustrating the fallacy in compiling a composite section measured over a wide expanse of outcrops.

is not truly representative of the complete stratigraphic column at any point, though it may be moderately typical for the area as a whole. On the other hand, the simple stratigraphic section may be as badly in error in details where dips are low and differences in elevation on the surface are small; for in order to measure a significant thickness of beds under these conditions, the line of section must be long, thus affording many opportunities for changes in the stratigraphy between the ends of the section traverse.

Figure 129 is a simple type of stratigraphic section measured along a single straight line from *a* to *f*. Upper formations have

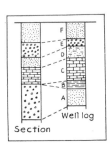

Section

FIG. 130. Comparison of the composite section and well log shown in Fig. 129.

been eroded away in localities where basal portions are exposed. It is clear that the thicknesses measured at the surface along the line of section cannot be combined into a composite that would be correct for any one point. Figure 130 is a comparison of the surface section and that penetrated by a well near point *f*. One overlapped formation does not crop out along the line of section.

When using this type of simple, continuous section or the ordinary composite section in stratigraphic mapping, the location of the control point on the map should correspond to the location where the formation was actually measured. In a series of stratigraphic maps, the control point for Formation *A* would be plotted at a different location than one for Formation *F*. A central location for the entire section would not do for certain kinds of mapping.

185. Measurement of Level Strata

There are no geometric problems involved in the measurement of thickness of a stratigraphic sequence lying essentially level. The *stratigraphic thickness is simply the difference in elevation* between the base and the top of the stratigraphic interval. The horizontal or map locations of control points have no bearing whatsoever on thickness determinations so long as the attitude of the beds remains horizontal.

Figure 131 shows a stratigraphic cross section of level beds. The interval to be measured is from *A* to *B*, and the course that must be followed in making the measurements is along the surface profile. Units 2 and 3 are measured on the small hill to point *a*, but the

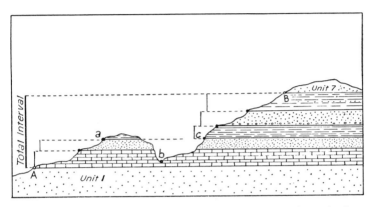

FIG. 131.   Measurement of stratigraphic thickness where beds are level.

level traverse is continued back down the section to point *b* in order to carry the elevations to the next hill, where the remainder of the section is exposed. In getting to point *c*, which is at the same horizon as *a*, Unit 3 and part of Unit 2 have been traversed three times. However, from the figure it is clear that the differences in elevation between *a* and *b* and *b* and *c*, are ignored in computing the thickness of the section.

Inasmuch as horizontal position of control points has no effect on the measurement of level strata, there is no need for plotting the locations of stations on a map or plane table sheet. Any instrument by which the difference in elevation can be measured is applicable to measuring horizontal beds. Where beds are exposed in vertical cliffs, a tape or calibrated cord with a suspended weight may be hung over the brink to measure the thicknesses of the units. Methods for measuring difference in elevation are given in Chapter IV.

186. Measurement of Vertical Strata with Constant Strike

The stratigraphic thickness of beds dipping at 90 degrees (vertical) is *the horizontal distance perpendicular to the strike.* It is evident in Fig. 132 that the difference in elevation between the various portions of the section in no way affects the measure-

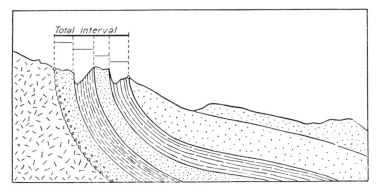

FIG. 132. Measurement of stratigraphic thickness where beds are vertical.

ment of thickness; therefore, no advantage is gained by running elevations.

Vertical beds of constant strike crop out as parallel straight lines, regardless of the amount or character of topographic relief. Because of this fact, the strike can be obtained exactly by sighting along the surface trace of any bed. The direction of section is at right angles to the strike or outcrop line. When the plane table is used, the strike line can best be established on the sheet by setting the tripod over a bed that can be traced for some distance and then sighting along the bed or on a distant rod held on the bed. A line drawn along the blade of the alidade is the strike on the sheet. A line is then drawn perpendicular to the strike and the alidade is placed on this line, and thus it is pointed in the direction in which the section is to be measured. Points on the ground lying on the line of section are noted and horizontal measurements of distance are made with a tape or stadia rod. Distances to points along the section are plotted on the sheet on a scale sufficiently large to permit scaling within the *allowable error in stratigraphic thickness.*

When only the Brunton compass and tape are used the bearing of the strike is first determined and then a compass bearing at 90 degrees is established and marked on the ground along the line of section. Where it is not convenient to mark points along the line of section, the tape may be oriented by compass while measurements are being made.

It should be kept in mind that the measurements of distance are direct determinations of stratigraphic thickness; therefore, an error in either the measurement of distance along the line of section or in plotting, when the plane table is used, results in an error of *equal magnitude* in stratigraphic thickness.

Under ordinary circumstances thick sequences of beds are not continuously exposed along a line of section normal to the strike. Topography often plays an important part in the distribution of outcrops. Similarly, adverse topographic conditions may prevent traversing a long, straight line. In such cases the section is measured by a system of offsets. Figure 133 is an areal geologic

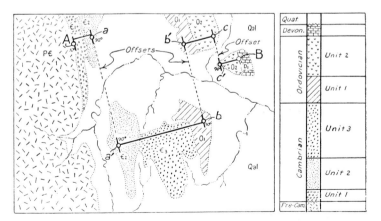

Fig. 133.   Measurement of vertical strata by offsetting along the strike.

map of an area in which it is necessary to measure the thicknesses of Cambrian and Ordovician sediments. Obviously, it is not pos-

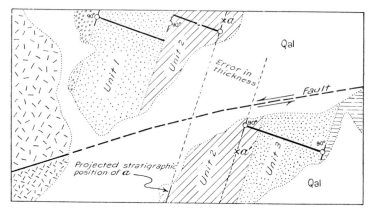

FIG. 134.   Errors introduced by obscure faulting when offsetting along strike.

sible to traverse the entire section on a continuous line. The segment Aa is measured and a point is sighted from a to a' exactly along the bearing of the strike. The second segment $a'b$ is run

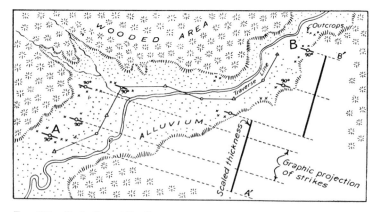

FIG. 135.   Projecting strike lines to reconstruct section where outcrops are widely scattered.

to any convenient point in the formation O_1 that can be seen in the northern part of the area, as at b', along the strike line. Similar offsets are made to the top of the section at B. Sighted offsets are used where key beds that can be identified in various outcrops do not occur in the sections exposed. No large errors will be

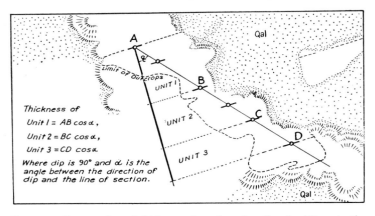

Fig. 136. Computation of thickness where line of section is oblique to the direction of dip.

introduced if the strike is constant and the offset lines are carefully sighted. Faults might be present in covered areas, yet not be suspected by changes in dip or strike in the exposed sections, as shown in Fig. 134. The field man must always be on guard to prevent errors such as that illustrated. The error in this figure is from a to a', resulting in an apparent thickness of Unit 2 that is more than twice too great.

As mentioned earlier, the course that must be followed in measuring a section may be determined by topography. Figure 135 shows a plane table traverse from which stadia shots are taken on random outcrops, identified in the figure as x-marks and dip and strike symbols. The thickness of the section is determined graphically by prolonging the strike lines so that they may be cut by perpendiculars. In the case illustrated, the distances normal to the strike (stratigraphic thicknesses where the dip is 90 degrees) are scaled along the two heavy lines. This method requires the plotting of distances and strike lines on drawing paper or a plane table sheet.

Figure 136 shows a line of section along a ridge where bedrock is continuously exposed. Because of the orientation of the ridge, the line of section cannot be run in a direction normal to the strike; however, the section can be laid out in a straight line without offsets. If the section is run by plane table, thicknesses may be determined graphically, as outlined in the previous paragraph. When it is not convenient to use a plane table, the measurements may be made with tape and compass, and thicknesses of the units determined mathematically, as follows.

$$\text{Thickness of Unit } 1 = AB \cos \alpha,$$
$$\text{Thickness of Unit } 2 = BC \cos \alpha,$$
$$\text{Thickness of Unit } 3 = CD \cos \alpha,$$

when distances are measured along a straight line of section, as A to D, and α is the horizontal angle between the line of section and the direction of *dip*.

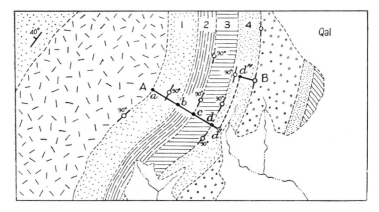

Fig. 137. Measurement of stratigraphic interval where the beds are vertical but the strike changes.

187. Measurement of Vertical Strata with Variable Strike

In areas where outcrops are numerous, the measurement of vertical beds is a simple process even though the strike changes considerably. Figure 137 illustrates a situation where changing strike must be taken into account. The section to be measured is from horizon *A* to horizon *B*. Various obstacles prevent running one straight, continuous line across the entire section. Inasmuch as the strike is constantly changing along any given horizon, the offset method given earlier cannot be used. A number of strikes is determined throughout the vicinity and a line of section is laid out in such a way that the strikes are intersected at 90 degrees. The most favorable terrain is from *A* to *d*. The unit contacts are established at *b*, *c*, and *d*. The top of Unit 3 is difficult to trace

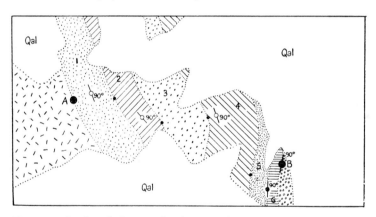

FIG. 138. Areal geologic map showing a section from A to B where it is impossible to obtain measurements along a continuous straight line.

laterally; so a horizon that can be traced is selected at *d'* and "walked out" to *d''*. At this location dips and strikes are determined, and the remainder of the section is measured to *B*. Either the plane table or tape and compass may be used.

Figure 138 shows somewhat similar field conditions but the

area of outcrops is less favorable. In this case only the plane table should be used because the determination of formational thicknesses is dependent on accurately plotted positions of dips and strikes (shown as symbols on the map) and stations on formation boundaries (solid black dots). Figure 139 is the graphic solution of the problem, which is performed as follows. At point a, near the base of the section, a long line is drawn perpendicular to the

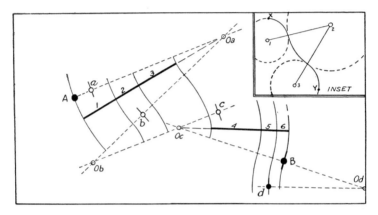

FIG. 139.   Method of measuring the section shown in Fig. 138.

strike, as shown by the dashed line. Next, a perpendicular is erected from the strike at b so that it intersects the first line at Oa. With a drafting compass, arcs are drawn through all located points on stratigraphic boundaries within the segment, in this case, 1, 2, and 3. The dip line at c is now extended to intersect the one from b at Ob, and arcs are drawn from this center within the segment formed by the two radii. These arcs must be extensions of, and tangent to, the first ones drawn from the center Oa. This procedure is followed for remaining dips and strikes. At Od the intersection (center for arcs B to d) falls on the opposite side of the outcrop bands, thus indicating a reversal in the curve of the strikes. Measurements of stratigraphic thicknesses are made along any radius normal to the arcs, as shown by the heavy lines in the figure.

This method is based on principles described in detail by H.G. Busk in *Earth Flexures,* Cambridge Press (1929). It presumes that strata within the area of investigation are essentially parallel and unfaulted, and the flexures are segments of circle arcs (see insert of Fig. 139). The accuracy of the method depends on how closely these conditions are fulfilled. As to the first two, the same assumption is made no matter what technique is used. Any mathematical curve can be approximated very closely by a system of circle arcs, provided sufficient control exists to correctly place the required centers. Therefore, this condition is met simply by determining a large number of strikes in the field; the form of the curves will then more closely approach that of the folding.

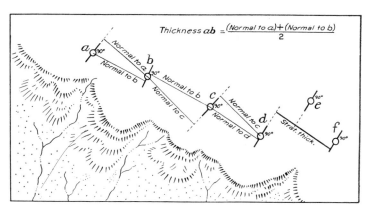

Fig. 140. A method of averaging the horizontal distances normal to the strike where the bearing of strike varies from station to station.

A method based on averaging the strikes is illustrated in Fig. 140. The strike line at a is prolonged so that a perpendicular (normal) can be drawn to pass through b. The length of this line would be the stratigraphic thickness if the strike were constant to this point. Now a normal to the strike at b is drawn to pass through a. This would be the stratigraphic thickness if the strike at b persisted to a. Inasmuch as the true thickness lies somewhere between these values, the average of the two is taken as the probable thickness. It is clear that if the strike at one point persists *nearly* to the other an error in thickness results by taking the average. Again, the best way to avoid such errors is to determine a larger number of dips and strikes in the field.

Another means of determining the distance between two differing strikes is shown in Fig. 141. This method consists in finding

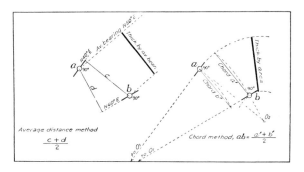

Fig. 141 Comparison of methods for obtaining the horizontal distance parellel to the dips where directions of strike are not constant.

the bearing of a strike that is midway between the observed strikes. Thus, the strike at a is N 40° E and at b it is N 60° E. The mean strike is N 50° E. Lines having this bearing are plotted through the points and the perpendicular is scaled for the distance normal to strike. In the figure is a comparison of the arc method, the "average distance" method, and the "average bearing" method. It will be seen that the results are nearly identical where the divergence in two adjacent strikes is not excessive. A modification of the average distance method is illustrated in the same figure. This method consists in extending the strike lines to intersect at 0_1 then striking arcs through a and b. The average of the chord distances a' and b' is taken as the stratigraphic thickness (where beds are vertical).

188. Remarks on the Measurement of Inclined Strata

The preceding articles deal with strata whose attitudes are either vertical or horizontal. The problems involved in measuring such sections are usually simple and the complications that do exist are generally related to the distribution and the size and character of the outcrops. The determination of stratigraphic thicknesses becomes more complex where beds dip at angles intermediate between the two extremes. However, some of the methods described in these earlier articles are applicable in part to the measurement of inclined strata. Methods for determining dip and strike (Chapter VI) should be reviewed in detail.

189. Measurement of Inclined Strata with Constant Dip and Strike

As in the measurement of level beds or vertical beds having a constant dip and strike, the determination of stratigraphic thicknesses of strata dipping at less than 90 degrees is simple where the dip and strike are constant, except when field operations are hampered by adverse conditions. In the following presentation, the

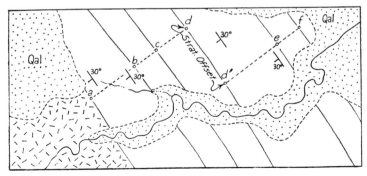

FIG. 142.   Measurement of a stratigraphic section where dip and strike are constant.

simplest examples are given first, the more complex toward the end of the discussion.

GROUND SURFACE ESSENTIALLY LEVEL

Figure 142 shows a succession of beds dipping at a constant rate with no change in strike. The surface of the ground is nearly level. Field work consists merely in measuring the widths of the outcropping stratigraphic units in a direction normal to the strike. Distances may be determined by pacing, taping, or by stadia, depending on the accuracy required.

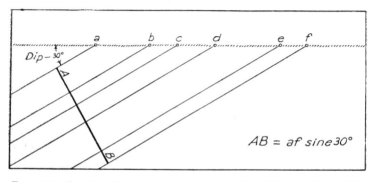

FIG. 143. Graphic determination of stratigraphic thicknesses from field measurements shown in Fig. 142.

Stratigraphic thicknesses are obtained graphically as shown in Fig. 143. Any graphic construction from which measurements are to be taken must be on a natural scale (no exaggeration of the vertical scale). Lines must be clear and sharp and carefully drawn. Points a to f are scaled and plotted along the horizontal line according to distances measured on the ground, and dips are plotted by protractor. Lines representing unit boundaries may be prolonged so that a single perpendicular line will cut several of the boundary lines; however, one should take care that the lines are not extended so far as to seriously affect the accuracy of the work.

Thicknesses are computed directly from field data by the following formula.

Stratigraphic thickness = Horizontal distance[1] × sine of dip angle

Where it is not practicable to traverse a continuous line at right angles to the strike, portions of the section may be offset by tracing a bed along the strike, identifying a horizon whose stratigraphic position is known in the measured portion of the section, or by projecting the strike line as stated in Article 186.

The Brunton compass (pocket transit) can be used alone to measure a section of steeply dipping beds on level ground. The method follows.

(1) While standing erect, measure the height from the eyes to the ground.

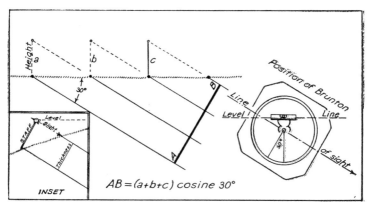

$$AB = (a+b+c)\ cosine\ 30°$$

Fig. 144. Measuring a stratigraphic section with the Burton arc set at the angle of dip. In the inset, an inclined Jacob's staff is used, thus eliminating trigonometric computation.

(2) Determine the dip and strike carefully. Verify at several places.

(3) Select a course to be followed in a direction normal to the strike.

[1] Normal to strike.

(4) Set the arc of the Brunton exactly at the angle of dip previously established. Check this setting frequently as work progresses.

(5) Use the Brunton as a hand level by sighting to points ahead with the bubble centered. The *line of sight* will be inclined at the dip angle, a necessary condition of this method.

In Fig. 144 it can be seen that the observer stands at one stratigraphic horizon while sighting a stratigraphically higher one, even though the elevations of the two points are equal. The geologist moves from each sighted point to the next, keeping a record of the number of sights for later reference. Computations are made from the formula

Stratigraphic thickness = Height to eyes × cosine of the dip angle.

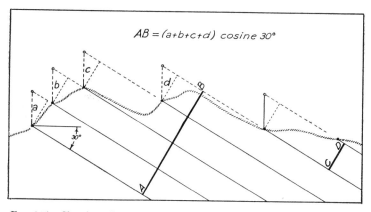

Fɪɢ. 145. Showing that topographic irregularities have no effect on the Brunton method.

GROUND SURFACE SLOPING

Figure 145 shows that the inclined sight method just described is applicable regardless of the nature of the topography over which the course must be run. It is most accurate where the beds are level, for then the arc is set at zero and the Brunton becomes a hand level and the stratigraphic interval is a direct measure of the difference in elevation. The method is not applicable at all where dips are in the order of 60 to 90 degrees.

A Jacob's staff may be used effectively in combination with the Brunton for measuring stratigraphic sections, provided dips are not too steep. The Brunton is placed on the top of the staff and the length from the end of the staff to the center of the compass is measured.

Set the arc of the Brunton to the angle of dip. Place the Brunton on the top of the staff, whose base rests at the starting point of the section (Fig. 144). Lean the staff forward until the level bubble is centered, then sight a point on the ground, as outlined in earlier discussions. It is apparent from the figure that the Jacob's staff is perpendicular to the bedding planes and, therefore, is a direct measure of stratigraphic thickness.

Where strata crop out in areas of significant relief, the difference in elevation as well as the horizontal positions of control points must be established in order to determine the stratigraphic thickness. In these circumstances the computations of thickness must take into account the relationships of direction and degree of topographic slope and the degree and direction of dip.

Dip Opposite Slope of Surface

Figure 146 is a topographic map on which the areal geology has been sketched approximately. An offset traverse is shown by solid lines. The traverse may be run by any method that will yield the required accuracy in elevation and position.

Figure 147 is a graphic construction of the "cross section" from which thicknesses are scaled. The profile of the surface is first plotted from field measurements of horizontal distance normal to the strike and the elevations of the control points. Vertical and horizontal scales must be the same. The graphic plot is simplified if cross-section paper of convenient scale is used, such as 1/10 inch. When the scale of the map differs from that of the cross-section paper, the conversion is made easier by reading the scaled

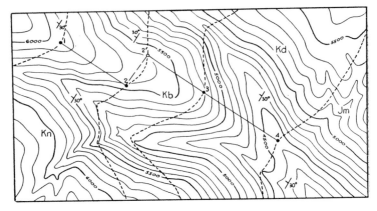

Fɪɢ. 146. Topographic map with formational boundaries shown by dashed lines. The dip and strike are constant. Notice offset from 2 to 2′ along the strike.

distances on the map in *feet of ground distance* and then plotting this footage to the scale of the cross section.

From the figure the following mathematical relations are apparent. The quantities known are the horizontal distance normal

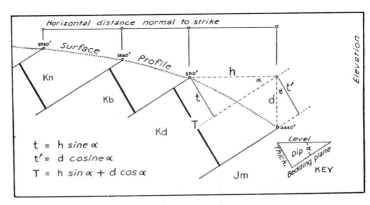

Fɪɢ. 147. Graphic and trigonometric determination of thicknesses from measurements indicated in Fig. 146.

to the strike (h), the difference in elevation (d), and the angle of dip (a). The stratigraphic thickness (T) is required.

$$T = h \text{ sine } \alpha + d \cos \alpha$$

Where the line of section is oblique to the direction of dip, the horizontal distance normal to the strike becomes

$$h = h' \cos \beta,$$

When h' is the field measurement of distance on the line of section and β is the angle between the line of section and the direction of dip. In this case the stratigraphic thickness is

$$T = (h' \cos \beta) (\text{sine } \alpha) + (d \cos \alpha)$$

DIP IN SAME DIRECTION, BUT LESS THAN SLOPE ANGLE

Figure 148 illustrates a case where beds dip "out of" the slope. That is, slope and dip are in the same direction but the angle of the slope is greater than the dip. The field methods employed are much the same as those described earlier; only the computations are different.

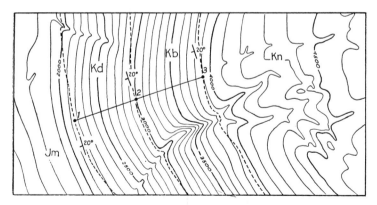

FIG. 148.   Measurements parallel to the dip where the slope angle is greater than the dip, but in the same direction.

Figure 149 shows that the following mathematical relationships apply to this situation.

In the diagram, h is the horizontal distance from 1 to 2 in a direction normal to the strike; d is the difference in elevation

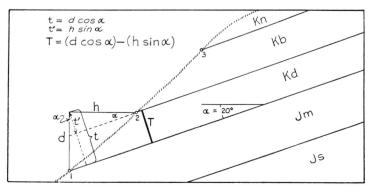

Fig. 149. Computation of thickness from data shown in Fig. 148.

between the two points; and α is the angle of dip (20° in the figure). The stratigraphic thickness of the unit Kd is T. The sides of triangles t and t' are shown merely to clarify the derivation of the formula

$$T = (d \cos \alpha) - (h \text{ sine } \alpha).$$

As stated in the preceding article, when the line of section (h') is oblique to the direction of dip (h) and the angle between these two lines is β, the length of h is h' cosine β, and the thickness of the strata is computed by the formula

$$T = (d \cos \alpha) - (h' \cos \beta)(\text{sine } \alpha).$$

DIP IN SAME DIRECTION, BUT GREATER THAN SLOPE ANGLE

The field conditions illustrated in Figs. 150 and 151 are similar to those just discussed, except that the slope angle is less than the

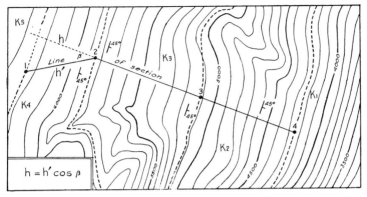

$$h = h' \cos \beta$$

FIG. 150. Topographic map showing the relations of dips and slopes. The segment of section from 1 to 2 is not parallel to the dip. The dip angle is greater than the slope angle.

dip of the beds. From the figures it is evident that the section from station 2 to station 4 can be computed by the formula

$$T = (h \ \text{sine} \ \alpha) - (d \cos \alpha).$$

The line from station 1 to station 2 is oblique to the direction of dip; therefore, this portion is determined by the formula:

$$T = (h' \cos \beta) \ (h \ \text{sine} \ \alpha) - (d \cos \alpha).$$

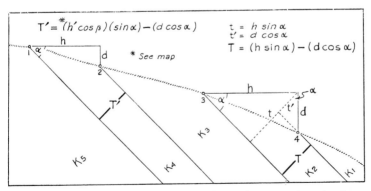

FIG. 151. Calculation of thickness where the dip is steeper than the slope, but in the same direction, as in Fig. 150.

190. Measurement of Inclined Strata with Constant Dip and Variable Strike

It has been shown earlier that it is sometimes necessary to measure stratigraphic sections in areas where considerable folding is present. Under such conditions it is usually impossible to select a line of section where both the dip and the strike remain constant over the full length of the line. Every effort should be made to plan the work so that the line of section avoids radical changes in dip and strike. The accuracy of computations of thickness will

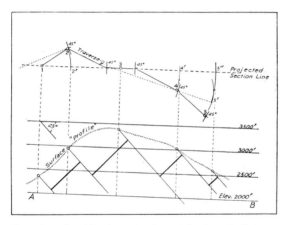

Fig. 152. Graphic determination of horizontal distances parallel to the dip where there is variation in the strike. Formation boundaries are projected perpendicular to this derived line of section to establish points for construction of the cross section.

normally be improved if the line of section is chosen where only the dip or the strike (not both) is changing. A situation where the rate of dip is constant, but the direction of strike varies from one outcrop to the next, is shown in Fig. 152. A plane table traverse is indicated by the solid line connecting stadia rod stations 1 to 5 on formational (or unit) boundaries. Dips and strikes are determined at these stations and at other nearby outcrops. These supplemental points should also be located on the sheet and their elevations established for later reference if needed. A straight line (dashed in the figure) is drawn the full length of the section in a position and orientation such that it nearly, or quite, corresponds with the direction and locations of some of the dips already established on the sheet, and at the same time separates divergent dips, as at 2 and 4. This is the best *average* line of section on which to base computations. Using the arc method described previously, strike arcs through outlying control points to intersect the projected line of section. Because of irregularity of folding or non-representative surface dips, complications may develop in the graphic constructions. In the figure, the intersection of perpendiculars from 4 and 5 falls on the point 4. An arc cast from this center through 5 would cut the line of section too near the projected position of 4, at 4'. To avoid this awkward and unrealistic situation, first draw the short arc through 5 from the center at 4 to a point on the produced dip line at 5'. Now using the center from which 4 was projected to 4', strike an arc through 5' to the line of section at 5". This is a compromise adjustment, but errors resulting from the methods will normally be within permissible limits.

The next step in the process is to drop perpendiculars to a base line *AB*, which is drawn parallel to the line of section. An alternative is to draw the perpendiculars upward from the line of section, in which instance the line of section is used as the base. Assign an elevation to the base line that is considerably lower than the lowest elevation on the traverse and plot the elevations of the projected control points on the same scale as that used for horizontal plotting. Never exaggerate the vertical scale in this kind of work. Plot the angle of dip at each of the stations and scale stratigraphic thicknesses along perpendiculars to the dip lines.

Stratigraphic thicknesses may be determined trigonometrically by formulas given in preceding articles, provided the positions of stations along the projected line of section have been established.

Scaled horizontal distances, differences in elevation between adjacent control points, and measured dips provide all the needed values. This procedure is advantageous in two ways: It reduces the probability of drafting errors or inaccuracies, and it avoids cluttering the plane table sheet with construction lines.

The surface "profile" obtained by drawing a line through stations plotted in the vertical plane is simply a step in the construction in order to better visualize field relationships; it is not a true surface profile. An elevation of a point to the side of the line of section may project to a point in space above or below the ground at the line of section; therefore, it is not a point on the profile. Obviously, the vertical plane drawing is not a cross section; but this fact in no way affects the determination of stratigraphic thicknesses.

191. Measurement of Inclined Strata with Constant Strike and Variable Dip

The strike may remain constant while the dip varies appreciably in regions of strike folding, strike thrusting, or on the flank of an individual anticline. In any case, the measurements of stratigraphic thickness across such structural variations are reliable only when a sufficient number of dips is determined to show precisely *where* the changes take place. Wherever possible the line of section should be oriented normal to the strike. If outcrops are widely scattered, offsets by projection of strikes, offsets by correlation, or lines of section oblique to the dip may be used. Horizontal distances normal to the strike are determined graphically as outlined in preceding discussions.

Figure 153A is a structural contour map on which is also shown the areal distribution of three formations (D_2, M_1, and P_1) whose thicknesses are to be determined. A line of section is selected at a location where the strike is constant. Dips, however, increase progressively down the flank of the anticline. Dips and strikes are plotted along the line of section at a, c, d, and f (formation boundaries), and additional ones at outcrops somewhat off the

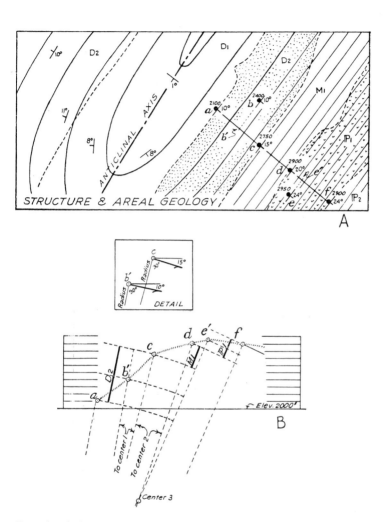

Fig. 153. A. Measurement of section on the flank of an anticline where the strike is constant but the dip increases, as shown by structural contours. B. Construction of the cross section.

line at b and e. These supplemental dips are projected parallel
to the strike into the line of section at b' and e'. Elevations are
established at all points.

Plot the cross section positions of the control points according
to the scaled distances along the line of section and the elevations
on vertical lines, as shown in Fig. 153B. With a protractor, plot
the dips at the space positions of the points and draw long lines
perpendicular to the dips, as indicated in the "detail" of the
figure. Where adjacent dips are the same, these lines will be
parallel; elsewhere they will intersect. These points of intersection
are centers from which circle arcs are drawn through the corresponding control points. The arcs are drawn only across the
segment bounded by the two radii. This procedure is repeated
for each adjoining segment until the "cross section" is complete.
The arcs pass tangentially into one another or into straight lines
where two adjacent dips are parallel, as at a and b', and at e' and f.

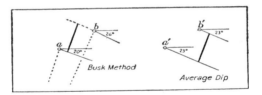

FIG. 154. Comparison of Busk's arc method and a
projection using the average dip. There is no significant difference in the thickness obtained if the
dips vary by only a few degrees.

Stratigraphic thicknesses are scaled from the section along radii
where dips are convergent and along perpendiculars where they
are parallel. This is Busk's method of section construction referred
to earlier. Its accuracy is dependent on the controlling dips being
placed (1) closely together, where the dip is gradually increasing
or decreasing; and (2) at points where changes occur if the variations in dip are irregular.

The graphic construction just described is identical to that used in the adjustment of variable strikes. One is in the vertical plane, the other in the horizontal.

If the difference in the degree of dip is not large between any two adjacent dips, an average dip may be used for calculating the thickness of the section, as shown in Fig. 154. The difference in thickness obtained by the two methods is negligible.

Stratigraphic intervals may be calculated mathematically by using the average dips as in the example illustrated in Fig. 154. Formulas that take differences in elevation into account have been discussed. The formula must be selected on the basis of the relationship of slope angle to dip angle.

192. Measurement of Inclined Strata where Both Dips and Strikes Vary

The measurement of stratigraphic interval where strikes are variable but dips are constant, and where strikes are constant but dips vary has been discussed in preceding articles. The methods employed where both dips and strikes are variable consist merely in applying the principles developed in the simpler problems. It is first necessary to obtain horizontal distances along a line normal to the strike. Once this has been done, either by direct measurement in the field or by projection, thicknesses are computed exactly as outlined in the preceding article.

193. Measurements Parallel to the Strike

In country of high relief the best exposures of bedrock are commonly found on the sides of tributary valleys near their junction with the main valley. The escarpment facing the main valley is often too precipitous for detailed work. If the beds dip away from the main valley or canyon, an ordinary condition where anticlinal folds are deeply breached by erosion, the best place to measure a section is up the side of a tributary along a line parallel to the strike. If the control points are placed along the same strike line, the only field measurements needed are differences in elevation. Figure 155 illustrates the situation described. The line of section on the ground is represented by the dashed line from A to d. Difference in elevation is determined by alidade, hand level, or altimeter. The locations of points need not be established. From the diagram, it is evident that the thickness is computed by the formula:

$$T = Ad \ \cos\alpha$$

when Ad is the difference in elevation, α is the angle of dip, and T is the stratigraphic thickness.

194. Evaluation of Errors

All the methods given for obtaining stratigraphic thicknesses are based on the assumption that the strata are everywhere parallel.

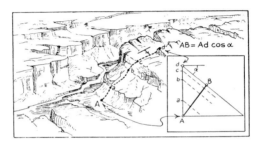

FIG. 155. Measurement of a section parallel to the strike. The plane of the triangle in the inset is parallel to the line of section (the strike).

This assumption is generally valid if the site of the section is carefully chosen, if structure is not too intense, and if the line of section is not too long. Whether valid or not, it is necessary to assume parallelism for purposes of calculation, for more than the thickness would have to be known in order to derive a formula that would account for attenuation of beds on the flanks of folds and other irregularities commonly encountered. Attempts have been made to derive such formulas; but it is doubtful that complex formulae produce more precise determinations of thickness than are obtained by simple trigonometric relations and graphic constructions. The following list of common sources of error emphasizes the importance of careful field work and the necessity for considering all phases of the field and drafting operations.

(1) Stratigraphic thinning or wedging of units within the area where measurements are made.
(2) Small exposures, necessitating short sight lines in establishing dip and strike.
(3) Near-surface weathering, sagging or slumping, incipient faulting.
(4) Irregular bedding "planes," resulting in inaccurate or unrepresentative dips.
(5) Attenuation of strata on the flanks of sharp folds and mashing and thickening in crestal regions.
(6) Sparse dip and strike control; especially important where there is appreciable variation.
(7) Inaccuracies in reading (or recording) all instruments.
(8) Careless plotting of control points and inaccurate drafting of graphic constructions.
(9) The use of scales too small for accurate plotting or reading.
(10) Gross errors in determination of distance or elevation.

The field stratigrapher is interested, not so much in the frequency or magnitude of these errors, but rather in the ultimate effect that the errors have on the calculations of stratigraphic intervals. In earlier discussions, it was stated that where strata are vertical, horizontal distances normal to the strike are direct measurements of stratigraphic interval. Therefore, the determination and plotting of distances must be commensurate in accuracy with that expected in stratigraphic thicknesses. Where beds are horizontal the thickness is the difference in elevation. If dips are in the order of 45 degrees, equal attention should be given to measurements of distance and difference in elevation.

A few examples will illustrate certain types of errors and their effects on the determination of stratigraphic thickness.

Errors in Bearings of Strikes

Errors in the bearings of strikes may occur as a result of miscorrelating a bed across a valley, obscure structural deformation,

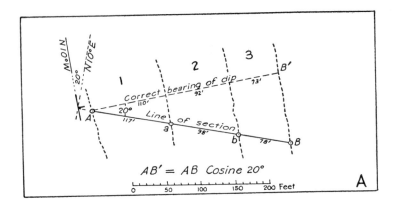

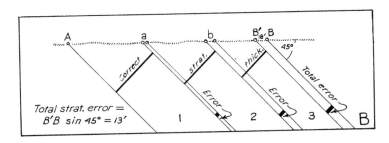

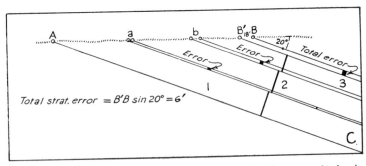

FIG. 156. Errors in stratigraphic thickness resulting from a mistake in determining the bearing of the strike.

poorly adjusted surveying levels, or misreading compass bearings.

Fig. 156A shows a line of section oriented normal to the supposed strike of the strata; however, the line of section was laid out on the strike bearing of N 10° E; the actual bearing is N 10° W—an error of 20 degrees in the orientation of the line. The resulting error in stratigraphic thickness is proportional to the *length* of the line of section and the *steepness* of the dip. From the figure it is clear that the error in horizontal distance normal to the strike *varies as the cosine* of the angle of error in bearing. The effect of this error is shown in Figs. 156B and 156C. Errors in horizontal distance (*B'B*) result in errors in stratigraphic thickness that *vary as the sine of the dip angle*. Therefore, such an error in field work is of greater consequence where dips are steep. For all practical purposes, it may be assumed that the error in thickness varies as the numerical value (in degrees) of the dip; that is, the error for a dip of 40 degrees is twice that for 20 degrees. The entire problem is expressed by the formula:

$$Te = (L - L \cos \beta) \times \text{sine } \alpha$$

when *Te* is the error in thickness, *L* is the length of the measured line, β is the angular error of the bearing of the strike, and α is the angle of dip.

ERRORS IN ANGLES OF DIP

Errors in the angle of dip may be caused by much the same factors that cause errors in strike. Compare Figs. 157A and 157B. In each case the error in the amount of dip is 10 degrees, but one occurs in a steeply dipping section, and the other where the strata are considerably flatter. It is quite evident that, with all other factors being equal, a given error in the angle of dip becomes more serious as the angle of dip decreases. In the examples cited, where the angle of dip is 40 degrees and the error is 10 degrees, the resulting error in stratigraphic thickness is 19.7 percent. On the other hand, where beds dip at only 10 degrees, the same discrepancy in the angle of dip produces an error of 96 percent in stratigraphic thickness. It is obvious that one must be especially careful in the field to determine dips exactly where average dips are low. The trigonometric relation expressing this error is

$$Te = D \text{ (sine } \alpha - \text{sine } \beta)$$

when Te is the error in thickness, D is the horizontal distance normal to the strike, α is the angle of true dip, and β is the erroneous dip.

A great deal of field time will be saved without sacrificing high quality standards if the contemplated field procedures are carefully analyzed with respect to the results desired. For example, if

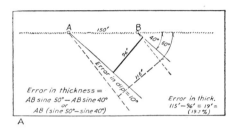

A

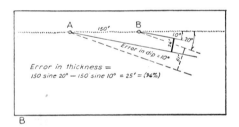

B

Fig. 157. Errors in stratigraphic thickness resulting from an error in the angle of dip.

the permissible error in stratigraphic interval is in the order of 10 feet per 1000 feet of section and unit boundaries cannot be identified more closely than two feet, it is a useless waste of the instrumentman's time to require elevations to the nearest tenth of a foot. He should read the rod to the nearest foot, thereby saving time in both reading the rod and computing elevations. If beds are dipping at high angles, the need for precise elevations is further minimized.

The effects of errors in dip and strike, elevations, and horizontal distances have been suggested or demonstrated in preceding topics. It is impractical to work out the optimum standards for all, or even a large number of, typical projects for the reason that an error of a specific magnitude in one department of work will result in varying ultimate errors in stratigraphic thickness, depending on the relation of the error to other aspects of the problem. Thus, approximate methods of measuring distance may logically be combined with precise methods for determining difference in elevation where dips are very low. In a long line of section containing a wide range of dips, it is permissible to vary the standards of field measurements if by so doing the accuracy of *thicknesses* is not jeopardized and a worthwhile advantage is gained in time, effort, or expense.

Before detailing of a section is begun, the *limits* of error should be decided upon. These limits must be gauged by the immediate objectives of the project and future usefulness of the section. The permissible limits of error are the key to selection of field methods and procedures. Choose all methods and set field standards such that the required accuracy in thickness determinations will be attained in the shortest time. Test each of the field procedures experimentally by computing the effects of *probable* errors, as demonstrated in the examples of the preceding article. Every precaution should be taken in phases of field operations that have the most direct bearing on thickness determinations. It should be kept in mind that the measure of effective field work is in the accuracy of the completed section.

195. Instrumental Control

The relative importance of accurate measurement of distance and difference in elevation and the ultimate effects of certain types of errors have been shown. Many of the hazards or inconveniences suggested can be avoided if time is taken to correctly appraise field conditions and then to plan the detailing operations accordingly. Of primary importance is the balancing of various operations with regard to relative accuracy and speed, and to appraise the application of certain methods to the problems at hand. In regard to the latter, it is difficult to substitute abstract knowledge for experience; but experience is not merely a product of time, for the measure of experience is one's ability to *effectively apply toward a practical end* what he has learned from study. Experience can be gained by learning from one's mistakes. But to learn by doing things right takes less time, is more gratifying, and may eventually become a habit. The "habit" of doing things right is acquired by *studying all phases* of a (field) problem *before* procedure is decided upon. This manual could not be kept within reasonable bounds if procedures were laid out for all conceivable combinations of circumstances. It can provide little more than a variety of methods from which to select.

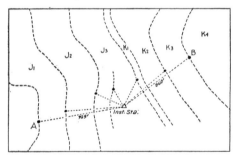

Fig. 158. Centrally located instrument station permits measuring the entire section without traversing.

One of the commonest errors in plane table surveying is in orienting the table. Since this is an angular error, the amount increases according to the lengths of the plotted distances. The large scales ordinarily used in measuring sections emphasize the scalable errors caused by misorientation. Two precautions should be observed: use the utmost care in orienting the plane table; and by careful selection of traverse routes, reduce the number of instrument stations to a minimum consistent with lengths of sights that will insure accurate reading of the rod. It is often possible to set up at such a location that the entire section can be "shot in" by stadia from one instrument station, as shown in Fig. 158. Similarly, by setting the instrument *within* the area to be measured, the number of stations can be reduced, as shown in Fig. 159. In

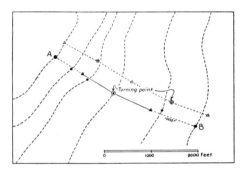

Fɪɢ. 159. Comparison of two traverse lines, one with three stations, the other with five. Lengths of sight are limited to 1000 feet.

this case, if the instrument had been set up at the base (or top) of the section, an extra station would be required. If there is much topographic relief, try to set the instrument at such an elevation that detailing rod stations will be both *above* and *below* the instrument, thus avoiding large corrections for horizontal distances. Corrections for horizontal distance must be made for smaller vertical angles when large scales are used. Determine from the anticipated lengths of sights (as 700 feet) at what vertical angle the error becomes plottable on the scale being used.

Depending on the detail and precision required, the placement of rod station control is within broad limits a matter for the field man to decide. In order to prevent gross errors in the overall thicknesses, wide spacing of rod shots should be avoided. Important lithologic units having thicknesses in the order of five feet or less should be measured or estimated on the ground, because the errors that develop in graphic constructions from plotted plane table positions will probably be disproportionately large.

The hand level, tape, Brunton, or Jacob's staff may be used effectively in combination with the plane table. In Fig. 160, rod stations are shown by double vertical lines. The boundaries of significant lithologic units between rod stations are determined by the supplementary methods, including estimation of thin members.

Fig. 160. Effective locations of rod stations along a section traverse. Intervening detail is established by hand level, tape, or estimation.

When using the plane table, locate rod stations at the base or top of prominent stratigraphic units, and locate intervening units by other methods. When the section is being measured from the base toward the top, place the rod shots at the bases of units. When measuring from the top downward, it is better to locate points at the tops of the units. This procedure facilitates the writing of descriptive notes.

In some regions there may be a wide selection of localities where sections can be measured. A careful examination of areal geologic and topographic maps and air photographs will aid materially in selecting a location for measuring the section. Assuming moderately uniform thicknesses of formations, the breadth of outcrop bands is dependent on degree of dip and topographic relief, both of which have a bearing on the proper selection of methods. Where the narrowness of outcrop bands is caused primarily by steep dips, the distance that must be traversed is shorter than where dips are generally low. Precipitous topography of high relief also produces narrow outcrop bands, but the advantage of a short traverse may be overcome by additional corrections for horizontal distance, high vertical angles, and roughness of terrain. Weigh the advantages of one site against those of the alternatives before plunging into the field operations.

196. Sequential Order of Field Measurements

From the field man's viewpoint it is often easier to measure and describe sections from the base upward. This procedure permits examination of the successive strata in the same relative sequence as the sedimentation events, and for this reason it may be somewhat easier to decipher unconformities, hiati, and other phenomena. Sections are commonly exposed with the oldest units at the lowest topographic levels. There is a decided advantage in being able to observe the section *ahead* of measuring and sampling operations. Where working upward the faces of ledges are presented to the observer, whereas they are not visible from above.

Certain advantages are gained by running sections from the top downward. If samples are being collected in quantity the load increases as work progresses. The increasing burden is less exhausting when being carried downhill.

It is common practice to collect samples in the field and later to examine them microscopically and plot the lithologies and descriptions as a columnar section. For various reasons it is difficult to plot a section from the bottom upward, and *especially* difficult to plot a section from the top downward if it has been measured, described, and sampled from the bottom upward. Therefore, when the plan is to run the samples under a microscope, plot the section in a column, and combine field and laboratory descriptions on the columnar section (or log), it is far better that the section be measured downward in the field.

197. Checking Station Numbers

When the plane table is used for measuring sections, the geologist should check station numbers with the instrumentman at frequent intervals. As a safeguard against confusing discrepancies, it is a good plan for the geologist to record the numbers of all instrument stations and turning points in his notebook even though they do not serve as stratigraphic control. Usually in section work the instrument station is sufficiently close to the site of the outcrop work that the numbers of new rod stations can be checked simply by calling to the instrumentman. A mistake in the numbering of a single station might be difficult to trace back and correct, and thus lead to a serious error in the stratigraphic sequence.

198. Remarks on Sampling Surface Sections

It is common practice to collect representative samples of rocks or fossils from surface sections, either concurrently with instrumental measurements of thickness, or at some later and more convenient date. Inasmuch as sampling may require considerably more time than measuring, this phase of stratigraphic field work should be planned in detail and coördinated with other operations in order to attain a high degree of efficiency from the field parties.

The advantages of measuring and sampling simultaneously are: (1) the section is traversed only once; (2) lithologic or paleontologic units are likely to be examined on the ground in greater detail, which permits more precise selection of stratigraphic boundaries and instrumental control points; (3) points used as control for measurement need not be marked on the ground or described in notes for later reference; and (4) the instrumentman and other assistants may aid the geologist intermittently in collecting, labeling, and transporting the samples.

The advantages of measuring and "staking" (marking control points on the ground) a section and then at a later time sampling the rocks are: (1) the essential services of assistants are required for a relatively shorter period of time; (2) the section may be sampled either upward or downward, thus permitting the numbering sequence in either direction; (3) the geologist can give full attention to examination of the rocks, without the interruptions necessitated by selecting points for instrumental control; and (4) a stadia rod need not be added to the burden of samples while working on the outcrops.

When sampling rocks for any kind of laboratory examination, the field man is responsible for obtaining specimens that are representative of lithologies of all stratigraphic units in the section. Sometimes there is a tendency to overemphasize (in sampling) unusual lithologies, or to dismiss them with the conclusion that they are local anomalies, and therefore of no great significance. Neither course is justifiable. A suite of samples should be sufficiently representative that laboratory descriptions of the specimens are adequate for plotting an accurate and realistic lithologic column.

199. Selection of Localities

The *freshness* of specimens is extremely important when the purpose of the work is to obtain materials for the laboratory analysis of lithologies. Weathered rocks may be severely altered either by the loss of soluble constituents or through the acquisition of secondary minerals from invading waters. A stratigraphic analysis based on the lithologies of altered surface rocks may be fundamentally wrong; therefore, the field man should give much attention to selection of localities where weathering would not be expected far below the surface.

Unweathered bedrock is normally found near the surface on the sides of topographically young (V-shaped) valleys where mechanical erosion is relatively rapid and the high grades of streams aid in removal of loose materials. Where streams are sluggish and meandering, appreciable erosion may take place only during periods of high water. In this type of valley the freshest samples are likely to be found along the outsides of bends where the current impinges on the banks. In regions where the climate is warm and humid, the rocks may be deeply weathered in low places and relatively fresh where drainage is good. Barren slopes or those on which vegetation is sparse offer better possibilities than wooded or grassy ones. Fresh bedrock may be found nearer the surface on the combs of ridges and spurs than on the flanks.

In country of low, rolling relief outcrops are generally sparse; however, samples of bedrock can be obtained from mines, railroad and highway cuts, irrigation or drainage canals, wells, "cave" cellars, and other excavations. Samples of shales and other soft rocks are sometimes brought to the surface from the burrows of various types of rodents. Slumps may expose unweathered bedrock or indicate places where shallow pits can be dug. When sampling in areas where slumping is prevalent care must be taken that the correct stratigraphic positions of samples are established.

200. Samples from Pits and Borings

Where much of the section is covered by alluvium, soils, sands, gravels, and like deposits, samples of bedrock are obtained by digging pits or trenches and by boring holes. A great deal of effort will be avoided if the sites for pits or borings are selected at localities where surface conditions are favorable. The topography should be studied in detail on the ground and from maps and air photographs. Select areas for digging according to suggestions given in the preceding article. A pit located on a hillside requires much less work than one on level ground. The amount of "spoil" excavated is much less and it need not be lifted so high. Try to select sites where full advantage can be taken of this fact. Long, narrow pits are more effective and require less work than equidimensional ones to the same depth. A narrow pit oriented normal to a slope is better than one parallel to the slope.

When an appreciable amount of pit digging is to be done, it is important to consider the best tools for the job. In addition to a field hand pick, the most versatile implements are a long-handled shovel with a rounded cutting edge, and a mattock of the type shown in Fig. 161. This type of mattock is equally effective in rocky ground or soils interlaced with tough roots.

The U.S. Geological Survey makes effective use of long, continuous trenches down slopes in search for, and appraisal of, stratified deposits of phosphates and other economically important rocks. Micropaleontologists sometimes employ similar techniques of sampling soft shale sections having sparse or spotty distribution of

FIG. 161. The type of shovel and mattock best adapted to pit and trench work.

microfossils. In some instances where the mantle is not too thick, a single furrow made with a "walking" plow down a hillside will save the geologist a great deal of time and hard work.

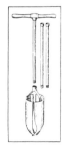

Similarly, bulldozers and ditch diggers can be employed in wastelands where no particular damage results.

If the loose mantle materials do not contain cobbles larger than two inches in diameter, an auger-type of post hole digger, shown in Fig. 162, is an effective means of obtaining samples of shales or clays down to depths of about 15 feet. Iron or steel pipe, threaded at both ends, and equipped with two-inch couplings comprise the extension handle. The sections should be about 30 inches in length. Wells 30 feet deep have been sunk with this kind of device, although the method is not practical for

FIG. 162. Post hole auger with threaded sectional shaft used for obtaining samples down to fifteen feet below the surface.

sampling to such depths. When the digger is withdrawn from the hole, loosened materials from the walls are likely to fall into the top of the tool, thus contaminating the upper portion of sample; therefore, the upper part of the load should be scooped out before the sample is removed from the tool. When the digger is in use (in the hole), never turn the T-handle counterclockwise, for there is danger of unscrewing the shaft and losing the lower portion of the tool in the hole.

201. Sampling Intervals

The stratigraphic intervals to be represented by one composite sample are determined by (1) the detail required in the described section, (2) thicknesses of beds, (3) diversity of lithologies or faunas, (4) total thickness of the section, (5) lateral continuity of individual beds, and (6) time limitations on the project. Usually, where formations and the total stratigraphic column are relatively thin, individual thin members have greater significance than similar units in sections where formations are thick. Therefore, it is common practice to sample thin formations in somewhat greater detail. Similarly, sections composed of rapidly alternating lithologies require more detailed sampling than do less diversified sections containing thick members.

Composite samples consist of several specimens, either of the same or differing lithologies, in one container, the entire assemblage to represent a specified stratigraphic interval. Thus, a 10-foot composite sample might contain six specimens chipped from the outcrop at two-foot intervals. Within this 10-foot interval there may be only one type of rock or several types. Figure 163 shows a stratigraphic section and points at which chips are taken to make up the composite samples. In this example each chip represents somewhat less than two feet of section. When several pieces of rock are put in the same envelope or bag, the relative positions should be indicated, either in the field notes or on the envelope.

Unit samples are made up from specimens taken from only one distinct stratigraphic unit. Figure 163 shows a stratigraphic sec-

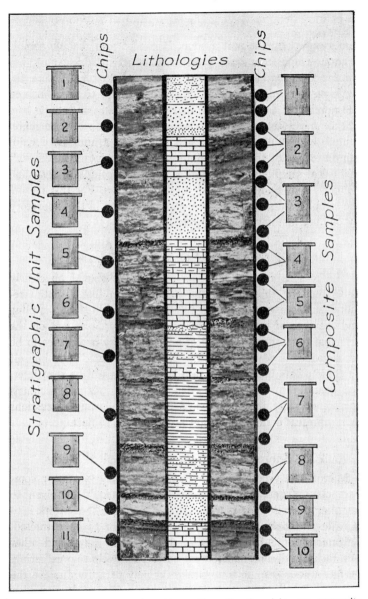

FIG. 163. Sampling a stratigraphic section. On the right are composite samples, each of which may contain several lithologies. On the left, only one type of lithology is contained in each sample.

tion sampled by the unit system. It can be seen that no sample contains chips from more than one distinct lithologic unit, but thick beds may be represented by several samples. Where the thicknesses of units vary greatly, it is customary to set a limit on the number of feet that shall be represented in one sample bag. If the limit is set at 10 feet, a 40-foot sandstone would be represented by four or five bags, each containing a number of chips representative of the 10-foot interval. The advantage in the unit method of sampling is that there is never any confusion regarding boundaries of significant stratigraphic members. For this reason, the samples are somewhat more easily processed in the laboratory by one not familiar with field relationships.

202. Quality and Quantity of Samples

The reasons for sampling surface sections should be clearly understood by those doing the field work so that essential requirements are certain to be fulfilled. The method of sampling and the type of specimen required are largely dependent on the principal purposes of the project and laboratory procedures to be employed. It is advisable for the field man to familiarize himself on these points before going into the field. As will be seen later, the quantity of materials needed and the kinds of specimens considered most important vary greatly. Following discussions briefly present certain important aspects of the subject.

203. Samples for Micropaleontological Study

Microfossils generally occur in limestones and shales or compact clays. Therefore, particular attention should be given to sampling these lithologies when the main purpose of the work is to provide materials from which microfossils are to be extracted. Calcareous forms often occur in shales, marls, clays, and other soft rocks, and consequently are quite vulnerable to weathering. Surface waters seeping into such rocks may partially dissolve the calcareous shells or tests before any other discernible alteration of the rock takes place. Inasmuch as the damage to the fossil content cannot be determined in the field, the only way in which the field man can avoid the possibility of collecting much worthless material is to make certain that the samples are taken from freshly exposed beds. He should be aware of the fact that very few of the microfossils are visible to the naked eye, many cannot be seen with a 15-power hand lens, and some cannot be seen clearly

under a microscope until the rock has been completely broken down or disaggregated by laboratory methods. Because the field man cannot evaluate the rocks by direct observation, it is desirable for him to collect much larger quantities than would be needed for most lithologic determinations. In sections that are suspected of leanness in fossil content, it is common practice to collect from one to two cupfuls of loose material. Lithified pieces of approximately the same volume may also be required, though normally the fossils are some-what better preserved in the hard rocks.

Fig. 164. Tying cloth sample bags so that the sample is secure but the knot or hitch can easily be untied.

Samples are usually put into muslin "ore" bags about four inches wide and six to eight inches long. The top is provided with a strong draw string and a stiffened cloth label is stitched along one side. The draw string should be pulled down tight and knotted so that the contents cannot leak out, yet the bag can be reopened without cutting the string. Figure 164 shows two types of knots that are satisfactory.

Microfossils commonly occur in abundance in thin layers of shales which are separated by comparatively thick barren zones. Since the identities of these fossiliferous layers are unknown to the field man, the best safeguard against collecting the barren rock at the expense of the more productive laminae is to make up the sample from *all* the beds or laminae. The following procedure is recommended for collecting from soft rocks.

With a shovel or hand pick scrape the loose, weathered material off the surface in a band across the bedding planes. Using the point of the pick, rake a shallow trench two to four inches wide

FIG. 165. Trenching a slope to obtain fresh and representative samples for micropaleontologic examination.

and two or three feet long. The length of the trench will depend on the interval desired for each sample. The accumulated heap of material at the end of the trench will contain portions of all the laminae cut by the trench. Thoroughly mix the chips so that the sample taken will be quite representative of the beds. This method of sampling is shown in Fig. 165. When samples are taken by continuous trenching, as described above, there is less danger of skipping a thin but highly productive bed than there would be by selective sampling.

204. Collecting and Casting Macrofossils

Large fossils occurring in hard, brittle rocks are difficult to remove by means available to the man in the field. Before attempting to break out an important specimen imbedded in hard rock, the immediate vicinity should be carefully searched for small fragments containing the same form. Frequently, the "weathered out" specimens are of better quality than those chipped out of the hard rock.

A few "cold" chisels of different sizes are of inestimable value to the collector of macrofossils. Only the highest quality steel should be considered for such use, for chisels of poor grade dull quickly when used on hard rocks. The chisels can be shaped and sharpened on an emery wheel. Star drills ranging from $\frac{1}{4}$ inch to $\frac{5}{8}$ inch diameter are sometimes used to remove fossils from the surfaces of large solid blocks of stone. A circle of shallow holes $\frac{1}{2}$ inch to 1 inch apart is first drilled around the fossil, then the circumscribed segment is further loosened and broken out with a chisel.

When a rare specimen is fully exposed on a weathered surface, it is good practice to make a mold before attempting to remove it from the rock. Molds can be made in a few minutes from plaster of Paris or a variety of compounds that remain elastic after they have set. These compounds are available at art and crafts shops. The flexible materials are better than plaster of Paris in that undercuts on the rock surface cause no difficulties whereas plaster would be firmly locked to the rock. When plaster of Paris is used, the surface of the rock and the fossil must be thoroughly covered with petroleum jelly, a mixture of kerosene and stearin, or glycerine. Wipe off the excess so that fine details of texture or sculpture on the fossil are not obscured. The setting time of plaster is greatly accelerated when a small quantity of salt is added

FIG. 166. Field casting fossils. A. A dam of art clay or mud is pressed on the rock. B. A flat board confines the plaster of Paris.

to the water used in making the plaster slurry. Grease-base art modelling clay (one or two pounds) makes the best retaining wall for holding the slurry around the specimen, and it can be reused for this purpose indefinitely. If the fossil occurs on a vertical face of rock, the mold is made as shown in Fig. 166A. A rope of "art" clay is pressed on the rock in the form of the letter U. Next, the grease mixture is applied to the surface inside the clay wall. A board or aluminum notebook cover is now pressed against the wall to form a plaster-tight vessel, as in Fig. 166B. Plaster slurry of the consistency of thick cream is poured into the top. The board must be held until the plaster has set. The setting point is indicated by a noticeable rise in the temperature of the plaster.

Plaster molds must be handled carefully when first removed from the rock, as they are quite fragile from the excess water.

This water is dissipated in a day or two, when the mold may be used for making "positive" casts. The inside of the mold must be greased before casts are made.

Fossils and molds or casts of fossils should be completely labelled as to locality, stratigraphic position, etc., and wrapped separately in paper before packing in boxes for transportation or shipment.

205. Samples for Determination of Lithology

The field geologist should clearly understand the main purposes of sampling a surface section, the uses to which the samples will be put, and the kind and quantity of material needed to meet immediate requirements and still insure a complete suite of representative chips for filing. Some laboratory techniques completely destroy the specimens, while others render them unfit for further analytical study. If it is likely that the samples will be subjected to destructive tests, the field man should collect enough additional material for a file suite. It may be almost as easy, and certainly safer, to make up duplicate sets of samples in the field. One set can then be used for all manner of tests and the other left intact for future reference.

Microsopic Examination of Rock Chips

As a means of obtaining better correlation between surface sections and well sections, the surface samples may be treated in the laboratory in exactly the same manner as cuttings from wells. The samples are examined under a binocular microscope with magnifications ranging from X9 to X18. The lithologies determined in this way are commonly plotted on a light-weight log strip in either color or black-line symbols. This method emphasizes the microscopic characters of the rocks and minimizes the gross outcrop habits. There should be no difference in the appearance of a surface section and the log of a well when this method is used. When comparisons of lithologies are to be made with well cuttings it is essential that the surface samples be selected from unweathered portions of the rock. Further details on microscopic examination of rocks are given in Chapter IX.

Rocks of essentially identical lithology may possess strikingly different outcrop characteristics. Some oölitic limestones weather to distinctly beaded surfaces, yet lithologically similar oölitic limestones weather to smooth surfaces with no suggestion of the granular structure. Field geologists make use of the weathering characteristics of strata, and for this reason it is sometimes desirable to include in the sample a representative chip of the surface of the weathered rock in addition to a piece of the fresh material. Of course, the specimens must be labeled so there will be no confusion when they are run under the microscope.

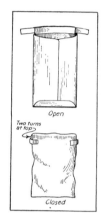

Manila envelopes whose dimensions are roughly 3 x 5 inches are widely used by oil companies for storing or filing well cuttings. These envelopes, shown in Fig. 167, are equally convenient for samples collected in the field. They will hold three to five chips about 1 x 1 x ¼ inches in size or an equivalent volume of fine, loose material. A flake of about these dimensions is sufficient for binocular microscopic examination

Fig. 167. A type of Manila envelope commonly used for well cutting and surface rock specimens.

and the few tests generally used in this class of analysis. Only a small portion of the rock is destroyed by these simple tests, thus leaving the bulk of the material for filing in a repository.

SAMPLES FOR PETROGRAPHIC THIN SECTIONS

Petrographic thin sections should be cut perpendicular to the planes of stratification in order to show as many lithologies as possible within the area of the section. Therefore, it is important for the field man to supply samples that will meet this requirement. There is considerable knack in spalling a thin flake from any massive rock, such as limestone, siltstone, or fine, indurated sandstone. Figure 168 shows how the chips are struck from the rock across the plane of bedding by means of a prospector's hand pick. The first blow, as shown in A, spalls off the weathered sur-

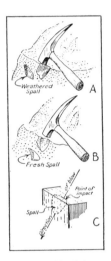

face. The second blow, as in B is directed exactly as the first, but ¼ to ½ inch deeper in the rock. The spall obtained by the second blow is freshly broken on both sides. The key to the operation is shown in C. It is quite easy to spall flakes from homogeneous massive rocks by sharp blows with a hammer, but relatively difficult if the rock is thinly stratified. In this case it is necessary to direct the hammer or pick so that a number of the laminae receive the impact directly, as shown in Fig. 169. It can be seen that the direction of the blow is parallel to the bedding planes. If struck in a direction normal to the bedding, there is a tendency to splinter the specimen, depending to a considerable extent on the degree of induration of the rock.

FIG. 168. Obtaining a flake with two fresh surfaces. A. A chip of the weathered surface is first spalled off. B. A second blow struck in exactly the same direction breaks out a fresh flake. C. Indicating direction of the hammer blow.

Soft or poorly cemented rocks should be sampled in lumps of such size that a thin section 1 inch square can be cut on a plane normal to the bedding. Soft rocks are likely to be broken in the sample container unless they are wrapped individually in paper and carefully handled thereafter. If the bedding planes are not apparent in the sample specimen, the top should be marked so the plane of the slice can be determined.

206. Oriented Specimens

Analyses of structure and structural deformations often make use of x-ray and petrographic studies of oriented specimens. The relations of strain patterns, microjoints, microfaults, and other minute structures are determined according to their positions in space and their orientations. When rocks are collected for the purpose of analyzing major deformations by means of microstructures the field specimens must be marked so that they may be arranged in the laboratory in exactly the same attitude that they had before removal from the outcrop. In fulfillment of the essential requirements, various reference marks must be made on the rock before it is broken out of the outcropping bed. Depending on the type of analysis anticipated, all or some of the steps given in the following discussion should be given consideration. Refer to Fig. 170.

FIG. 169. Obtaining a transverse chip from thinly laminated beds.

(1) Record the exact location and the elevation of the point where the specimen is taken from the outcrop.

(2) If the location is on a local structure, indicate the structural position, such as low on west flank, or near axis.

(3) Scratch or clearly mark a north line on the portion of rock to be removed as a specimen.

(4) Indicate on the rock the directions of dip and strike.

Figure 170B shows how to draw an accurate north line on the surface of the rock even though it is steeply dipping. By using a book or any rigid, flat *nonmagnetic* object as shown in the drawing, the compass may be held in a level position against the side of the book and a true north line drawn along the edge resting on the rock surface. The surface may be too rough at the exact site of the specimen to permit reading an accurate dip and strike; however, the dip and strike may be determined nearby where conditions are more favorable, and then be scratched on the specimen by duplicating their bearings. All markings on the specimen must be made before it is broken from the bed. Much

needless work may be avoided if the locality is carefully investigated for a segment of a bed *in place* that can be removed
simply by prying it out with a pick or bar. When the oriented

FIG. 170. Oriented speci-
mens. A. The true dip
and strike of the strata
and the north line are
scratched on the surface
before the sample is
removed. B. Method for
establishing the north
line on an inclined sur-
face is shown.

sample must be taken from solid, unjointed
beds, it may be loosened by a star drill and
chisels as shown in Fig. 170A.

Another method commonly employed is
much more simple than the one just described.

The ' dip" and "strike" of any flat surface is determined with the Brunton. This
plane will be placed in the same attitude
in the laboratory; so it is immaterial that
it be a bedding plane. The true dip and
strike of the strata may be determined
where convenient for possible later use.
This method of orienting a specimen is
ordinarily used in crystalline rocks that
contain no stratification.

The specimen may first be broken out
of the outcrop and then carefully replaced
in its original position. The orientation
readings are then indicated on any plane
surface. This procedure avoids destruction
of predetermined reference lines.

207. Samples for Special Uses

Surface or near surface samples are collected for specific types
of analyses. The determination of minute quantities of hydrocarbons, trace elements, organic matter, and the like require sampling techniques peculiar to the particular substance being sought.
The method of collection and precautions to be observed are
dictated by requirements of such work, and these requirements, in
turn, are subject to certain theories regarding the significance of
the geochemical or other analyses contemplated. The techniques

of various organizations and institutions differ radically, and the geologist must perform his duties in accordance with the practices of his organization. For these reasons, a discussion of special sampling techniques in this manual would be of little use; for it also would no doubt reflect personal preferences not in basic accord with all endeavors in this field of investigation.

208. Labeling Field Samples

A surface sample or specimen is practically worthless if the stratigraphic position or geographic location is unknown. Therefore, every sample bag or envelope must be marked by some means that will insure permanency of the identifying label. From the day a sample is collected until it is finally filed away it may be handled many times, subjected to rubbing in the collecting bag and shipping boxes, or become wet from rains or other causes. There is little consolation in the knowledge that samples were completely labeled in the field, if for any reason the markings have become illegible. The mark of a soft pencil on cloth labels or paper envelopes withstands much moisture, but smears easily when rubbed. Common fountain pen inks withstand rubbing, but smear or wash out altogether when moistened. The advantage of one over the other is entirely a matter of circumstances. Certain types of ball point (cartridge type) pens are satisfactory, but the lines should be tested for resistance to water and rubbing before they are used in the field. Wax-base colored pencils (not indelible) are quite resistant to moisture and moderately resistant to erasure. Waterproof (India) drawing inks make the most permanent label, and there are several types of fountain pens designed for these inks.

The task of completely labeling each sample in the field can be reduced appreciably by stamping a large portion of the label on the envelopes before they are taken into the field. Rubber type sets in various sizes can be purchased at small cost, and special waterproof stamp pad ink is available for use with rubber type.

LOCALITY IDENTIFICATION

When samples from a number of sections, localities, or regions accumulate in a laboratory or repository there are many possibilities for portions of suites from different sections to become mixed. Unless each sample is completely labeled it may be diffi-

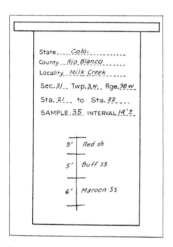

cult to correct such mishaps. The likelihood of mixing samples from two or more sections is reduced by adhering to some uniform pattern in the label. Figure 171 illustrates one type of form that may be set up as a rubber stamp with which all the envelopes or bags are printed in waterproof ink. The blank lines are filled in by hand lettering or rubber type, as mentioned in an earlier article.

FIG. 171. Rubber stamp form used on Manila sample envelope. Sketch at bottom identifies relative positions and approximate thicknesses of units represented by sample chips.

STRATIGRAPHIC IDENTIFICATION

When sections are measured by the plane table method, there always exists some danger of confusion regarding the stratigraphic position of the sample relative to a stadia control point. Although these relationships are usually stated in the field notes, it is a good practice to also show on the envelope the approximate position of the sample site above or below the nearest stadia station used for control. Thus, a series of samples taken in numerical sequence might be labelled as follows:

> At sta. 10
> Sample 17 (1 ft.)
>
> Between sta. 10 & 11
> Sample 18 (5 ft.)

Between sta. 10 & 11
Sample 19 (5 ft.)

At sta. 11
Sample 20 (5 ft.)

The intervals in parentheses are estimated or measured by hand instruments, and are therefore subject to adjustment.

A supplemental sample taken along the same stratigraphic horizon as another should bear the same number, but with a subsidiary letter. This letter indicates that the sample is not in stratigraphic sequence with the others, but is located laterally from one in the regular series. For example, if the bed from which Sample 20 is taken exhibits wide variations in lithologies in short distances, it would be desirable to collect supplemental samples somewhat off the line of section, which would be designated as follows: Sample 20-A, 20 ft. east; Sample 20-B, 25 ft. west.

LABELING BY NUMERICAL SEQUENCE

Sequential numbering of samples holds several distinct advantages over other systems in common use: (1) Sample numbers are easily and quickly checked, for they are readily comprehended by one who may have had no part in the field work; (2) numbering is independent of stratigraphic interval, though estimated intervals may be shown; (3) there is somewhat greater flexibility and simplicity for adding any number of stratigraphically equivalent specimens without confusing the numbering sequence; and (4) short, simple numbers may be shown on a plotted standard three-inch log strip without excessive crowding in the limited space.

The label on Sample 1 should always indicate where (stratigraphically) the section was started—top or bottom. Because of the possibility of this envelope being lost or the label becoming illegible, the next few consecutive envelopes should bear the note "Near base of section" or "Near top of section." These safeguards take only a moment in the field, and they may prevent much lost time, confusion, and serious errors later.

LABELING BY STRATIGRAPHIC POSITION

This method is applicable only where stratigraphic thicknesses are computed concurrently with sampling, as, for example, when hand leveling horizontal strata. The principal advantage is that the sample number indicates the stratigraphic position above the base or below the top of the section. The numbers on the samples are analogous to depths on a well log; for instance, if the section is measured from the base upward, the successive samples are labeled 0-10, 10-20, 20-32, etc. The base of the third sample interval would be 20 feet stratigraphically above the base of the section, and the top would be 32 feet. The same principles govern the numbering when the section is measured from the top downward, but in this case, the first number designates the stratigraphic thickness from the top of the section to the top of the sample interval.

Some geologists like to "tie" all detailed sections into some well-known stratigraphic horizon, even though this horizon is not included in the sampled section. Thus, if the top of a distinctive and widespread formation occurs 250 feet below the point where detailing begins, the first 10-foot sampled interval would be labeled 250-260 (feet above the top of formation X).

A variation of this sytem consists of the stratigraphic thickness to the base (or top) of the section followed by the sample interval, as, for example, 250-12, 262-5, 267-8.

LABELING BY STADIA STATION NUMBERS

When the section is measured by plane table and stadia, samples may be referred to rod stations either by number or estimated interval. Samples numbered above station 15 would be designated $15+1$, $15+2$, $15+3$; those below the station would be $15-1$, $15-2$, etc. The subnumbers begin anew at each successive rod station, as $16-1$, $16-2$, etc. Lateral supplemental samples are indicated $16-2A$, etc.

The principal advantage of this system of numbering is that the sample designations indicate the map locations; hence, it is a simple matter to place the positions on the plane table sheet without reference to the field notes.

209. Stratigraphic Field Notes

Field notes reflect the competency of the field geologist. The ability to discriminate between important and inconsequential details, to organize various phases of the work, and to recognize the necessity for recording observations in concise and specific terms is gained through experience. But, as mentioned earlier, *experience* is a relative quantity, not necessarily a product of *time* alone. Constructive experience is gained by effectively relating and directing academic knowledge to practical accomplishment. In terms of time spent in the field, relative levels of effectiveness can be reached quickly or slowly, according as the man applies himself and his academic training to the task at hand. Field notes indicate to what extent the geologist has comprehended basic field problems and his ability to attack these problems in an effective manner.

Good field notes provide all the data necessary for achieving the objectives of a project. If they fail to do so, then the project has failed accordingly. They should be neither too brief, for extreme brevity may result in inadequate treatment of descriptions; nor too voluminous, because very detailed notes are extravagant of field time. Ideal field notes meet the requirements of the project.

Notes should be lettered, not written in longhand. Variations in styles of handwriting may lead to errors in interpreting the notes. Abbreviations should be used extensively as a means of saving time. An explanatory list of the abbreviations used should be included in each notebook. Every field book must contain specific identification as to locality, name of section, associated plane table sheets, etc.

SUPPLEMENTAL NOTES FOR SAMPLED SECTIONS

When samples are collected for analysis in the laboratory or field office, the stratigraphic notes need not treat details of the lithologies, for microscopic determinations of the samples will provide better lithologic descriptions than can be achieved in the field; therefore, much duplication of effort will be avoided if only gross characters, which can be determined at a glance, are re-

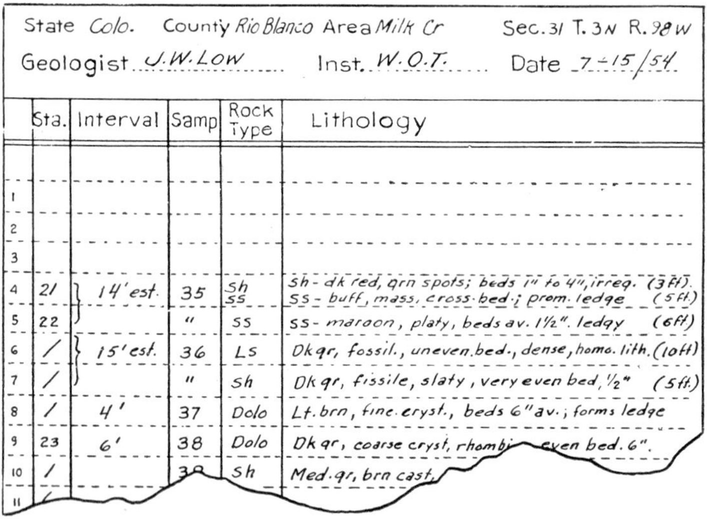

State _Colo._ County _Rio Blanco_ Area _Milk Cr_   Sec. 31 T. 3 N R. 98 W
Geologist _J.W. Low_   Inst. _W.O.T._   Date _7-15/54_.

	Sta.	Interval	Samp	Rock Type	Lithology
1					
2					
3					
4	21	14' est.	35	Sh SS	Sh - dk red, grn spots; beds 1" to 4", irreg. (3 ft).
5	22		"	SS	SS - buff, mass, cross-bed; prom. ledge (5 ft)
6	/	15' est.	36	LS	SS - maroon, platy, beds av. 1½". ledgy (6 ft)
7	/		"	Sh	Dk gr, fossil., uneven bed., dense, homo. lith. (10 ft)
8	/	4'	37	Dolo	Dk gr, fissile, slaty, very even bed, ½" (5 ft.)
9	23	6'	38	Dolo	Lt. brn, fine. cryst., beds 6" av.; forms ledge
10	/		39	Sh	Dk gr, coarse cryst, rhombi even bed. 6".
11					Med. gr, brn cast.

FIG. 172. Portion of a page from a field notebook showing the kinds of data that should be recorded. Any blank notebook may be ruled to meet other requirements of an investigation.

corded. The field man should observe and record characters and stratigraphic relationships that cannot be deduced from examination of the specimens, such as types of bedding, weathering habits, continuity of lithologic units, and unconformities. These facts can then be combined with microscopic descriptions of lithologies when the samples are processed in the laboratory.

Figure 172 represents a page from a geologist's notebook used on a plane table survey of a sampled section. The form shown may be varied to meet special requirements or personal preference. However, the figure illustrates a system which meets the basic requirements in a simple and easily understood manner.

DESCRIPTIVE NOTES ON UNSAMPLED SECTIONS

If a section is not to be sampled and no laboratory work is contemplated, it may be necessary, and generally is desirable, to describe details of lithology rather completely in the field. In order to accomplish this objective, the geologist should carry a

State.......... County......... Area.............. Sec....T.... R... .

Geologist...................... Inst. .... Date ....

	Sta.	Interval	Samp	Rock Type	Lithology
			None Collected		*(Note: Measured from top downward)*
1	8	5'	)	Ss	*Grains av. 0.3mm, ang., qtz., trace feldspar, poorly cem. with clay, pink to buff., soft.*
2		3'	)	Sh	*Gr and brn, mottled, fissile, hard, tr. carbon. matter*
3		6'	)	Ss	*Grains 0.2 mm, rnd, frosted, cross-bed., pink, red*
4	9	2'	)	Sh	*Gr to black, beds 2", much pyrite; weath. lt, gr.*
5		3'	)	Ls	
6	10		)		
7			)		
8			)		

FIG. 173. Page from field notes where samples are not collected for laboratory examination. Rock descriptions include features, such as grain size, normally deferred for microscopic examination.

pocket lens of 9- to 15-power. Where carbonate rocks are prevalent in the section, a small bottle of dilute hydrochloric acid will aid in differentiating limestones and dolomites. Figure 173 represents a page of notes for a section where samples are not collected.

SKETCHES AND DIAGRAMS

Simple sketches, diagrams, and cross sections clarify complex relationships of stratigraphy more effectively than word descriptions, and sketches can be drawn in less time in the field than comparable descriptions can be written. Sketches and diagrams should be made in the notebook, not on a separate sheet of paper, for then they become a part of the permanent record of field observations. Always show an approximate scale or dimensions and points of reference to the stratigraphic section. Figure 174 is a simple notebook sketch showing how to relate definite points in the drawing to the field notes.

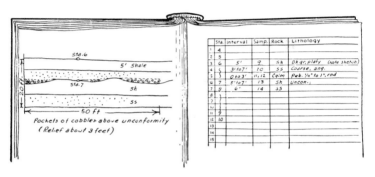

FIG. 174. Field sketch showing relations of the diagram to points established by surveying methods. Notice that an approximate scale is given.

PHOTOGRAPHS

Photographs, especially those in color, go far toward bringing to the laboratory the concept of field relationships. Their value, however, is largely dependent on the manner in which they have been taken and identification of details in the picture that are referenced to the measured section.

CARBON COPIES OF FIELD NOTES

Carbon copies of field notes require very little additional time in the field, yet they may serve a number of useful purposes. The field notebook is vital to the processing of surface sections. If it were lost the job could not be completed and much of the work would have to be repeated. When copies of the field notes are available to the office or laboratory man, the laboratory phase of work can be carried on concurrently with the field work; otherwise, it must be deferred until the notebook can be submitted. One notebook may contain several stratigraphic sections, and for this reason they are difficult to file. Carbon copies can be filed separately for each section according to location, name of section, etc.

Sheets of white paper and carbon paper are cut to sizes somewhat smaller than the notebook page prior to going into the field. One day's supply may be placed in the back of the book and held in with rubber bands. When in use, the carbon and white paper are fastened to the notebook page with small paper clips.

CHAPTER VIII

Mineral Exploration[1]

210. Introduction

Igneous and metamorphic rocks are commonly referred to as "hard rocks," and sedimentaries as "soft rocks." The terms are ambiguous, however, for certain sedimentary rocks are normally harder than some varieties of igneous and metamorphic rocks, though the "hard rock" distinction is generally valid. As a whole, igneous and metamorphic rocks are more dense, unyielding, and are considerably harder than the ordinary varieties of sedimentaries. Perhaps the term *hard rock* has more significance with respect to the commercial objectives of those who are concerned with their occurrences and characteristics. The distinction between hard rocks and soft rocks is also applied to those who work habitually, or primarily, with one group or the other. The hard rock geologist is mainly concerned with igneous and metamorphic, and to a lesser degree, with the sedimentary rocks. With the exception of purely academic or scientific investigations, the objectives in mapping and deciphering the complexities of hard rock areas are to precisely locate, measure, and evaluate mineral deposits of commercial worth. Inasmuch as the majority of commercial deposits of metallic ores occurs in igneous and metamorphic rocks, the term *hard rock geologist* is considered by many almost synonymous with mineral exploration geologist.

The difference between a hard rock geologist and any other "kind" of geologist is only a matter of specialization. Generally

[1] Material in this chapter was prepared by Robert H. Carpenter.

speaking, a good field geologist has a "working" knowledge of all kinds of rocks; but the hard rock man usually has a more intimate and detailed knowledge of igneous and metamorphic rocks. Similarly, he is more concerned with the processes of mineralization, hydrothermal alteration, contact and regional metamorphism, and the like, than with the processes of sedimentation. It is through his ability to correctly observe and to interpret field observations with respect to geological processes that his success as a mineral exploration geologist will depend. Obviously, the hard rock geologist must have extensive knowledge of rocks and minerals, igneous and metamorphic processes, modes of mineral segregation, and a three-dimensional grasp of structural relationships in order to project his geologic conclusions into areas or depths where direct observations are impossible.

Although the hard rock geologist may have less interest in sedimentary rocks, he must have a working knowledge of them, for some of the world's great ore deposits are in sedimentary rocks or in metamorphosed sediments. The key to regional interpretation of igneous and metamorphic processes may be found in closely associated sedimentary formations.

The detailed mapping of hard rocks in a number of respects is more difficult than the mapping of stratified sedimentaries. Sedimentary rocks generally exhibit greater lateral continuity and vertical differentiation; therefore, observations and measurements on isolated outcrops can be projected into the subsurface or across alluvium-covered areas with some assurance. In contrast, the behavior of igneous intrusions, irregular masses, and alteration zones of hard rocks is difficult to predict, and extrapolation from widely separated outcrops is relatively more hazardous. In general, the necessary observations of hard rocks are in finer detail than are required for most mapping of stratified rocks, although there are notable exceptions where sediments are thick and homogenous and stratigraphic relationships can be determined only by microscopic examination of the rocks.

211. Reconnaissance

As in all other types of mapping projects, reconnaissance of the entire area is essential to effective planning of mineral exploration. In so far as the instrumental phase of the work is concerned, reconnaissance is basically the same for all kinds of mapping, such as the tentative selection of triangulation stations, base lines, traverse courses, and other features that will affect the course of the work. But when reconnoitering an area for mineral investigation, especial attention should be directed toward the geologic features and relationships pertinent to the principal objectives of the survey. These objectives will vary according to the geology of the region and the types of ore deposits sought. Ordinarily the reconnaissance would include all features having regional significance, such as faults or fracture zones, bearings of lineation, dikes, and areas of strong mineralization.

A generalized small scale map or air photographs are invaluable in reconnaissance work. Photos are especially useful for the reason that most features of immediate interest are readily identifiable and are already located. Transparent overlay sheets of acetate or vellum may be stapled or clipped to the prints so that unlimited sketching may be done without impairing the photos for later use. Areas of particular interest but of differing character may be outlined in colors and appropriately annotated.

Diagrams and plans sketches together with brief notes will be found useful during the course of the detailed work to follow.

The reconnaissance phase of the project may include the measuring of stratigraphic, metamorphic, or volcanic sequences for the purpose of correlation, comparison, or preliminary relative evaluation of the different localities. Even if measurements are not made at this time, estimates of thicknesses or areal distribution of certain rocks or sequences should be recorded in the notebook or on a sketch map. Methods of measuring stratigraphic sections are given in Chapter VII.

212. Base Maps

Topographic maps, whose construction is discussed in Chapter V, provide an excellent base for accurately locating geologic features, provided the scale is sufficiently large to show the detail desired. Existing maps may be enlarged by photostat or photographic methods, but errors in the original maps are likewise increased—a fact which must be taken into account if a high degree of accuracy is required. Enlarged maps may be checked for accuracy by comparing distances, bearings, and elevations on the sheet with corresponding measurements made on the ground by plane table, transit, or tape. A few such comparisons made locally will demonstrate the accuracy that might be expected over the map area.

Air photographs are sometimes used directly in the field for delineating geologic features and later are adjusted for correct positional relationships. The positions of points or boundaries are corrected by radial-line or projection methods. Base maps showing drainage patterns, landmarks, roads, trails, and earlier survey marks can be constructed from air photos by several photogrammetric methods. However, all these methods, except the radial-line, require special instruments which may not be available. Methods for constructing maps in the field are presented in other chapters in this manual.

213. Map Scales

A wide range of scales is employed in the search for, and development of, commercial ore deposits; therefore, it is important at the outset of a project to review the objectives, the field methods to be used, and various other factors to ascertain the most appropriate scale for the required results. Only the most important topics for consideration in selecting a scale are mentioned below. Local conditions will to some extent introduce additional ones.

TOPOGRAPHIC RELIEF

The character and amount of relief of the surface should be shown on contour maps which are needed, not only as a base on which to show the geology, but also to plan development once ore deposits have been found. The contour interval selected should be such that the significant relief features will be shown. The ground spacing of contours is determined by the steepness of slopes (Article 111). Once the spacing is known, the smallest scale on which this spacing can be shown is easily computed. It is impractical to space contours closer than $\frac{1}{32}$ inch.

SIZE AND DISTRIBUTION OF OUTCROPS

The scale must be large enough to accurately display small, yet important, outcrops and the relationship of one outcrop to another. A trial sketch will indicate the minimum scale required.

GEOLOGIC DETAIL

The scale of detail maps may be governed by the size and complexity of geologic features, such as fault systems, zones of alteration, thickness of veins, and fracture or joint systems. In some instances the complexities of local areas may require very large-scale maps of small areal extent. Such special sheets should be tied into the regional maps so that exact interrelations are evident.

INSTRUMENTATION

Detailed precise maps can be made only by use of precise instruments and appropriate field methods. No advantage is gained by increasing the scaling properties of the map beyond the measuring limits of the available instruments or the prescribed methods to be used.

MAP SCALE AND WORKING TIME

If an area can be mapped on one plane table sheet on a scale of 1 inch = 2000 feet, it requires four sheets to map the same area on a scale of 1 inch = 1000 feet; and if the scale is increased to 1 inch = 500 feet, 16 plane table sheets will be needed. All the sheets must be properly matched together—a meticulous and time-consuming task. If only a few triangulation or accurately located traverse stations have been established for control, increasing the scale may result in an unusable distribution of points. Three well-placed points may be adequate for controlling one sheet; but three triangulation stations will not suffice for more than one; therefore, a great deal of supplemental control would have to be run if the scale were increased.

Costs in field and drafting time and in materials increase at a disproportionate rate with increase in scale.

From the foregoing it is obvious that the selection of a map scale is a matter not to be taken lightly. Perhaps the best rule is to *adopt the smallest scale that will satisfy all requirements of the project.*

214. Structural and Lithologic Framework

One of the principal purposes of reconnaissance is to clarify and define major problems. When the problem is clearly understood, the next step is to devise economical means of solving it. A phase of field operations, for which there is no convenient term, consists in setting the stage for detailing. It is neither reconnaissance nor detail, but somewhere between.

When the broad problems are defined and methods of attack have been devised, the project has been reduced to a series of technical operations. It is very important to direct these operations or field procedures toward ultimate objectives and to proceed in a manner that will achieve these objectives with a minimum expenditure of effort, time and money. Probably the worst possible course to pursue is to plunge prematurely into fine detailing at completion of reconnaissance.

Close detailing must be conducted within an accurate framework based on structure, lithology, petrology, or stratigraphy, depending upon geologic conditions. In establishing such a framework, only methods suitable for detailing are used, for the design of the skeleton determines the overall accuracy of the detail map.

Figure 175 is a map of an area in which certain major features are accurately located, but those of secondary magnitude are omitted. Only the readily identifiable features are considered at this stage of the work, for the identification of obscure faults, folds, unconformities, and geologic boundaries must be deferred until the rocks and their interrelationships can be studied more closely.

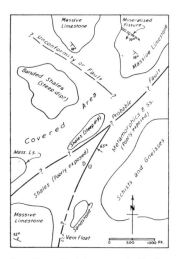

FIG. 175. Sketch map indicating the manner of subdividing an area into major geologic elements during reconnaissance work.

215. Filling in Detail

The purpose of the preliminary mapping is to subdivide the area into segments bounded by major geologic features. Each of these segments, or areal units, may be characterized by certain peculiarities in the finer details, which, in turn, are the result of the local geological environment. When examining one of these segments and filling in detail, the significance of observable peculiarities should be considered in relation to the regional and local setting. As will be shown later, the form and orientation of minor structural features are indicative of large structural units and the stresses and processes that caused them. Mineralization and metamorphic processes commonly bear a close relationship to local structural, stratigraphic, and lithologic features; hence, if the locality can be evaluated in terms of these geologic features, the mineral potentialities can be inferred.

Most "hard rock" work is done on intermediate or large scales, which demand precision methods and instrumentation. Plotting and drafting of maps must be correspondingly accurate in order to show small but very important veins, faults, dikes, and altered zones in correct dimensions and relationships. Many of the details may appear to have little significance in early stages of the work, but as the map develops they will fall into place as integral parts of the overall complex. For this reason all outcrops are accurately located and adequately described in the field book, even though their value to the project may not be known at the time.

216. Field Identification of Rock Types

Specific identification of igneous, metamorphic, and some sedimentary rocks ordinarily requires laboratory techniques; hence, such work must be deferred until the end of the field season, except under special circumstances. Nevertheless, it is necessary to efficient field operations that all rocks observed be classified in general terms for purposes of correlation or comparison. The tentative names given to certain varieties in the field may be changed later as a result of petrographic analyses; but the tentative classification will have served a useful purpose during the course of field work. Terms that are somewhat descriptive of constituents are best for field use; thus, a flow rock may be called a fine-grained, quartz-bearing extrusive during the conduct of a survey, though, later, it may be more specifically identified as a dacite or rhyolite.

Tentative generalized descriptions of all rocks observed should be made at the outcrop. No description should be trusted to one's memory. Patterns or colors can be used, preferably on overlay sheets, to designate the different rock types as determined in the field. As the work progresses, areal patterns develop and areas of abnormal lithologic distribution become apparent. These areas may require more intensified work or detailed sampling. It is disconcerting to have such anomalies come to light as a result of laboratory determinations after the parties have left the field.

217. Standardization of Descriptions

A rock description or a specimen is of no use if it cannot be identified with respect to the location of the outcrop from which it was derived. Similarly, an error in correctly relating description to location can cause a great deal of trouble or a serious error in geologic interpretation. It is for these reasons that the simplest possible system of mutual identification should be used, and this system consists of *consecutive numbers*.

In order to avoid possible confusion, numbers used in the notebook should be in consecutive order and this should be the order in which descriptions *are made* or samples collected, as the case might be. It is bad practice to *anticipate* numbering of samples not yet collected or to reserve numbers for rock descriptions prior to actual examination of the rock.

When a numbered entry is made in the notebook, the same number should be placed immediately on the map at the correct location. Occasions arise when it is necessary to return to a locality for additional detail. Some geologists prefer to refer the second series of numbers to the first by adding distinguishing subscripts or letters to the original numbers. This practice can result in confounding the descriptions. It is better to give the new description a new number, and designate its location with reference to a preëstablished ground point by including the station number in parenthesis. Thus, a second run of numbers would be 112 (31), 113 (29), and 114 (35). The original rock descriptions and stations would have been numbered 31, 29, and 35.

The descriptions of rocks should be governed by some sequential order of characters, which may be devised at the beginning of a project. The order of topics for sedimentary rocks is suggested in the following outline.

    (1) Name of rock, if known (sandstone, quartzite, etc.).
    (2) Granularity (grain or crystal size).
    (3) Texture (grain shape).
    (4) Sorting (grain size distribution).
    (5) Grain materials (identifiable minerals).
    (6) Induration (hard, soft, brittle, etc.).
    (7) Cementation (degree and material).

(8) Color (on fresh and weathered surfaces).

(9) Accessory constituents (fossils, carbonaceous materials).

(10) Thickness of rock unit.

(11) Stratigraphic relations (cross bedding, sedimentary peculiarities, alternations of unlike lithologies, or recurrence of similar lithologies).

(12) General effects of weathering, hydrothermal alteration, and mineralization.

(13) Structural features.

Descriptions which adhere to such a plan are much easier to correlate from well-organized written notes than are those which do not follow any particular order.

In order to save field time it is permissible to simply refer in the notes to a description already recorded. Thus, in describing rocks along the strike of a bed, it may be that at station or locality 31 the rock is exactly the same as at locality 30. Instead of repeating the description, enter in the book the notation, "31—Sandstone, same as (30)"; or with slight variations, "31—Sandstone, same as (30), except somewhat harder, no fossils."

Descriptions of igneous rocks should likewise follow a uniform sequence, which, because of the basic differences, must be different from that employed for sedimentary or metamorphic rocks. An example of such an outline follows.

(1) Name, if known, or generalized group name.

(2) Color. (The color may be most important in quickly identifying a sample or in correlation or comparative work).

(3) Minerals. (Identify, or give superficial description, with estimated percentages).

(4) Texture and textural variations.

(5) Maximum and median crystal size.

(6) Structure (jointing, flow banding).

(7) Contact relationships with other rocks.

(8) Metamorphism (local, contact, etc.).

(9) Mineralization and hydrothermal effects.

(10) Degree of weathering.

218. Concealed Areas

In many regions the most serious problem facing the geologist is the paucity of outcrops. Broad areas concealed by alluvium, soil, glacial till, talus, and other surface materials must be filled in by projection of observations and measurements made at isolated localities. The "hard rock" geologist is especially concerned with projecting features such as fracture zones, faults, fault zones, and unconformities, where hydrothermal, solution, and other processes of mineral emplacement or enrichment may occur. Where outcrops are sparse some of the manifestations of unconformities are similar to those of faults. Table 10 (appendix) presents some common criteria for detecting these features where outcrops are insufficient for direct identification. Folding can normally be projected into covered areas where dip, strike, and elevation control can be established at critical locations.

219. Minor Structural Features of Metamorphic Rocks

Of the three major rocks groups, metamorphics are the most complex, for their genesis begins with whatever complexities existed in the parent rock, and the molding of their characteristics is subject, not only to their original constitution, but perhaps even more to the types and intensities of outside influences that have been responsible for modification of the parent rock. In order to understand metamorphic rocks, one must be familiar with the mineral compositions and structures of igneous and sedimentary rocks. Original structures may either be retained or completely obliterated depending upon the intensity of metamorphism, and if extremely severe, entirely new mineral constitution and structure may evolve from the parent rock. Because of these complexities the histories of metamorphic rocks are difficult or impossible to decipher.

Mild or low-grade metamorphism ordinarily does not materially affect gross structural features and only partially changes such features as bedding, cross-bedding, banding, lenticularity, and the like. Figure 176 shows an area wherein low-grade metamorphism has occurred. Parent sedimentary rocks have been altered to poorly developed slates and marbles, metaquartzites and sericitic and graphitic schists. Although schistosity, transverse cleavage, drag folding, and thermal alteration partially obscure small sedimentary features, the major stratigraphic aspects of the rocks still persist.

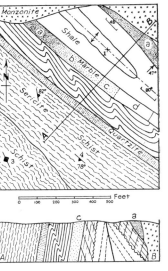

Certain structural features are characteristic of metamorphic rocks, and it is well to have them clearly in mind when engaged in field examinations. Extreme contortion, folding, attenuation, and cleavage are commonly exhibited. By analyses of the small or microstructures it may be possible to reconstruct the stress framework within which they originated. The following descriptive classification of cleavage aids in evaluating the features observed.

FIG. 176. Metamorphosed area where characteristics of the sedimentary section are still retained despite considerable lithologic alteration.

Splitting parallel to mineral orientation of the rock

Slaty cleavage—closely spaced planes of splitting are parallel to the orientation of microscopic mineral grains.

Schistosity—closely spaced planes of splitting, as in schists and gneisses. These "planes" are commonly much contorted.

Bedding cleavage—splitting planes essentially parallel to the inherited bedding planes.

Splitting not parallel to mineral orientation

Fracture cleavage or closely spaced jointing—planes of splitting spaced from about a millimeter to a centimeter. Distinguished from ordinary jointing only by the small scale.

Slip cleavage—closely spaced faults of extremely small displacement, generally in the order of one to several millimeters.

Cleavage in rocks develops in response to stresses applied. If the rock itself tends to flow under stress, the constituent minerals

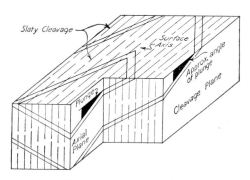

Fig. 177. Block diagram showing the relationships of cleavage planes and major structural features.

are reoriented, and splitting planes will develop parallel to the mineral orientation. On the other hand, the rock may yield to stress by shearing.

Slaty cleavage and *schistosity* are generally ascribed to rock flowage, although under certain conditions the splitting planes may develop in the direction of shear. *Fracture* and *slip* cleavages ordinarily result from shearing stresses. *Bedding cleavage* may result from (1) flowage and recrystallization parallel to bedding; (2) recrystallization parallel to fissility, which in turn may or may not be parallel to bedding; and (3) splitting parallel to the beds and axial planes in isoclinal folding.

The stresses that cause major structural features also produce the characters common to metamorphic rocks, and owing to this cause-and-effect relationship, minor structures can be very helpful in regional structural analysis. There are numerous examples of the parallelism of slaty cleavage and the axial planes of folds; therefore, a persistent orientation of cleavage planes suggests the attitudes of associated axial planes. The plunge of a fold can be established approximately as the angle between the horizontal and the trace of the stratification as it appears on the "axial plane" cleavage surface. These relationships are shown in Fig. 177.

When stratified sedimentary rocks are folded, fracture cleavage is likely to develop in the less competent members of the sequence. Figure 178A shows the relationships that might be expected. It can be seen that the acute angle between the cleavage and the bordering structurally competent bed points in the direction of the *relative* movement of the competent bed with respect to the incompetent one. The axial planes of drag folds respond in a similar manner, as shown in Fig. 178B. Relatively, the upper bed moves toward the axis of the anticline and the lower, toward the syncline.

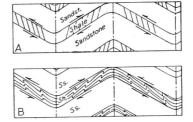

FIG. 178. A. Cross section indicating the inclination of cleavage planes with respect to the axes of folds. B. The major structures are suggested by drag folds. Arrows show the relative slipping of beds during folding.

The line of intersection between fracture cleavage and bedding is parallel to the plunge of the fold. Consequently, both the direction and inclination of plunge can be determined by analysis of the fracture cleavage.

The foregoing illustrates ways in which minor structural details of metamorphic rocks might be of assistance in solving difficult structural problems, but it should be emphasized that it is hazardous to place complete confidence in methods which depend solely upon minor structural details revealing the true aspects of major structural phenomena. Gross features must be observed and measured wherever possible, utilizing such minutia as are applicable to bridge over the gaps in information. One must always be cognizant of the fact that cleavage, foliation, imbrication, jointing, and similar features can be developed at any time in the history of the rocks; and the stresses which created these characters may or may not be the same ones that produced the major structures now observable at the surface. The relationships between minute and gross characters must be established for each area before it is reasonably safe to rely upon minor structures of the rocks as indicative of major structural features.

220. Field Relationships of Metamorphic Structures

The preceding article is concerned with the more common attributes of metamorphic rocks. Some of these details are so small as to require the use of a hand lens or even a microscope; others, though small in relation to regional features, are easily observed in the field and are of considerable importance in solving structural problems. Figure 176 is an idealized representation of field conditions showing how measurements of minor details can suggest the presence of larger structural features.

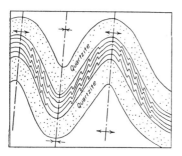

FIG. 179. Areal geologic map showing the parallelism of drag folds and principal structural features. Drag folds are developed in the less competent members of a stratigraphic succession.

As mentioned earlier, where a succession of competent and incompetent strata is strongly folded, the upper portions of the incompetent members are commonly dragged toward the crests of the anticlines and the lower portions. Figure 179 is an areal geologic map showing drag folds in slaty shales that lie between two beds of quartzite. Notice that the plan of drag folds is similar to that of the anticline and syncline. Such drag folding may occur in moderately indurated beds where main structure-making stresses are borne by the more rigid members of the succession. High temperatures and pressures reduce the inherent strength of the rock so that drag folding and flowage can take place. As indicated in the figure, the axes of drag folds approximately parallel the axis of the "parent" structure.

221. Structural Features of Igneous Rocks

Ore deposits commonly occur along the contact of an intrusive body with the country rock, and for this reason the field geologist must be especially watchful for clues that reveal or suggest such relationships. Structures within the intrusive body may indicate the most favorable conditions or areas for the development of important mineral deposits.

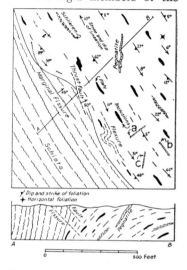

FIG. 180. Orientation of igneous features suggesting gross structural aspects of an area. Transverse, longitudinal, and diagonal joints are shown at *a*, *b*, and *c*.

A cooling igneous mass ordinarily passes through three phases or stages: flow, or liquid; transition, or plastic; and solid.

FLOW STAGE

In the flow stage, circulation within the magma tends to reorient all constituents having unequal dimensions (such as tabular minerals, elongate rock fragments, and spindle-shaped schlieren) parallel to the long axis of the intrusive body. Figure 180 illustrates the lineation associated with an intrusive body cutting a metamorphic series. Notice that the lineation is independent of the strike of the strata.

TRANSITION STAGE

Between the flow and solid stages magmas pass through a plastic phase. Tabular and columnar elements in the magma are usually flexed and contorted by differential stresses, especially where drag folding has occurred along the contact with the country rock.

SOLID STAGE

All magmas cool and solidify from the outer surfaces toward the center; hence, all three phases exist contemporaneously in different parts of the body. Tremendous stresses are set up during the cooling process. Relief of these stresses is attained by the formation of faults and complex joint systems in the solidified portion of the mass. All types of faults and joints may be represented, depending somewhat on the size and shape of the igneous intrusion, the temperatures, and the time involved. Pegmatite or aplite magmas may be emplaced in open joints or faults to form dikes, or along certain stratification surfaces in the country rock as sills. As the interior of a large igneous mass cools and shrinks, structures in the outer "shell" may be modified in adjusting to the smaller volume occupied by the body. This shrinkage is also increased by the escape of vapors and gases. As a result of the contraction anomalous relationships in the faulting, fracturing, and jointing may exist locally.

Lineation generally is oriented parallel to the long dimension of an intrusive body and is inclined parallel to the plunge of the body. Similarly, foliation is approximately parallel to the roof or hood and the flanks of the intrusion. Mica flakes, platy inclusions, and pancake-shaped accumulations of schlieren tend to form a halo in the outer parts of the intrusive body and thus reflect the configuration of the adjacent country rock.

Solid stage structures normally develop within the marginal regions of the intrusive body and extend well into the fringe of country rock. In Fig. 180, transverse joints are shown at *a*, longitudinal joints at *b*, and diagonal joints at *c*. All three types may be more or less equally developed, or one or two sets may predominate. Marginal fissures or normal faults dipping toward the intrusive body at approximately 45 degrees are commonly present. Thrust faults of small throw may be present in the fringe zone or in the hood. The thrust planes generally dip toward the intrusion; therefore, relative to the igneous body, thrusting is outward.

222. Surface Observations of Mineralization

Inasmuch as the field geologist is primarily concerned with mineral deposits, most of his time will be spent in observing and evaluating mineralization. In the very early stages of the work most attention may be given to mapping the obvious gross features of the geology. But as the work progresses, a greater proportion of the effort will be directed toward determining the causes of mineralization and controls of the processes. It is not practicable within the scope of this manual to consider the many combinations of field relationships that are normally encountered in the course of mineral exploration; therefore, only three rather typical examples are given as illustrative of features and relationships to be sought and mapped.

PYROMETASOMATIC SCHEELITE DEPOSIT

Figure 181 shows a small monzonite intrusive body partially covered by basalt. A scheelite ore zone in silicated limestone occurs along the eastern edge of the body, and copper mineralization has taken place in the central region. A blanket type of hydrothermal alteration appears within the intrusive mass and as a peripheral halo in the intruded rocks. It is not uncommon for silication to occur adjacent to igneous contacts, particularly in carbonate rocks. Silication probably occurs contemporaneously with intrusion of the magma, whereas hydrothermal alteration generally is later and is most likely related to solutions emanating from deep still-cooling portions of the igneous mass.

The exploration geologist must have considerable knowledge

of the processes of thermal and additive metamorphism in order to correctly interpret their various manifestations in the field. The original compositions of the rocks may be drastically altered where these processes have been active; and correlation with unmeta-morphosed rocks would be exceedingly difficult if the nature of the alteration were not clearly understood.

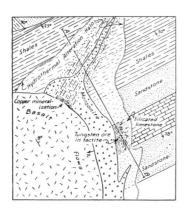

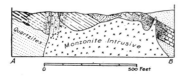

Since scheelite is difficult to recognize in a silicated rock, the tactite zone may profitably be examined at night with a fluorescent lamp to establish the relationships of the fluorescent scheelite to specific rocks or beds that can be identified and mapped during daylight. The fluorescent patches may be outlined with chalk or crayon to facilitate daylight studies.

FIG. 181. Mineralization along the fringes of an intrusive body. Copper and tungsten mineralization is related to the extensive hydrothermal halo in the sedimentary rocks.

If the metasomatic halo is relatively narrow and without major faulting, key marker beds are traced into the silicated zone, and progressive mineralogic and textural changes are observed along the strike of the strata into this zone of alteration. Even though all vestiges of the marker beds may disappear in the tactite zone along the contact, sufficient framework may be established marginally to enable the geologist to project significant beds or fracture systems into the obscure region and ultimately into the subsurface.

COPPER MINERALIZATION

In Fig. 181 copper mineralization is indicated by stippling in a zone along the dike and under the cover of small basalt flows.

The copper occurs within the alteration halo, and is controlled by post-intrusion fracturing roughly parallel to the trend of the dike. Generally, bodies of disseminated copper, such as this, consist of scattered chalcopyrite and pyrite in hydrothermally altered intrusive or country rock and as a filling in hair-like cracks and in joints. In order to delineate such a zone the geologist should attempt to associate the mineralization with specific joint or fracture sytems, hydrothermal alteration, or rock types. The effects of oxidation should be carefully examined with the possibility in mind of a secondary enrichment zone occurring at the water table.

SILVER-LEAD VEIN

Figure 182A is a map showing a braided vein system with several strands developed in a zone ranging in width from 75 to 115 feet. This zone consists of a number of normal faults successively downthrown in step-like fashion to the west. Fault planes dip from 53 to 76 degrees and the average throw in the volcanic "host" rocks is about 40 feet. The vein system and associated hydrothermal alteration zone are offset by the long post-mineralization fault.

The first step in mapping such an area is to measure and plot one or more columnar sections (Chapter VII) in localities where the rocks are relatively undisturbed by faulting. In the figure, this section consists of an upper dacite flow, intermediate tuffs, and a lower basalt flow. These sections are quite essential in projecting observable features along strike into the vein system. When measuring the sections, and later when mapping, particular attention should be given to the tops and bottoms of flows; sedimentary channel fills of reworked tuffs; mud flows; flow banding; columnar, platy, and other joint systems; slump features; and relative permeabilities of mappable rock units, with the intent of projecting them along "strike" into the vein system. It is commonly the association of one or more of these features with the fracture or vein system that results in rich mineral concentrations.

The vein system itself should be mapped in detail to determine

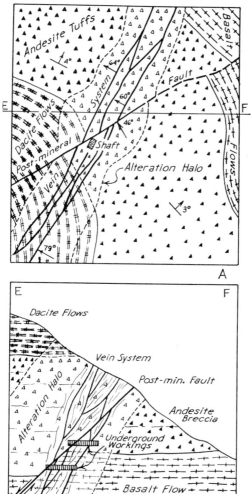

Fig. 182. A. Map showing a braided vein system and the associated hydrothermal halo. B. Underground relationships

if there is any relation between vein width and changes in trend. Of course, the vein materials are carefully sampled to appraise distribution of ores in relation to vein widths and intersections, wall rock alteration, and specific features of the volcanics. High metal content is frequently associated with a specific stratum, silicification and kaolinization, and the wider portions of the vein system.

The fault zone is mapped on the surface and projected into the subsurface. Ordinarily, it is difficult or impossible to observe all important characteristics of faults at the surface, but if surface observations can be correlated with underground workings, the significant features can generally be resolved. Figure 182B illustrates the subsurface relationships between the fault, the vein system, and the volcanics.

223. Underground Mapping Procedure

The principal objective in mapping a vein system in underground workings, such as that discussed in the preceding article, is to establish the specific controls of ore deposition, the extent and rake of ore shoots and post-mineralization fault relationships as an aid in further exploration for new ore shoots and evaluation of ore reserves.

All accessible mine levels, sublevels, stopes, and raises are mapped in detail. Although the plane table is occasionally employed in this work the transit and tape are generally more satisfactory, especially if the mine is wet. Where mining operations are going on, the new workings are added to the maps as a routine matter so that geologic interpretations are kept up to date.

The primary control consists of a transit-tape traverse, established near the center line of the mine workings. Permanent marks are established overhead on the back (roof) in order to avoid obliteration by mining operations. These fixed points are the basis for all sketching and extensions of the survey. The ground (wall) line is determined by measuring outward at right angles from the "center" transit traverse. It is common practice to fasten the tape

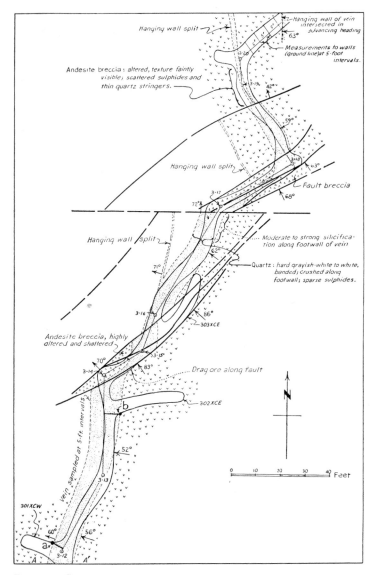

FIG. 183. Complex relationships mapped by transit-tape traverse in underground workings. Permanent survey stations from 3-12 to 3-20 are marked on the back (roof) of the main tunnel. Cross measurements to the wall and ground line are shown between station 3-20 and the mine heading.

at two stations in order to free the men on the survey party to make necessary measurements to features along the walls or to determine the ground line. The intervals at which the distance to the ground line is measured are generally five or ten feet, depending on the accuracy required. The transit line and measurements to the ground line are indicated at the top of Fig. 183.

Underground workings are generally referenced to a coördinate grid system whose point of origin is to the southwest of the workings; thus all locations are designated as so many feet north and east of this point.

The scale of underground maps obviously must be gauged by the complexity of the geology and the detail required. Commonly used scales are one inch to 20 feet and one inch to 40 feet. As a matter of convenience it is good practice to choose a scale that is a common denominator of the surface map.

When the underground maps are completed they can be traced on to note sheets of hard surface paper, $8\frac{1}{2}$ x 11 inches in size, and ruled in one-inch coördinates. These sheets are convenient for geological sketching and preliminary planning of survey extensions. The sectional map fits into an aluminum notebook on the back of which are loops for pencils, scales, and a pencil sharpener. The transferring of map data must be carefully performed so that scaling properties are maintained. Be certain that coördinate lines on the sheets are properly registered over coördinates of the grid on the level maps. Inasmuch as the long dimension of the sheets may be oriented either east-west or north-south, a north arrow, as well as the scale and survey stations, is shown on each sheet.

For underground work the geologist should wear a "hard hat," heavy shoes or boots, and other clothing found satisfactory by those working habitually in mines.

The datum level of underground maps is generally selected at waist or chest height, whichever is more convenient for sketching. All features such as veins, faults, and geologic boundaries are projected on to this imaginary "plane." As suggested previously, locations of points along the walls are determined by measuring at right angles from the tape, as shown at *a* and *b* in Fig. 183. Points located in this manner control the lateral sketching of all geologic features. Features on the back (roof) are projected on to the map datum level according to their inclination. Thus, the only back structures that would project directly downward to the datum plane are those having a 90 degree dip. More commonly, back features project diagonally. In some instances, faults, veins, and similar features are shown outside the ground line, as indicated in Fig. 184.

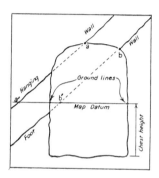

Fig. 184. Diagram illustrating the manner of projecting wall and back features on to the map datum plane. Notice that the footwall appears inside the ground lines at *b'*, and the hanging wall projects outside the ground line at *a'*.

The principle structural framework or skeleton of the map is formed by lines and points representing the most significant geologic or mine features. Details are filled in according to measurements or estimation of positions.

It is common practice in mining geology to indicate the banded character of veins by a series of sweeping pencil lines. The veined zone, as a whole, is carefully located, and details within the zone are sketched in with care; country rock types are indicated by symbol, and supplementary descriptive notes and sample data are lettered along the margins of the map.

Various colors are used to represent types of features (e.g., faults in blue, vein material in red). The depth of color indicates the degree of development of the feature. Practices in the uses of color on maps are not uniform among the companies and institutions concerned with hard rock geology. The exploration geologist should obtain and employ the color symbols desired by the organization which he represents.

224. Geochemical Prospecting In Mineral Exploration

Geochemical prospecting consists of collecting and analyzing soil, rock, plant, sediment, and water samples. In recent years, it has become one of the most valuable tools available to the exploration geologist. The concentrations of metals present are determined and recorded in parts per million or in parts per billion. An appreciable increase in metal content over the average background of the area is suggestive of possible commercial accumulations.

Geochemical prospecting may be used in reconnaissance in the search for mineralized areas or it may be employed as a detailing tool to outline the outcrop limits of a mineralized area beneath a soil cover. In the course of reconnaissance, analyses of stream sediment may point up areas worthy of further investigation, as for example within a particular drainage system. When detailing, soil, plant, and rock analyses are utilized.

Under normal conditions three soil zones are developed in most areas. In Fig. 185, A is a zone of decaying organic material and leaching; B is a zone of accumulation of materials leached from A; and C is partly decayed rock fragments from underlying bedrock.

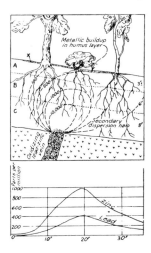

FIG. 185. Metalliferous enrichment of soils from an oxidizing vein. The intensity of the secondary dispersion halo is indicated by "contours" whose values are in parts per million. The graph represents the tenor of the soils in the *B* zone. Notice the down-slope shift of the peak in the graph.

Preliminary studies should be made over the entire area to determine the degree of development and characteristics of these soil zones in order to select samples which will be representative.

In one case the upper *(A)* zone may contain high metal values resulting from the decay of plants or trees whose roots have penetrated to the depth of an oxidizing orebody, and thus be a direct indication of mineralization. In other instances, the increase may be a result of accumulation of metals by plants or trees whose roots penetrate only zones completely devoid of mineralization. They accumulate widely dispersed amounts of metals normally present in all soils. These plants are known as *accumulators* and include such trees as white birch, ash, and alder. Usually, the B zone yields the most reliable and consistent results. Where the upper zone (A in figure) is thick it may be too costly to sample the underlying B zone; in this instance the A zone is sampled. In areas where the buildup of metal content is appreciably above background, sampling of the B horizon is warranted despite the relatively higher costs.

In the figure cited, the dispersion halo, forming outward from the outcrop of the orebody is commonly distorted downslope. Usually, the halo is well developed in B, as will be evident when this zone is sampled. Toward the base of C, the dispersion halo may become narrow toward the oxidizing orebody; therefore, either pattern or random sampling along the bedrock surface might fail to include the small area of enrichment.

Residual soils, or those developed essentially in place, are the most reliable, and should be sought when sampling an area. Transported soils, if they are not recent accumulations, may contain dispersion halos similar to those in residual soils. However, if the transported soils are very recent, time may not have been sufficient to allow for the formation of effective halos. Slump soils may yield an anomaly related to upslope mineralization.

225. Field Methods of Soil Sampling

A survey grid on 100 or 200 foot centers is commonly used in pattern sampling for analysis. If the vein trend is known, the grid should be oriented obliquely to the trend rather than parallel to it, as in Fig. 186. Soil samples are collected at or near each station.

Rock or plant samples may be collected in addition to, or in place of, soil samples if soil conditions are not favorable.

It has been found from experience that fine materials in the soil which pass through an 80-mesh screen generally are representative in the metal content of the entire sample. It is common practice to dry sieve each sample in the field through an 80- or 100-mesh stainless steel or cloth screen, discarding the coarser portion. The sample may be used for the analysis without further crushing or grinding.

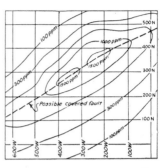

The samples are analyzed for the metal or metals of primary interest. The values in parts per million are plotted and contoured. Areas with values above the aver-

Fig. 186. Geochemical sampling grid and a geochemical anomaly suggesting the presence of a subsurface fault or fracture.

age metal content of the rocks of the region stand out as anomalies, as illustrated in Fig. 186. Intermediate samples at 50, 25, or perhaps even 10 foot centers may be collected and analyzed to establish a more exact pattern of metal distribution.

Apparent geochemical anomalies may result from nonrepresentative sampling or from errors in analyses. It is sometimes difficult to distinguish between an apparent, though erroneous, anomaly and a valid one. For this reason all phases of the geochemical work should be checked. It is generally hazardous to rely solely on the results of geochemistry. Geological and geophysical methods should be employed to bolster the evidence of anomalies derived from geochemical investigations.

226. Rock and Plant Analyses

Geochemical analyses of rocks recovered from diamond drill core holes and exploration headings are quite useful in the detection and evaluation of primary mineralization and hydrothermal halos adjacent to ore bodies. Rock samples taken every foot or at intervals of several feet outward from a vein or an ore body commonly show a percentage increase in certain metalliferous constituents toward the ore body. Figure 187 illustrates the idealized lead and zinc curves resulting from dispersion of these metals outward from a vein or mineralized zone. Rock analyses are most reliable where samples are taken well below the ground water table where oxidation or secondary enrichment a l o n g joints and small fractures will not have obscured the hydrothermal effects.

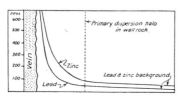

FIG. 187. Graph plotted from geochemical analyses showing the rapid buildup of lead and zinc above the regional background for these metals.

Biochemical or plant analyses are sometimes used with considerable success in determining mineralized localities. Most of these techniques are not yet widely used by mineral exploration geologists, but where conditions are favorable, these methods can contribute much to the general understanding of an area.

227. Types of Chemical Tests

In order to cope with the large number of samples that must be analyzed in mineral exploration, rapid semiquantitative and inexpensive methods of analyses have been devised. These methods are designed to yield useful results at a rate of 30 to 100 analyses per man-day. Specific chemical tests for about 20 different metals have been worked out by the Geochemical Prospecting Laboratory of the U.S. Geological Survey. The chemists and geologists in this laboratory have pioneered in the development of geochemical prospecting in the United States. Further research at this laboratory, at colleges in the United States, Canada, England, and elsewhere, as well as by several large mining companies is aimed at extending the list of specific tests and simplification of techniques.

Generally speaking, geochemical field tests fall into two categories—one is *colorimetric,* the other is a *confined spot.* The colorimetric method involves a separation of a colored metal complex by an immiscible solvent. The spot method consists in concentrating a colored precipitate of the desired metal in a spot, the color intensity of which is a measure of the amount of metal present.

Field kits for analysis of metals in waters, sediments, and soils are available at moderate cost. The analyses are made in the field in a few minutes' time, thus permitting the geologist to follow up interesting leads without delay.

EXAMPLES:

Colorimetric Citrate Soluble Heavy Metals Test

A 0.1 gram sample is placed in a glass stoppered cylinder. Five milliliters of buffer solution, and 1 milliliter of green dithizone solution are added. The cylinder is shaken for 15 seconds and the color noted. If the color is red, more dithizone is added with shaking until the solution is blue. The volume of dithizone solution used to titrate the blue color is proportional to the heavy metals extracted. This type of test is called a cold extraction method because no preliminary sample digestion by hot reagents is necessary, whereas most field tests do require this initial step to take the metals into solution.

Confined Spot Test for Nickel

A 0.1 gram sample is fused with $KHSO_4$ and brought into solution with sodium citrate; the pH and volume are adjusted. A 0.2 milliliter aliquot of the sample solution is placed on a piece of filter paper which is enclosed in the confined spot apparatus. The aliquot is slowly pulled through the filter paper and the colored reaction products are collected on a spot about $\frac{1}{4}$ inch in diameter. The spots are then compared with a standard series of spots of known values prepared in the same manner.

228. Geophysics in Mineral Exploration

Geophysical methods, instruments, and interpretations are too complex for even introductory treatment in this manual. However, the field geologist should acquire some knowledge of the various techniques, for he will often encounter problems that can be solved by no direct geologic approach. It is important for the field man to recognize a situation where some geophysical method can be applied effectively and be able to analyze field relationships with regard to the selection of a particular geophysical method that stands the best chance of providing the required data. A highly successful method for one locality might be of little value in another where geological and physical conditions are quite different.

Geophysics, in conjunction with sound geology, is an extremely important branch of mineral exploration, and the success of many ventures can be credited largely to the intelligent application of one or more geophysical methods. There is little doubt that their applications will be even more extensive in the future.

Of the many devices and methods that might under certain circumstances be useful, all fall in the general classification of magnetic, electrical, gravimetric, and seismic (seismological) in approximately this order of importance.

MAGNETIC METHODS

Magnetic methods employ a number of instruments including the dip needle, Hotchkiss Superdip, and the magnetometer, the last being the most sensitive and widely used. All measure particular variations of the magnetic field of the earth. The ground magnetometer may record either the relative vertical or horizontal components, whereas aerial magnetometers measure the total field.

This method is effective in outlining areas of magnetic intensities greater than regional background or intensities less than background where hydrothermal alteration has destroyed magnetic minerals to give a negative anomaly. This method is widely used to trace dikes and contacts between crystalline rocks and sediments. It is particularly valuable as an aerial tool over bodies of water and for regional studies in inaccessible areas.

ELECTRICAL METHODS

The principal electrical methods used in mineral exploration are self (spontaneous) potential, resistivity, potential drop ratio, and electromagnetics.

Certain rocks in place possess a natural electrical potential; and from measurements of the difference in potential from one point to another specific geologic relationships can be inferred, provided sufficient geologic data are available. This natural property is called the *self potential* of the rocks. When an ore body is oxidizing in the presence of downward percolating ground water, a strong electric field may be created in the immediate vicinity. Such a field will appear as an anomaly with respect to the background, and thus may reveal the presence of a mineralized body. Self potential results are entirely qualitative. Instruments used in this type of work are essentially some form of potentiometer.

Resistivity, the reciprocal of conductivity, has been used for many years as an exploration tool in mineral exploration. Nonmetalliferous rocks free of moisture are nonconductive—highly resistive—to electrical currents. Conversely, rocks high in metals exhibit relatively lower resistivity. Therefore, a measure of the current from one electrode to another, placed in the ground at carefully determined positions, provides an indirect means of determining lithologic anomalies. The depth to which investigations are made is determined by the distance separating the sending and receiving electrodes; therefore, it is possible to estimate the depth and size of a mineral deposit simply by changing the spacing of the electrodes. Resistivity methods are especially useful in layered or stratified rocks of alternating lithologies, if structure is not complex, or where the rocks have a wide conductive contrast.

Electromagnetic methods have been developed rather recently, but they have become an exceedingly useful tool in exploration. Massive sulphide ores are particularly amenable to these methods, because they are conductive. Their primary application is in delineating steeply dipping sulphide ore bodies by using a vertical transmitting loop which induces a current into the body, thus resulting in a secondary field. The total field is measured. The frequency may vary, depending upon the particular type of unit used and the specific geologic relationships. Airborne electromagnetic equipment has been used in recent years with unusual success, especially in Canada, in locating mineralized areas.

GRAVIMETRIC METHODS

Instruments used in gravity measurements are the pendulum, torsion balance, and gravimeter (gravity meter). Only the gravimeter is widely used in exploration.

The gravity meter measures anomalous gravitational attraction. The intensity is dependent principally on spatial disposition of rocks of differing densities. The gravity response to rocks in the subsurface is affected by the depth, the size and shape of the body and by the density contrast between it and the surrounding rocks. This method is most effective in mineral exploration where topographic relief is low and the difference in density of the various rocks is large, and where these rocks having different densities occur within 200 feet of the surface.

SEISMIC METHODS

The seismograph is a large, complex instrument which graphically records the length of time of arrival and character of a shock wave that has been transmitted through rocks below the surface from a point where the shock originates. The wave is generated by an explosive charge set off either above the surface of the ground or in a "shot hole" drilled for the purpose, or the energy may be derived by the dropping of a special heavy weight to the surface of the ground. The compressional waves thus generated radiate downward and outward at velocities that are dependent on physical properties of the rocks. These waves are both reflected and refracted when passing from rocks of one velocity to those of different velocity. Both refracted and reflected waves are utilized, depending upon the type of investigation. Devices called seismometers are placed at specific locations at the surface, where they respond to the returning reflected or refracted wave. The seismometers are synchronized so that their response to the waves is accurately recorded in time by the seismograph on the *seismo-gram* or *seismic record*. The distance that the wave has traveled is then computed from the velocity and time, and the path of the wave in the subsurface is charted accordingly.

The seismic method is useful in determining structure of strati-fied rocks, tracing obscure faults and intrusive bodies, and defin-ing the configuration of the surface of deeply buried bedrock. In some instances the general character of the rocks can be inferred from the character of the waves, but usually this is not possible. Instruments designed for shallow seismic work have been found to be particularly applicable to mineral exploration, whereas instru-ments with greater depth penetration are in general use only in petroleum exploration.

229. Geophysics and Underground Exploration

Most electrical conductive methods are of little use in mine workings because of the large amount of steel and iron in pipes, rails, mine cars, and similar artificial materials. Resistivity can be employed provided all such materials are removed from the area being investigated. Insert units have been used successfully for electromagnetic methods applied in downhole investigations of diamond bore holes. This type of equipment may be used either above or below the surface.

230. Combining Methods

From the foregoing discussions it is evident that different methods yield different types of data. The field geologist seldom has all the information desired for evaluating an area or prospect; so it is advantageous to combine methods where no large increase in cost or time is involved. Geochemistry and various geophysical methods may be combined with little additional effort on the part of the field man. In some cases the use of a second method only serves as a check on the first, but generally there is a net gain in useful information. Figure 188 is an example of combining methods to obtain a more complete appraisal of a promising zone. Several feet of talus covers much of the vein system. A magnetometer is used to delineate the mineralized halo adjacent to the vein. Slightly magnetic pyrite in the vein material and magnetite in volcanics within the alteration halo have lost most of their magnetic properties by the hydrothermal processes. This results in a negative magnetic curve, as shown in Fig. 188B. Results of soil sampling for combined base metals (copper, lead, zinc) along the same traverse are shown in Fig. 188C, indicating a buildup of metal ions in the soil above the outcrop of the vein. Resistivity and self potential methods are used in detailing the vein within the mineralized zone; one serves as a check on the other, as suggested in Fig. 189. Electromagnetics may also be used instead of resistivity, or as a primary method instead of magnetics.

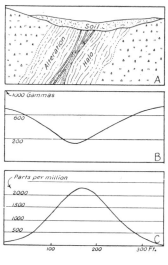

FIG. 188. Diagram illustrating the relationships of magnetic and geochemical responses to a mineralized zone.

Geochemistry may be dovetailed readily with geophysics. This requires but a small amount of the field man's time because the surveyed grid and cross-traverse stations established for the purposes of geophysical methods are utilized in locating sample spots for geochemical analyses. The results of geochemical analyses can be plotted by parts per million on a coördinate graph similar to that used for geophysical profiles so that all the methods of investigation can be compared directly. The major, and possibly minor, veins or mineralized zones may be clearly indicated where peaks or depressions of the various curves coincide.

231. Exploration for Radioactive Minerals

The development of sensitive semiquantitative instruments for the detection of radioactive materials has been greatly accelerated by the growing need for atomic energy. Old instruments have been improved and new ones devised. The two types in wide use are the *Geiger counter*, which measures gamma ray intensity, and the *scintillometer* (or similar instruments), which measures both gamma and beta ray intensities. The Geiger counter is less sensitive to radiation, but it has proved to be quite effective in general exploration for uranium. Scintillation instruments can measure small differences in the intensity of radioactivity, and for this reason, instruments of this type are commonly used for evaluating properties in considerable detail.

Radioactivity emanating from bedrock is dampened or shielded

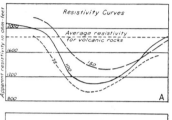
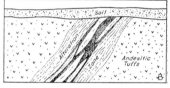
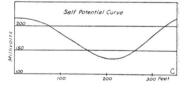

Fig. 189. Diagram showing the relationships of resistivity and self potential curves over a mineralized zone.

by very little overburden. Surface intensity may be reduced to a level below the detection limit of the instruments by only a few inches of alluvium lying on the bedrock. The difficulty is circumvented in the field by the use of probes attached to cables which are lowered into shallow bore holes. This method is used in evaluation work where the exact positions and approximate thicknesses of the radioactive mineralized zones or strata must be determined.

Airborne geophysical instruments, such as scintillation equipment or the magnetometer, are sometimes used in uranium exploration in locating areas of mineralization. Anomalies are then checked on the ground with a scintillometer or Geiger counter.

232. Sampling Mineralized Zones

Mineral exploration consists of several phases, starting with *reconnaissance*, which seeks to subdivide large regions into areas of good and poor prospects; *detailing*, whose objective is to establish geologic relationships and obtain three-dimensional measurements on mineralized zones; and *evaluation*, the purpose of which is to establish the value of ores, cost of exploitation, and the ultimate tonnages that can be mined at a profit. Before the third phase can be attacked it is essential to collect *representative* samples, analyze them, and compute the net extractable metal content. It is clear that errors in sampling are multiplied thousands of times in application to the entire deposit, and it therefore follows that the sampling of rocks and ores must be carried out in a careful and completely objective manner.

Sampling, itself, should be considered as having two objectives which are distinct and only remotely related to each other. The first is the sampling for *geologic* information. This type of sampling is guided by geologic conditions and it seeks to clarify geologic relationships. The second objective is economic, and its objective is to accurately represent the richness and leanness of rocks that must be mined or processed. The most difficult task for the geologist is to maintain an unbiased attitude and to guard against the natural inclination to select the richest specimens rather than the typical.

Ore bodies and mineralized zones, as intimated earlier, are characteristically irregular, both in outline and in richness. For this reason the plan distribution of sample points must be determined by field relationships, not by some preconceived pattern. In other words, where the apparent quality of material varies abruptly or where geologic features are complex the density of sample points must be higher than in those localities where conditions are more uniform.

The average density of sampling (number of samples per unit area) is usually determined by the accuracy required or the time available for the work. Where the richness of the ores varies radically within small areas, an extremely large number of specimens would be required to obtain a reproducible evaluation within a small margin of error, and the expense of such sampling would probably be prohibitive. In the final analysis, it is the judgment and experience of the geologist that should determine sampling procedures.

233. Methods of Sampling

Types of ore and mineralized rock sampling are designated *channel, chip, muck pile, car,* and *core* or *drill cuttings.*

Channel sampling consists in cutting channels into fresh rock across outcrops or underground exposures at selected intervals. The exposed rock is first prepared by removing the bulk of weathered portions. Fine crushed material can be removed by washing or sweeping with a stiff-bristled brush. Next, two parallel lines are marked along the course. These lines serve as guides for cutting out the sample material. Instead of a double line, a single one may be more convenient and a wooden block cut to the desired dimensions is used for maintaining a constant width. A more or less standard size of channel sample is three inches in width and one inch in depth. It is necessary to exercise some care in holding to these dimensions in order to insure adequate representation of the outcrop.

Channel samples may be taken normal to the vein or grain as a composite to represent all bands, or as separate samples for each band or mineralized zone. The composite samples provide material for bulk analysis and appraisal and samples of selected bands represent more clearly the associations of ores and gangue materials. Figure 190 is a comparison of the two procedures.

Inasmuch as a channel may cross one vein at right angles and another obliquely, the three-inch strip would be disproportionately long for the latter, and the final analysis would be correspondingly erroneous. Therefore, the actual widths of the veins should be determined and the amount of material collected should be ad-

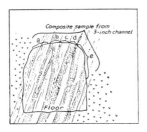

justed accordingly. The sample obtained from interval *e* of Fig. 190 should be reduced to two thirds because of the oblique angle of sampling.

The spacing of channels is a matter that must be decided according to circumstances. Although five-foot intervals is common practice, the spacing may be anything from one foot to ten feet, depending upon the uniformity of the mineralization.

Fig. 190. Composite and individual samples from a channel.

Channel sampling is laborious and expensive, and for this reason the method should be employed only where necessary to obtain the required accuracy.

Chip sampling, as the name implies, consists in obtaining chip specimens from the rock along a line or on a grid system. This method is rapid; hence, it is widely used in reconnaissance or semidetail work. Chip sampling provides a fair appraisal of the general distribution of minerals, but is not sufficiently representative for quantitative computations of minable reserves of ore or ultimate metal recovery. Despite these shortcomings, sampling of this kind, if properly carried out, will indicate where and how the more tedious channel sampling should be done.

Muck pile sampling is simply the collection of representative specimens from piles of ore that have been knocked down in the course of mining operations. Scoops of ore are taken at random, placed in a box, and then quartered. This is one of the oldest methods of sampling, and good results can be expected, especially when the ore is friable and finely divided.

Car (or chute) sampling is similar to muck pile sampling. Scoops of ore are taken from each mine car while in transit to the mill, or the sample may be taken from the chute. Samples from each active stope may be segregated so that the average grade of ore from different workings may be determined. This form of sampling is commonly used by mine operators. Samples collected by automatic devices at the mill are called *mill head* samples. These samples serve the purpose of checking averages obtained by car or chute sampling at the mine. Car and chute sampling is of greater use to mine operators than to the exploration geologist; but there are circumstances where this method is applicable to exploration work.

Diamond and *churn drill hole* sampling is widely accepted as an exploration and evaluation method. Various procedures and location layouts are employed. In areas marginal to ore bodies both cores from diamond drilling or cuttings from churn drilling, and the sludge are assayed at regular intervals, such as two or five feet. When the prospective ore body is intersected it is usual to sample each band or zone irrespective of the intervals. Sludge containing very fine rock debris from the hole is collected in cans, allowed to settle, and the water poured off. Or, the sludge stream can be routed through a sample box having a series of baffle strips on the bottom behind which the sample material settles.

Bore hole samples are subject to certain deficiencies. Water lost during drilling may carry away fine fractions of the rock, and this might either increase or decrease the assay values, depending on the type of material lost. A similar loss may occur in sampling of the sludge. Contamination may occur through sloughing of weak portions of wall into the hole.

234. Sampling Tools

Personal preferences enter into the selection of sampling tools, but generally the following pieces will suffice: A piece of drill steel 1 to 1½ inches in diameter, 6 to 18 inches in length, and tapered to a point; a "single jack," which is a short-handled sledge hammer weighing about three pounds; and an ordinary geologist's or prospector's pick. Two or three heavy cold chisels ground with short bevels may be useful in scoring rock surfaces for breaking out with heavier tools.

Depending on the scale of operations, sampling is performed by two to six men. Where the rocks are especially hard the samplers work in pairs, alternating the work and rest periods. Samples are usually collected and carried in a wooden box, though heavy canvas bags are also used. It is well to have a piece of canvas to lay out beneath the sample spot when channeling. The canvas catches much material that would otherwise be lost. Of course one must guard against extraneous materials falling on to the canvas.

235. Labeling Samples and Recording Data

Individual samples are usually put into canvas bags, tied, and carefully labeled. Any sample whose identity has been lost or obscured is worthless; hence the labeling of bags is extremely important. The safest procedure is to attach one tag securely to the bag and place a duplicate inside the bag. Various methods of marking have been tested under varying conditions. As a general guide, it should be kept in mind that loss of identity is caused by (1) obscuring the label by rubbing against some object or material; (2) wetting, which may blur or completely wash off the markings; (3) smearing by mud or grease; and (4) loss of the tag itself. Whatever method of labeling is used, precautions should be taken against these hazards. Experience and special tests indicate the following.

TAGS

Tags used on the outside of sample containers should be made from water-resistant materials, such as specially treated high rag stock paper, plastic, or metal. The material must also retain identifying marks despite rubbing or wetting.

ATTACHMENT

The tags should be attached to the sample by strong cord or soft wire. If wire is used with paper tags, care must be taken that the tag is not cut by the wire.

MARKING MEDIUM

Hard graphite pencil marks withstand repeated wetting; however they are liable to become dim and difficult to read with slight abrasion. "Ball point" pen marks withstand both wetting and abrasion, but they are difficult to use on paper that has been treated to resist moisture. Neither pencil nor ball point pen is satisfactory on plastic or metal tags. Waterproof black drawing ink is excellent when used on absorbent paper, but washes off nonabsorbent surfaces. Drawing inks are inconvenient for field use. Wax-base crayon or "china marking" crayons are highly resistant to both wetting and abrasion. They are convenient to carry and use in the field, but since they cannot be sharpened to fine points the lines are coarse, and this necessitates large labels. These wax- (or oil-) base crayons can also be used on plastic and metal.

Sample data are recorded in a notebook by letter or number according to the system used on the tags. Booklets for this purpose are available on the market. These booklets are similar to a check book in that they contain tear-out tags and stubs which are retained in the book. Identical data are recorded on the tag and stub. After assaying, the results may be entered on the stubs.

Sketches of the vein or mineralized area showing the relative locations of samples in the channel can be made in the field book or on tag stubs to further guard against possible confusion.

236. Reduction of Sample Volume

Samples weighing one to five pounds are customary. If the initial sample exceeds this size it is reduced by a process called *quartering*. The sample is put on a piece of canvas or any smooth, clean surface and divided into four approximately equal portions. Two opposite samples are combined to make up a new sample; i.e., the four quarters are recombined to make two new samples, one of which is sent to the assayer, the other being kept for future reference. The process of quartering may be carried out to any degree, depending on the size of the initial sample and the size of sample needed for assaying. Mechanical samplers do this job effectively and rapidly.

In order to get an equable distribution of materials, the initial sample is first crushed to a maximum chip size of about 1/8 inch (for samples of one to five pounds). Small portable crushers are available at supply houses. Reducing hard rock to small chip size by pounding with a hammer or sledge is a time-consuming and laborious task, though it is necessary to resort to this means when samples are prepared for shipments far from the operating base.

237. Calculation of Ore Reserves

One means of classifying reserves of ore in a mine is to list the reserves as proved, probable, and possible. The first is blocked out by mine workings on all sides, the second, usually by levels above and below, and the third by one level and favorable geologic relationships.

In order to estimate the tonnage and grade in each block, the widths of veins and assay values of the samples must be averaged together. If the assay interval is uniform and the vein width is constant, the values are totaled and divided by the number of samples. If the widths vary it is necessary to weight each sample as follows:

Sample Number	Width in Feet	Assay (% of Lead)	Width × Assay
1	6.1	8.4%	51.24
2	4.3	5.2%	22.36
3	7.8	9.4%	73.32
4	5.2	6.2%	32.24
	23.4		179.16

$$\frac{23.4}{4} = 5.85 \text{ feet (average width)}$$

$$\frac{179.16}{23.4} = 7.65 \text{ (average percent of lead)}$$

The total of the widths in feet is divided by four, the number of samples used to determine the average width. The total of the widths in feet is divided into the total of the product of widths times assay value to determine the average percent of lead present.

If the width of the ore is less than the required mining width, considerable submarginal or barren rock may be broken along with the ore. In this case the sample across the barren rock may be averaged with the ore samples, as shown in the preceding table, or this rock may be considered as containing no significant values and therefore a dilution in proportion to the width.

Where the sample interval is not uniform, the intervals, representing the total of half the distance on either side of each sample to the adjacent samples, are multiplied by the widths of the vein, totaled, and divided into the widths times the intervals times the assay values to obtain the grade. The average width is derived by multiplying widths times intervals, totalling, and dividing by the interval total, as shown in the following table.

	Width	Interval	Width × Interval	Assay	Width × Interval × Assay
1	3.6'	7.0'	25.2	6.2%	156.24
2	4.9'	5.7'	27.9	8.3%	231.57
3	6.4'	10.3'	65.9	12.1%	797.39
	14.9'	23.0'	119.0		1185.20

$$\text{Average width} = \frac{119}{23} = 5.17$$

$$\text{Average grade} = \frac{1185}{119} = 9.9\% \text{ lead}$$

The individual bands within a channel cut may be sampled separately. If so, they are averaged together before the channel samples are combined and averaged.

Tonnages of ore are calculated by multiplying the square feet in an ore reserve block by the average width. This volume in cubic feet is converted to tons according to the weight per cubic foot, which in turn depends on the specific gravity of the material. A ton of sulphide ore is approximately 10 cubic feet; quartz vein material about 12, phosphate rock about 14, and coal about 25 cubic feet.

If metric tons are desired in a foreign operation the volume in cubic meters is divided by the specific gravity to obtain tonnage.

238. Calculation of Tonnage by Drilling

Thick, bedding replacement, or other flat-lying ore bodies may be sampled by vertical drill holes. If the holes are drilled on a uniform grid with equally spaced holes the average grade is obtained by multiplying the thicknesses times the grade and dividing the total of this product by the total of the thicknesses.

Another method of determining the tonnage and grade is to construct a series of cross sections through parallel rows of holes. The total cubic feet in the orebody is established by totalling the intervals between cross sections, if the intervals are equal, or the sum of half the distances between adjoining sections, and multiplying by the average area of the cross sections; or, the cubic feet may be calculated between each pair of cross sections, and totaled.

239. Placer Deposits

Preceding discussions have dealt with mineral deposits formed more or less in place. Placer deposits of economic metalliferous materials differ from others fundamentally in that the area of origin may be situated far from the deposit. Water transportation of the materials forming the deposit is a basic factor in segregation and accumulation, and search for placer prospects must be predicated on this fact. Inasmuch as placer deposits are the result of sedimentation processes, the problems of exploration should be approached from the viewpoint of the sedimentologist, and in this particular instance, the background preparation can be narrowed down to studies of topography, hydrology, and the basic principles of hydraulics.

It might be necessary in preliminary studies of a region to consider the topics referred to with regard to present and past conditions. Many important placer deposits occur in plains regions where there is little or nothing at the surface to suggest their presence. Under these conditions the core drill and geophysical methods are employed, but in either case the most effective application of these tools must depend to a large extent on the directing geologist's ability to interpret sparse, scattered data in terms of paleotopography and paleohydrology and the mineral and rock assemblages present in the region.

Surface placer prospecting is simpler and more direct than subsurface. Drainage patterns, stream gradients, the areal geology of headwaters regions, and various topographic features should be examined in detail. For preliminary regional work topographic and geologic maps and air photographs are invaluable. In the study of maps, or direct observations of ground conditions, the following topics should be given especial attention.

(1) The segregation of certain minerals and rocks in a placer deposit is controlled primarily by the specific gravity of the material and/or the relative sizes and shapes of the grains. It is quite common to find placer gold associated with magnetite, hematite, and ilmenite (all having high specific gravities), and coarse sands or gravels composed largely of quartz, quartzite, and other low specific gravity materials. In other words, in a hydraulic system small grains of high specific gravity will be deposited with larger grains of low specific gravity. Knowing the kinds of rocks and minerals common in the region, the normal associations can quickly be determined in the field.

(2) Wherever the velocity of a sediment-laden stream is materially reduced, a part of the load (heavy minerals and large grains) will be deposited. Reduced transporting capacity occurs at sharp bends, wide channels, and gentle bed gradients; therefore, these are the places to observe carefully.

Paleotopographic surfaces and buried stream courses may be destroyed by a later stage of *geomorphic* development. For this reason, it is important to correlate geomorphic events. Some recent placer deposits may also be second-cycle in origin; i.e., derived from the materials of older placers. This type of deposit is related to recent topography, but the ultimate volume of economic minerals is entirely dependent on the size of the original deposits.

240. Economic Aspects of Placer Deposits

The geologist's work is not completed when a placer deposit is discovered. Although the final appraisal of a deposit may be made by engineers, tentative, yet reasonably accurate, estimates should be made by the geologist before leaving the area. In estimating the worth of a prospect, the following should be considered.

RICHNESS OF THE MATERIAL

This can be roughly approximated by estimating the total volume of material to be moved to obtain a certain volume of mineral concentrate. If gold, silver, platinum, or similar minerals are the objective, they will generally be found in the "fines" of the aggregate. The fines are separated by panning. If water is not available, the fine material may be obtained by dry *sieving*. Several locations in the deposit should be sampled.

TOTAL VOLUME

The total recoverable volume of material should be estimated. In the following article a method for precisely measuring volumes is described. This method would not be applicable before accurate topographic maps are available, but the basic principles involved can be applied in a general way.

OVERBURDEN

The rich portions of placers often occur only in lower bands, but the worthless overburden must be removed in order to expose the metalliferous sands. The thickness and approximate volume of the worthless upper deposits should be estimated.

WATER SUPPLIES

The available water supply should be investigated for possible use in mining operations. The volume of flow can be gauged approximately as follows. Select a straight stretch of the stream 50 to 100 feet long and measure its average velocity in feet per second by timing a floating chip of wood along a measured interval on the bank. Next, measure depths along a string stretched at right angles to the two banks across the stream. The intervals at which depth measurements are made may be 1, 2, 5, or 10 feet apart, depending on the size the stream, the regularity of the bottom, and the accuracy desired. From these measurements, draw an accurate cross section of the stream from the bottom to the water surface. Now, by planimeter or triangles and scale (see following article) determine the cross sectional area in square feet.

The volume of flow in second-feet is this area times the velocity. Because the middle surface waters of a stream move faster than edge or bottom waters, it is common practice in making estimations of flow to reduce the calculated volume by 10 to 20 percent. If considerable accuracy is required, measurements should be made at several places where depths, widths, and velocities differ.

241. Volumes of Irregular Bodies

A rough approximation of the volume of material contained in a placer deposit, mine dump, or other irregular body can be obtained from a *planimetric* map of the boundary and a few measurements of thickness; but unless a large number of depth (or thickness) points is used, the final results may be seriously in error. A better method for measuring volume employs maps made specifically for this purpose.

An isopach map is a map on which contours, or *isopachs,* are lines connecting points of equal thickness. From such a map very accurate determinations of volume can be made.

Figure 191 is an isopach map of an *alluvial* deposit. The control points are auger holes bored to bedrock and located by plane table. As is evident, the isopachs are drawn by *interpolation* be-

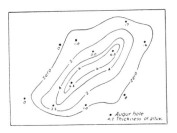

tween control points. The thick axis in the central portion of the map is caused by a stream channel in the bedrock. When the isopach map is completed, the volume of the alluvial deposit is determined as follows:

With a polar *planimeter* measure the area enclosed by the zero isopach (the boundary of the deposit). Next, measure the area within the 2-foot isopach.

FIG. 191. Isopach map controlled by auger holes and pits through the alluvial deposit.

The volume of aluvium between these two isopachs is:

$$V_1 = \text{First area} + \text{Second area} \times \frac{Isopach\ (contour)\ interval}{2}$$

The next step is to measure the area within the 4-foot isopach. The volume of material between the 2-foot and 4-foot isopachs is:

$$V_2 = \text{Second area} + \text{Third area} \times \frac{Isopach\ interval}{2}$$

Proceed in this manner for each isopach. The total volume is:

$$\text{Total volume} = V_1 + V_2 + V_3, \text{etc.}$$

For more rapid, though less accurate, determinations, alternate isopachs may be used, but one must be careful that the correct isopach interval is used in calculations, thus:

$$V = \text{Area within 0 isopach} + \text{Area within 4-foot isopach} \times \frac{2 \times 2}{2}$$

A planimeter may not be available to the field geologist, in which case areas are subdivided into rectangles and right triangles by means of drafting triangles. These geometric figures are scaled and the areas computed accordingly. Figure 192 shows an irregular area subdivided for scaling. It can be seen that the largest possible rectangles are drawn first, then the largest possible triangles. Marginal triangles are placed so that the meandering boundary will equalize (by inspection) small areas falling outside and inside these marginal figures.

Where unconsolidated deposits rests on a moderately regular bedrock surface, the isopach map is derived by a procedure different from that discussed earlier.

Figure 193A is a topographic map of a mine tailings dump. The problem is to determine the volume of unconsolidated material resting on the bedrock surface. In B of the

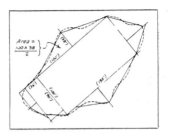

Fig. 192. Subdivision of an irregular area by means of a straight-edge and a drafting triangle.

figure, contours on the exposed bedrock surface are sketched by inference beneath the dump. The margin of loose material is indicated by the dotted line. The thickness of tailings is indicated at every point where a topographic contour on the dump intersects a projected contour beneath. Thus, at point a, the higher contour has an elevation of 960 feet and the lower, 900 feet; therefore, the thickness of the dump at this point is 60 feet. It is apparent that this map contains all data necessary for the construction of an isopach map.

Fasten a piece of tracing paper over the map having projected contours, and plot a point at each contour intersection. Obtain thicknesses by subtraction, as stated, and draw the isopachs as shown in C of the figure. Volumes are now determined from the tracing in the manner described earlier.

The volumes obtained by these methods are obtained in cubic feet. To reduce to cubic yards, simply divide by 27. If tonnage is required it is necessary to know the average specific gravity of the material *as it exists in place*. This may be determined by carefully

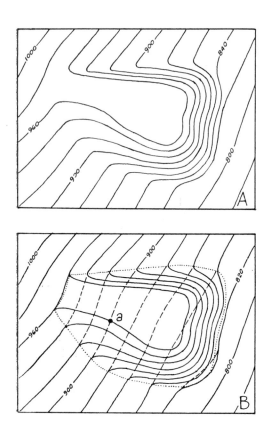

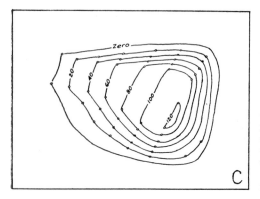

Fig. 193. A. Topographic map of a mine tailings dump. B. Contours are projected beneath the dump material to approximate the concealed ground surface. C. Contour intersections obtained from B provide the control for the isopach map.

laying off an area, say, 4 square feet, cutting out and saving the material to a given depth, and weighing the material removed. In other words, the volume is determined by the size of the hole, not by measuring the disturbed spoil. A large diameter auger may be used in the same way. The volume of an irregular pit can also be determined by filling it with a measured quantity of loose dry sand.

$$\text{Weight per cubic yard} = \text{pounds per cubic foot} \times 27$$

$$\text{Cubic yards per ton} = \frac{2000}{\text{Weight per cubic yard}}$$

In foreign countries where the metric system is used, areas are determined in square meters and contour intervals are in meters.

CHAPTER IX

Subsurface Methods

242. Introductory Remarks

Subsurface geology (structural and stratigraphic), derives its name from the fact that data employed are obtained principally from wells. It should be emphasized that subsurface geology is only an extension of surface (field) geology into a realm of investigation in which the methods are different but the objectives are the same. Too often the geologist confines his interest and efforts to either surface or subsurface work without regard to the advantages that the other may offer. Few geologists familiar with both surface and subsurface methods would ignore either in an area where both phases of investigation are practicable.

In a general sense, though there are notable exceptions, outcrops provide areal control for maps, and wells provide depth control. This is not always true, however, for much depends on the topography, area of rock exposure, and complexity of structure on the one hand; and the depth, density, and distribution of wells and the method of bore hole sampling on the other. For the purpose of comparison, certain attributes of data obtained by both methods are given in the tabulation on pages 385-386, but it should be made clear that there are many exceptions to the generalizations presented.

It is clear that the geologist can learn much more about the geology of any region by studying the formations at both outcrops and in wells than he could by limiting his work to only one method.

Geophysical methods, employing the seismograph, gravity meter, magnetometer and similar instruments, are essentially subsurface. However, the physical principles on which they are based, the complexities in their application, and means of interpretation of data obtained constitute a type of geologic investigation too complex and extensive for consideration in this book. Similarly, an exhaustive treatment of electric, magnetic, and radioactivity logging is impracticable because of space limitations. For these reasons, the remainder of this chapter is devoted to methods especially useful to the geologist who would broaden the area and technical scope of surface work.

	Outcrops	*Wells*
Stratigraphic relationships	Observable features are characters of strati-graphic contacts	Contacts, bedding, cross-bedding, unconformities can be seen only within diame-ters of cores or inferred from cuttings
	Regularity of bedding	Cross-bedding
	Interfingering, pinchouts	Interfingering or pinchouts inferred from well-to-well correlation
	Relationships of super-position	Superposition of thin beds ob-servable only in cores
Lithologic properties of sediments	Colors commonly result of weathering	Colors commonly original
	Soluble minerals often leached out	Soluble minerals usually (though not always) present
	Many minerals suscepti-ble to oxidation	Oxidation of deposited minerals not common
	Porosity and permea-bility of rocks un-reliable	Porosity and permeability from cores more representa-tive
	Degree of induration not always depend-able as being char-acteristic of the for-mation below surface	Induration usually representa-tive

	Outcrops	*Wells*
Structural relations	Accuracy of dip and strike dependent only on quality of bedding or surficial distortion (slumping)	Dip and strike determinate only for diameter of core or hole (with dip-meter). Subject to errors of recording and deviation of bore
	Faults observable	Faults determinate only by comparison with other logs
	Flexures and other features directly observable in outcrops not correlatable over wide areas	Flexures and other structural features between wells are indicated only by elevations of correlatable horizons drilled
Formation fluids	Usually not present	Obtained by various methods (drill stem tests, swabbing, pumping, or flow)
	When present (as in seeps) often greatly altered and not representative of characters even at shallow depths	Physically and chemically representative in most cases
	Degree of saturation indeterminate	Degree of saturation is measurable

243. Relations of Well Cuttings and Drilling Methods

Two basic methods of drilling are in common use, and it is essential to understand the principles of each in order to correctly interpret the rock samples cut by the bit.

The *cable tool,* or percussion, drilling rig is the older method. This type of rig drills by impact, and in the process of penetrating the formations, it pounds, chisels, and crushes the rocks. For this reason, the material brought to the surface for analysis is normally in a finely disaggregated or pulverized state.

The cable tool drill is a fluted steel billet varying in diameter from 3 inches to 18 inches or more, and in length from 4 to 8 feet. The "cutting" end of the drill is a very broad V-shaped chisel. The upper end is threaded for attachment to the drill stem, which is a steel bar somewhat smaller in diameter than the drill, and many times longer. The drill stem helps to maintain a straight hole and provides the weight for driving the drill into the rocks. A steel cable fastened to the drill stem lifts the bit assembly a few feet and by a "walking beam" or similar mechanical arrangement at the surface, permits the drill to drop to the bottom of the hole. Because of a torque put in the drilling line by the driller, the bit rotates slightly on each stroke. Water or thin mud is lowered into the hole in a bailer and freshly cut fragments are mixed into the fluid by the churning action of the drill. When a few feet of new hole is made, the bit is withdrawn from the hole by winding the drilling line on a large reel. The bailer is then lowered into the hole, agitated in the fluid at the bottom of the hole to remix the cuttings, and then is withdrawn to the surface with a load of cuttings and drilling mud.

The bailer is dumped into a box which leads into the "slush pit." Samples of the cuttings are collected from the box, washed, dried, and placed in bags or envelopes, which bear the identity and location of the well and the depth interval represented.

As stated earlier, cable tool samples are usually quite finely ground, and for this reason, some of the grosser characters of the rocks are destroyed. As a rule, very large fragments appearing in the samples are knocked from the wall by the whipping action of the drilling line or by the bailer gouging into the wall. These large pieces should be ignored when analyzing the cuttings. Some of the up-hole cavings eventually reach the bottom of the hole where they are ground under the bit and mixed with freshly cut material. These cavings are difficult to distinguish from the representative cuttings.

It is common practice to run casing rather frequently in cable tool wells because there is no other means of preventing collapse of the hole. For this reason there is no great amount of uncased hole above the bit at any time; so any cavings which do occur in the sample come from a rather short distance above the bit.

The *rotary* method of drilling is entirely different in principle from cable tool drilling, and the cuttings, likewise, differ materially.

The rotary bit consists of three or four rotating cutters or cones similar in appearance to conical gears. These cutters are mounted on a short steel cylindrical billet with vents through which drilling fluid is continuously ejected to wash the cone teeth and remove the rock cuttings. The tool joints are very heavy walled pipe to which the bit is attached. The drill pipe (stem) is screwed on to the tool joints at the bottom and to a squared pipe at the top which is called the "Kelley." The "Kelley" passes through a square hole in the rotary table on the derrick floor so that it rotates when power is applied to the rotary table. A flexible "mud line" is attached to the upper end of the "Kelley." The mud line leads to "mud" pumps where drilling fluid (a compounded mud) is pumped from the mud pit and forced through the drill pipe assembly under considerable pressure. The mud passes out through the vents in the bit and returns to the surface in the annulus between the drill pipe and the wall of the hole, carrying a continuous load of cuttings from the bottom of the hole. Cuttings are removed from the mud stream either by passing over a vibrating screen called a shale shaker or by settling to the bottom of a mud pit.

Samples of the cuttings are collected from either the shale shaker or from a special sample box (a trough) through which a portion of the discharge stream is diverted.

The boring of a hole by a rotary (rock) bit is essentially a chipping action. The chisel-like teeth on the bit cones roll on the bottom of the hole under the great weight of the tool joints and drill pipe, and the effect is to flake off the hard rock in tabular pieces ranging in size from $\frac{1}{4}$ to $\frac{3}{4}$ inches and from $\frac{1}{16}$ to $\frac{1}{4}$ inch in thickness, depending on certain characters of the rocks and other factors.

The drilling mud builds up a thin, tough layer on the walls of the hole, thus preventing the wall from caving. However, for a number of reasons, this layer may occasionaly fail and permit up-hole materials to enter the annulus and mix with the freshly cut materials. These cavings are collected along with representative cuttings, thus complicating the microscopist's interpretations.

244. Sample Intervals

The samples from rotary wells drilled by oil companies are usually taken for five- or 10-foot depth intervals, though the practice is by no means uniform. When more detail in the stratigraphy is required, the sample interval may be as small as one foot. When cable tools are used, samples are taken whenever the bailer is run into the hole; and since this operation is governed largely by drilling conditions, the interval is seldom uniform.

245. Discrepancies in Representation

Well samples normally are not strictly representative of the strata from which they were derived, and a literal logging of all lithologies present is bound to result in many errors. The microscopist is obliged to *interpret* the cuttings in the light of his knowledge of the stratigraphy of the area, the behavior of certain rocks or formations when subjected to the drill, and the characteristics of cuttings from rotary and cable tool rigs.

A sample of cuttings from a 10-foot sample interval may contain chips of sandstone, shale, and two distinct types of limestone, or any other combination of lithologies. These lithologies may be described in the utmost detail, but it is not possible to determine with certainty the relative positions of the strata within the interval. Electric and other types of "mechanical" logging, discussed later, may provide the necessary clues. From a general acquaintance with the formations of the region, as observed in surface work, it may be known that the normal sequence is, from the base upward, sandstone, clastic limestone, shale, and crystalline limestone; therefore, when logging these lithologies, they would be placed in the same relative positions.

Certain rock types are more subject to caving than others, yet no fast generalization in this matter can be made because a given type will react differently where subsurface conditions vary. For example, the degree of induration of a sandstone or the cementing material may control its caving properties. The most common lithologies contaminating samples are fissile shales, or shales containing bentonite or salt; poorly lithified claystone, gypsum and anhydrite; or other rock types containing large percentages of these minerals. Faulting or intense fracturing of the formations may cause them to cave and reappear in samples far below the point where they were penetrated.

As mentioned earlier, cable tool samples are usually much more finely ground than rotary samples. In general there is less caving in a cable tool hole but when caving does occur it may be more difficult to detect because the material is ground under the bit so that it is similar to the freshly cut rock. In contrast, a rotary hole, whose walls are held only by the mud filter cake, may yield extraneous materials at any time and from any place; but rotary cavings usually occur as large, irregular pieces, or if the rock is soft, as large much-rounded fragments. With some experience the microscopist is able to distinguish cavings from representative cuttings.

Depending on the characters of the formations drilled, the samples from cable tool holes may be somewhat out of balance in so far as the relative percentages of different lithologies present are concerned. For example, in the drilling of a series of interbedded sandstones and shales, the shales are likely to be so finely pulverized that they become an integral part of the mud, which is washed away when the "box" samples are washed. The resulting dried samples will contain too high a percentage of sandstone.

246. Extraneous Materials

In addition to cavings, discussed in the preceding article, other materials appearing in well cuttings are constantly posing problems for the microscopist. Identification and elimination of these materials is an important part of sample examination.

SURFACE CONTAMINATION

Unless the sample box or collecting board on the shale shaker is cleaned each time a sample is collected, a certain amount of mixing of cuttings from one interval to the next is almost certain to occur. The geologist seldom knows how carefully the samples are collected, but he should be alert to the possibility of contamination above ground. Similarly, gravel, sand, and other soil or rock particles may inadvertently be put into the sample envelope.

DRILLING FLUIDS

Drilling fluid is a compounded mud; that is, a wide variety of compounds and finely ground natural rocks and minerals are added to the fluid to produce desired characteristics. These additives have often been logged erroneously as drilled material. Some of the minerals commonly used in drilling are barite, bentonite, gypsum, anhydrite, lime, salt, and oxides of iron. When such materials appear persistently in the samples, especially in association with different kinds of rocks, the presence of dried drilling mud should be suspected. Information on the composition of the mud can usually be obtained from the operator or contractor who drilled the well.

When drilling fluids are lost into porous rocks, coarse, fibrous or bulky materials are added to close the pores and thus prevent further loss. Woody additives, such as cotton seed hulls, corn stalk fiber, and the like, are readily recognized under the microscope; but cellophane flakes and other organic compounds may simulate certain minerals like mica or selenite. Simple tests will quickly reveal their identity; for example, all the organic materials will burn when held in forceps over a match flame.

Sometimes drilling fluids have an oil or oil emulsion base. Samples recovered from these muds will be oil-stained; therefore, those rocks which actually bear oil are difficult to differentiate in the cuttings. Persistent oil-staining should be sufficient reason for inquiry into the type of drilling fluid used. Iron oxide, sometimes used for "weighting" the drilling fluid, tends to stain the cuttings a red or russet color. Break the chips to ascertain that the color is present throughout the rock.

CEMENT

Portland and other special kinds of cements are used in wells to stop lost circulation of drilling fluid, influx of bothersome water from formations, and to set casing. After cement has been used, a considerable quantity will appear in the cuttings. There are few microscopists who have not at one time logged cement as limestone, marl, chalk, or some similar rock type; for it is difficult for the novice to recognize differences and equally difficult to explain how to distinguish one from the other. Generally, the cements contain a liberal sprinkling of minute black specks and lack crystallinity or any observable granularity under low or intermediate magnification. Again, a drilling record of the well is the best safeguard.

STEEL SHAVINGS

Hard sandstones, cherts, or cherty carbonates gouge small particles of steel from the drill bit. These minute grains soon rust and sometimes stain a large portion of the sample, thus contributing to erroneous interpretation of lithologies. The steel shavings are quickly removed by first laying a piece of paper over the dry cuttings and then passing a strong horseshoe-type magnet over the paper. The paper and magnet are moved away as a unit, then the magnet is lifted and the shavings fall. The paper prevents the particles from clinging to the magnet.

OIL STAINS

It is difficult to determine all the lithic characters of a rock that is thoroughly saturated with petroleum. Oil not only changes the color of the rock, but also interferes with certain physical and chemical tests. Most of the residual oil in cuttings can be removed by first soaking and then agitating in solvents such as ether, acetone, or uncolored gasoline. Great care must be exercised when using any of these solvents as all are highly inflammable.

DUST COATING

Dry chips are sometimes completely covered with very fine dust so that the surfaces appear earthy under the microscope. Such samples are quite difficult to describe. Spread a large piece of wrapping paper on the floor and set an electric fan at one end. Take a small amount of the cuttings at a time and lightly rub between the palms of the hands, and let the chips fall slowly on to the paper through the air stream. The dust blows away, leaving the chips immediately in front of the fan relatively clean.

MUD COATING

Improperly washed cuttings from a rotary rig may have a thin coating of drilling mud. After the mud has dried, it is not easily removed. The cuttings should be soaked in water a few minutes, agitated, and then dried before microscopic examination. Drying can be hastened if the cuttings are spread evenly on an absorbent material, such as paper toweling.

247. Descriptions of Well Cuttings

The characters of rocks as seen under the microscope or interpreted from various tests differ considerably from those observed in the field. Grain sizes can be measured more accurately, lighting is more uniform, acid reactions are more definitive, and minute structures are apparent. For these reasons, it is sometimes difficult to correlate a microscopic description with one made on the outcrop where conditions of observation are radically different. When correlation from subsurface to surface rocks is important, yet difficult, it becomes necessary to treat samples collected in the field in the same manner as those obtained from wells. In other words, the field specimens are examined under microscope in the laboratory, and the characters sought and described are the same as those predominating in well sample determinations.

The manner in which specimens should be described is a subject of some dispute, and the limitations of space here do not permit a discussion of different preferences. The following sequential order of characters is widely accepted because it has a few practical advantages when used on graphic logs. This presentation is based on what is commonly accepted as the important visible attributes of each group of sedimentary rocks.

Coarse clastics
    Name (sandstone, conglomerate, graywacke)
    Grain size and shape, constitution of grains, degree of induration, cementing material, color, microstructure.
    Example: Sandstone—0.1 mm to 0.3 mm, quartz with trace of orthoclase, biotite, hard and dense, clay cement, pink and light gray mottled, laminae 0.2 inch.

Fine clastics
    Name (siltstone, graywacke, shale, claystone)
    Color, minor constituents (quartz grains, siderite, calcite dolomite, etc.), structure (fissile, massive, fractured)

Carbonates
    Name, impurities, color, induration, granularity (crystallinity, fragments, fossils, etc.)
    Microstructures (stylolites, veins, etc.)

Evaporites
    Name, color, crystallinity, minor constitutents, impurities.

This system is entirely descriptive of the rocks and does not consider the possible or probable origin. There is little room on a standard three-inch long strip for description. Supplemental notes may be made according to one's interpretation of the origin of the sediments, but space on the log should be utilized for descriptions of the cuttings.

248. Abbreviations on Strip Logs

It is common practice with oil companies, the U.S. Geological Survey, and commercial well log companies to reduce time in logging and conserve space by abbreviating most of the rock and mineral names and descriptive terms. Many of these abbrevia-

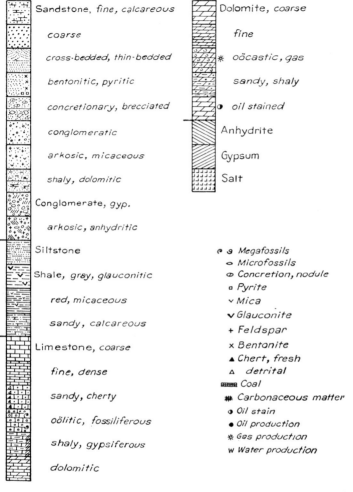

Sandstone, *fine, calcareous*

    coarse

    cross-bedded, thin-bedded

    bentonitic, pyritic

    concretionary, brecciated

    conglomeratic

    arkosic, micaceous

    shaly, dolomitic

Conglomerate, *gyp.*

    arkosic, anhydritic

Siltstone

Shale, *gray, glauconitic*

    red, micaceous

    sandy, calcareous

Limestone, *coarse*

    fine, dense

    sandy, cherty

    oölitic, fossiliferous

    shaly, gypsiferous

    dolomitic

Dolomite, *coarse*

    fine

    * *oöcastic, gas*

    sandy, shaly

    ● *oil stained*

Anhydrite

Gypsum

Salt

● ᵃ *Megafossils*
ᵒ *Microfossils*
⊙ *Concretion, nodule*
▫ *Pyrite*
ᵛ *Mica*
ᵛ *Glauconite*
+ *Feldspar*
× *Bentonite*
▲ *Chert, fresh*
△ *detrital*
▦ *Coal*
⚹ *Carbonaceous matter*
◐ *Oil stain*
● *Oil production*
✳ *Gas production*
w *Water production*

Fɪɢ. 194. Symbols in black-line patterns for plotting surface sections and well logs. (From L. W. LeRoy and Julian W. Low, *Graphic Problems in Petroleum Geology,* Harper & Brothers, 1954.)

tions are widely accepted and, therefore, might be considered standard. There are, however, variations in usage. Table 11 in the appendix is based on the most prevalent forms. In some instances an isolated abbreviation might be ambiguous, but in context the meaning is clear. For example, *gr* could mean gray, green, grain, or ground; and it has been used to abbreviate all these words. If the associated words do not make the intended meaning entirely clear, one should not abbreviate. As a rule, it is better to avoid abbreviations for very short words, such as pink, soft, and few, and save space by abbreviating the longer words.

249. Graphic Symbols

As in the case of abbreviations, there is considerable variation in symbols used by different organizations to represent rocks and minerals. Figure 194 shows common lithologies as they would appear on a well log. Obviously, the symbols shown do not represent all characters of sedimentary rocks—additional ones have to be invented to designate other lithologies or accessory constituents. When a new symbol is introduced, care should be taken that it does not conflict with one already in use.

The advantage in black-line symbols is that they are economically reproduced by offset or blue print methods.

Well logs plotted with a combination of black line and color symbols are more easily compared and correlated with others than are those on which lithologies are shown by only black lines and figures. Most oil companies, the U.S. Geological Survey, and other organizations engaged in stratigraphic work use colored strips in practically all lithologic logging.

Although there is no actual standardization among these organizations in the colors used or the manner in which they are used, considerable progress toward uniformity has been made in the past dozen years, and some practices have become quite widespread. The following discussion deals with the broader aspects of the subject.

In the selection of colors care should be taken that those adopted to represent major *lithologic* groups will not be confused with the common colors of the rocks.

These groups are shown as follows.

Canary or lemon yellow: Coarse terrigenous clastics (Conglomerates, sandstones, arkoses, etc.) are identified by yellow. Distinction between these members can be shown by patterns, such as stippling and small circles.

Light sky or cerulian blue: These colors are used for all carbonate rocks. Some organizations and individuals prefer purple for dolomite, whereas others use a blue diagonal ruling for dolomite and solid blue for calcitic limestones.

Natural rock colors: Red, gray, green, and brown are used for shales and clays. Siltstones and graywackes are shown by alternating diagonal bands of the rock color and canary yellow.

Black lines: The evaporites, as shown in Figure 194, are represented in this manner.

The logs are colored with the indelible or "water color" type of pencil because the color can be smoothed by light buffing with a charcoal drawing stump or a scrap of blotting paper.[1]

250. Equipment for Sample Examination

There is scarcely any limit to the types of examination and analysis that may be applied to well cuttings, cores or surface specimens. The brief discussion in this chapter is concerned chiefly with a type of analysis which will permit generally accurate determinations within the limitations of plotting lithologies on a standard well strip on a scale of $1'' = 100'$ or $1'' = 50'$. Largely because of limitations of plotting and space for descriptions, there is little advantage in examining specimens under very high powers of the microscope which reveal minute characters of the rock. Special training and experience are needed in this kind of work,

---

[1] Details of procedure and a color plate showing examples are given in L. W. LeRoy and Julian W. Low, *Graphic Problems in Petroleum Geology,* Harper & Brothers, 1954.

and only specialists in petrography and similar subjects are capable of correctly interpreting such examinations.

The *binocular microscope* with powers ranging from x6 to x20 is universally employed in the logging of well cuttings. Powers up to x90 are required for micropaleontologic work. This type of microscope has a wide field of vision which greatly facilitates direct comparison of chips, and reduces the time of examinations.

A micrometer scale in the eyepiece is an important feature of the microscope, and is used mostly for determining grain and crystal dimensions. In addition to the micrometer, the scoop-tray should contain a *grid* on a scale of about 0.5 millimeter. Appraisal of grain-size count is faster on such a grid. The eyepiece scale reads directly at only one magnification of the microscope. If the power is changed, measurements made with the scale must be multiplied by the appropriate factor. This is a time-consuming operation. Measurements made on the tray scale are unaffected by different magnifications.

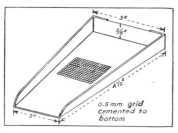

FIG. 195. Sample tray made from sheet aluminum. A paper grid is cemented on the bottom for measuring grain sizes and estimating grain distribution.

A type of *tray* in common use is shown in Fig. 195. This tray is tapered so that the cuttings are easily returned to the manila envelopes after examination.

The *lamp* best adapted to sample examination is one which provides adequate light on the specimens and also on the log. If the light is too intense, colors are "washed out" so that subtle differences are indistinguishable. Similarly, features of relief, such as sand grains, are emphasized in moderate light. Various types of double-tube fluorescent lamps meet the requirements of sample examination and logging.

Accessories needed for this work vary somewhat according to

circumstances, but the following should be considered in preparation for sample work.

The *acid container* should be of glass, heavy, and low, so that it cannot be upset easily. The glass chair leg coasters obtainable at any five-and-dime store are ideal.

A *plotting templet* as shown in Fig. 196 serves several purposes. It holds the log strip firmly on the table, protects the paper from dust and soiling from the hands, and aids in uniform and rapid plotting of log symbols.

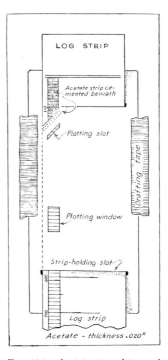

The templet is cut from cellulose acetate ranging in thickness from 0.015 to 0.02 inch. The templet shown in the figure is cut for plotting symbols, but if other symbols are preferred, additional slots can be cut accordingly. When the templet is in use, the log strip is "threaded" through the wide slots at the ends and then the acetate is fastened to the table at the most convenient position and angle by means of drafting tape.

Small strips of acetate cemented on the under side and near the slots lift the edge slightly off the paper so that inking can be done safely in the slots with a fine pen.

Fig. 196. Acetate templet used for uniform plotting of well logs on standard card strips.

Incidental materials include: Hunt #104 pen and holder; red, blue, and black waterproof ink; pencils, H to 5H; soft eraser; three or more pointed charcoal stumps (blenders); steel teasing needle; small-bladed knife; carborundum stone; steel forceps;

and colored pencils. Colored pencils should be selected with care. The water-soluble, rather than the wax-base type, such as the "Mongol," is best in that the color can be burnished smooth with a dry blender. Model airplane clear lacquer ("dope") and a half-inch artist's bristle brush are needed to coat the colored column of the finished log so that colors will be permanent and unaffected by light or moisture.

251. Special Tests

Tests ordinarily used in the laboratory in the identification of minerals are usually not applicable in sample analysis because of the small sizes of particles and grains. For this reason, the tests employed are somewhat different and are considerably less exact.

Hardness

The hardness of a mineral is an important diagnostic property. Hardness of constituent minerals is difficult to establish in an aggregate rock because of the tendency to crush the grains. Only approximate hardness can be determined.

Place a chip of the rock on the flat side of a steel knife blade and rub it lightly back and forth. Examine the knife blade under the microscope for scratches. Next, examine the specimen. If the blade is scratched and minute particles of steel are lodged in the rock, the abrasive grains have a hardness of about 6, or greater, (quartz, feldspar, chert, etc.). If this test is negative, perform the test with a copper penny; if positive, the hardness is in excess of 3. Tests of hardness below three are unreliable.

Organic Constituents

Bituminous and carbonaceous materials often occur as grains or laminae in sandstones and other clastic rocks. All these organic substances will burn when held in a flame. Take a chip in forceps and hold in the flame of a match. Withdraw, and determine the odor of the fumes from the hot chip. Carbonaceous material smells like coal smoke; bitumen, like burning oil. Under the microscope, burned carbonaceous matter leaves a white ash; bitumen, asphalt, and like substances leave a "molten," spongy residue. So-called "oil" or kerogenous shales are difficult to wet in water, and if rich in kerogen or wax, the chip will float.

COLOR

The colors of rocks are the result of a number of factors such as the pigment in the grains and cement, the refractive properties, and the color and intensity of the light under which observations are made. The colors of rocks appear deeper and more brilliant when the specimen is wet or examined through water. Dark gray shales may appear black when wet. For comparative work in color it is essential that all samples be examined under exactly the same conditions. Describe color from the surface of a freshly broken chip.

252. Acid Tests

Acid used for testing carbonate rocks should be prepared by adding seven parts of water to one part C.P. hydrochloric acid. This concentration is best for most tests.

The acid test for calcitic and dolomitic limestones is difficult for the novice, and it is only after considerable experience with specimens of known composition that intermediate mixtures can be determined with passable accuracy. The following tests must be performed carefully. Observe the reactions under the microscope. The specimen should be immersed under at least $\frac{1}{3}$ inch of acid so that the rate of effervescence can be observed in detail. The test specimen should be about $\frac{1}{4}$ inch square or smaller, and about $\frac{1}{8}$ inch thick. The acid must be moderately cold.

LIMESTONE

Effervescence is violent and audible, acid frothy. Specimen floats from energy of the reaction, and dissolves completely in two to five minutes, depending on degree of porosity in the rock.

DOLOMITE (OR MAGNESIAN LIMESTONE)

No effervescence, minute beads of gas form very slowly on surface of specimen, and there is no movement of the submerged chip.

DOLOMITIC LIMESTONE

Effervescence is moderate. There is a steady flow of carbon dioxide beads, and specimen may skid about or move slightly off the bottom of the container.

LIMY (CALCITIC) DOLOMITE

Effervescence is weak. There is a thin flow of gas beads to surface, and chip may rock back and forth but does not move along bottom of container. The reaction slowly accelerates after a few minutes of immersion.

The acid reactions of clayey or anhydritic calcitic limestones are in some ways similar to those of dolomitic limestones, in that the normal reactions are inhibited. There are two means of distinguishing between them.

(1) The reaction of dolomitic limestone gradually accelerates. The reaction of clayey or anyhydritic limestone is brisk at first, then becomes more subdued. The apparent reaction may cease altogether after a few minutes.

(2) If clay or anhydrite is suspected, granulate the specimen in a mortar and dissolve in hot acid. Dolomite or calcite will dissolve almost immediately with strong effervescence. As soon as the reaction has ceased, examine the container for slowly soluble or insoluble residue.

Most of the *chlorides,* such as halite, are readily soluble in water, and for this reason, they are generally not present in drill cuttings even though present in the strata. There may be a sufficient quantity to yield a salty taste, but "salt base" drilling fluid will also impart a salty taste to cuttings. Check drilling fluid records. Examine shales and carbonate rocks carefully for characteristic cubic salt molds left in the insoluble matrix.

Gypsum (selenite, alabaster) usually can be identified by its appearance or low degree of hardness. When ground in a mortar, it dissolves in a minute of boiling in dilute hydrochloric acid. When in solution, the sulphate comes down immediately as a heavy milk-white precipitate when an aqueous solution of barium chloride is added.

Anhydrite is usually amorphous-appearing, in contrast to the crystallinity or earthiness of gypsum. It cannot be scratched with the fingernail as can gypsum. It is very slowly soluble (or insoluble) in boiling hydrochloric acid.

253. Microstructures

Small grains, oölites, microfossils, fractures, and the like are difficult or impossible to observe in detail on the broken surface of a chip. However, a planed surface may be obtained quickly by holding the chip on a small crank-type abrasive wheel which can be clamped to the edge of the table. If a wheel is not available the chip can be faced by rubbing on a medium-grained carborundum stone or a fine machinist's file. It is not necessary to polish the surface for viewing the microstructures. Simply moisten the surface with water or a drop of light machine oil before examination under the microscope.

254. Concurrent Examination and Plotting

It is a common practice among oil company geologists to plot the graphic log, together with descriptions, as the samples are examined. Usually this plot is made in color which later may be transcribed into black line symbols if there is need for a number of copies. The advantages in the concurrent plot are (1) that logged material reappearing as cavings is more readily identified when lithologies up the hole are always in view of the microscopist; (2) tentative correlation of rock units can be made as the log develops, thereby revealing gross errors in sample interpretation; and (3) shale colors are determined by matching with the specimens. Lithologic descriptions which are made for later plotting on a strip must be in greater detail than the supplemental descriptions lettered on the plotted graphic log.

255. Electrical Logging

Electrical and radioactivity logs are graphic representations of certain physical properties of rocks. Through much laboratory research and comparative work in the field, a number of mathematical relations have been derived whereby several of these properties, such as porosity, can be computed with considerable accuracy. However, it is far beyond the scope of this chapter to go into the details of indirect logging and the quantitative interpretation of electrical logs. Such information can be obtained from the companies which make such logs and are constantly improving the methods of logging and the geological interpretation of the logs.

The field geologist is interested in electrical logs to the extent that they aid immeasurably in the construction of accurate lithologic logs from well cuttings. As mentioned earlier, up-hole cavings may complicate the interpretation of cuttings, and electrical or radioactivity logs help to fill in portions of the log where samples are unreliable. Even where samples are of fairly good quality, it is sometimes difficult to determine the exact boundaries of lithologic units or formations. These "tops" may be quite important to the field geologist carrying his work into the subsurface, and electrical logs are commonly the best means for accurate determination of lithologic boundaries.

For the field geologist who uses electrical logs only occasionally, the empirical approach is probably better than the mathematical or physical. The various curves of the electrical logs should be compared with sample logs in the region in order to establish the characters of the curves relative to known rock types or formations. However, there are a few principles of electrical logging that should be known in order to improve interpretations.

A typical electrical log consists of one curve on the left side of the column, known as the *spontaneous potential,* and one to three curves on the right side, which are specific measures of electrical resistivity, and are called resistivity curves. These curves are briefly explained below.

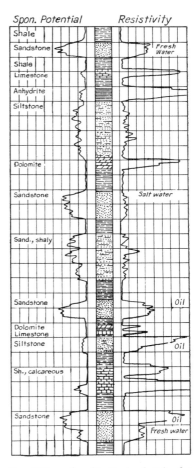

SPONTANEOUS POTENTIAL

An electrical potential exists between rocks of different lithology and between the rocks of the bore hole walls and the drilling fluid filling the hole. This potential is affected by the penetration of the drilling fluid into pores of the wall rock, and therefore is a *relative* measure of porosity and permeability. Inasmuch as shales are relatively impermeable, and uniformly so, the S.P. curve in front of the shale formations is a straight, nearly vertical line. Because of the generally constant position of this line, it is called the *shale base line.* The shale base line is a reference for appraising the S.P. curve in front of other types of lithology which are more permeable than shales.

The magnitude of the S.P. curve is controlled to a large

FIG. 197. An idealized electric log showing relationships between spontaneous potential, resistivity, and lithology of the rocks.

degree by the relative salinities of the drilling fluid and the fluids in the formation. Figure 197 is a schematic electrical log showing "normal" relationships of the various lithologies and S.P. and resistivity curves. The S.P. curve is typical of porous formations containing salt water and drilling fluid having a much lower salinity. If the salinity of formation and drilling fluids is nearly equal the S.P. curve lacks character. If the formation water is fresh and the drilling fluid is considerably more saline, the S.P. curve is *reversed* opposite porous formations. Other factors, such as bed thickness and types of solids in the drilling fluids, also affect the character and amplitude of the S.P. curves.

RESISTIVITY

Most of the minerals that make up sedimentary rocks are poor conductors of electricity; therefore, since resistivity is the reciprocal of conductivity, most rocks possess a high intrinsic resistivity. Absolutely pure water will not transmit an electrical current; hence, pure water is also highly resistive. With the addition of soluble salts, water becomes conductive, and the higher the concentration of salts in solution, the *lower* the *resistivity* becomes. Essentially all sedimentary formations contain some conductive minerals and some water, and formational waters always contain dissolved salts, ranging from mere traces to complete saturation. Furthermore, even "dry" formations contain water, which can be freed only by high temperatures, yet in sufficient quantity to serve as a conduit for electrical current along the surfaces of constituent grains. It can be concluded, therefore, that practically all rocks are to some degree conductive and that the conductivity (and resistivity) will vary according to composition, porosity, and the nature of the interstitial fluids.

In general it may be stated that anhydrite, gypsum, and salt have very high resistivities because of their extremely low water content. Coals, likewise, are normally quite resistive, though under some circumstances they may have rather low resistivities. Shales, clays, mudstones, and similar fine-grained clastics are characteristically highly porous (though impermeable) and the pores are filled with waters of high salinity; consequently these rocks exhibit very low resistivities. Porous and highly permeable rocks, such as sandstones, dolomites, limestones, some arkoses, and the like, have widely varying resistivities. The carbonate rocks, in particular, are subject to extreme variation, and, except where highly porous and permeable, are nearly as resistive as anhydrite.

In logging, the resistivities of the formations are measured in ohm-meters. Resistivity curves appear on the right side of the electric log. On most logs are three or more such curves which are differentiated by the type of line—light, heavy, dashed, or dotted—as shown by legend in the log heading. The difference between the types of curves is controlled by the spacing of

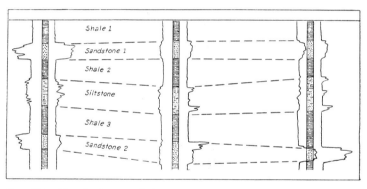

Fig. 198. Electric log correlation where the curves of the logs exhibit widely different characteristics.

electrodes in the hole and the scale on which the curve is plotted. These curves are designated by terms such as normal, amplified normal, long normal, lateral, and long lateral, all with reference to electrode spacing or amplification of scale. The microlog is a resistivity curve resulting from very close electrode spacing in a mechanical arrangement which holds the electrodes in contact with the walls of the hole.

Many geologically unrelated factors modify the character of both the spontaneous potential and resistivity logs, and for this reason correlations based on *similar appearance* of the curves may be entirely wrong. Figure 198 is an example of differing characteristics. Of course, these few illustrations by no means represent the variability that can be expected in the entire field of electric logging. They are given here primarily to emphasize the hazards of *literal* graphic interpretation.

256. Radioactivity Logging

Radioactivity logs are quite similar to electric logs in appearance, but there the similarity ends. This log consists of a gamma-ray curve on the left and a neutron curve on the right. The two curves measure quite different properties of the rocks.

Fig. 199. Schematic diagram showing the relative radioactive values for common lithologies.

The gamma-ray log is a measure of the natural radioactivity in the rocks, caused by the presence of minute quantities of radioactive materials. The neutron curve represents the response of the strata to a bombardment of high-velocity neutrons from special chambers, resulting in an excitation of gamma rays, which, in turn is recorded as the curve on the log. Hydrogen retards or stops the neutrons; consequently, where hydrogen is present in the rocks, as for example, in interstitial fluids, the value on the curve is correspondingly low.

As in the case of electric logs, certain lithologies can be inferred if the general stratigraphic characteristics of the region and bore hole conditions are known. Figure 199 shows the relative radioactive values for a number of rock types. These relative values, as they appear on the log, would be modified by formational and bore hole conditions.

When determining the boundary between two lithologies on a gamma-ray log, it is necessary to select a midpoint on the slope of the curve from one value to the next, as shown in Fig. 200.

In most areas, shales are identified by high radioactivity values, and within the shale range, the darker the color, the higher the value (i.e., black shales have higher values than gray or brown shales). If sandstones or limestones contain large amounts of radioactive materials, as they occsasionally do, the response on the gamma-ray log may be very similar to that of shales, and therefore difficult to distinguish. Coal exhibits very low values.

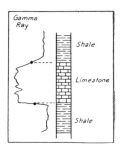

As mentioned, the neutron curve is affected by the presence of hydrogen in the formation fluid (oil, gas, and water); therefore, since practically all lithologies have interstitial fluids, the neutron curve must be interpreted by what is known

Fig. 200. Gamma ray curve showing that stratigraphic boundaries should be picked midway on the sloping leg of the curve.

about the lithologies, either from gamma-ray or electrical logs or determination of cuttings and cores.

A summary of idealized characteristics of electric and radio-activity logs in relation to certain lithologies is illustrated in Fig. 201. The fact that this representation is only schematic, and does not take into account the many variations, is strongly emphasized. When these logs are used empirically for purposes of correlation or lithologic interpretation, it should be with the awareness of their changing characters relative to the rocks involved.

257. Correlation of Surface and Subsurface Work

Most geologic projects employ several types of investigation and are therefore involved in many different techniques; methods of observation and analysis; and finally, and most important, the integration of all data into a feasible overall geologic concept.

In both area and depth most of the sedimentary rocks of the earth are hidden from view, and we must determine their characters and distribution, as well as their riches, by means that are indirect. The field geologist who is fortunate enough to work

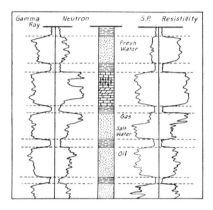

Fig. 201. Ideal relations between gamma ray, neutron, spontaneous potential, and resistivity logs and lithologies. (Modified after L. W. LeRoy, *Subsurface Geologic Methods,* Colorado School of Mines, 1950).

where outcrops abound may feel secure in his knowledge of an area. At best his *absolute* knowledge can extend only as wide and as deep into the earth as outcrops permit. Beyond these limitations, knowledge is but inferential. It must be granted that often the inferences are remarkably near the truth, yet geologic interpretations between outcrops and deep in the subsurface are always subject to revision when methods other than surface are brought to bear on the problems.

Next to observation of extensive outcrops, the data obtained from deep borings constitute the most direct means of deciphering lithologic and stratigraphic relationships of a region. Geophysical methods, including electrical and radioactivity logging which are also geophysical, add much to our knowledge of the subsurface.

Often, however, the results of these methods are not available to the field geologist, and cannot be effective in supplementing or bolstering his interpretations of subsurface relationships.

In the case of bore holes, within or near the map area, there is less excuse for his not augmenting surface data with subsurface information. Usually, the data from wells are easily obtained, and the kinds of data derived from various types of logs, cuttings, and cores are directly correlatable with those collected in the field. Well information will not only make possible the extension of surface observations, but will greatly strengthen subsurface interpretations.

Sections plotted from field examinations and descriptions of lithologies are sometimes difficult to correlate with detailed well sample logs. The reason for apparent discrepancies is generally twofold: (1) surface rocks are commonly much altered by weathering, and (2) gross aspects of the rocks are seen in the field and minute characters are seen under the binocular microscope. Therefore, if it is anticipated that subsurface work will be done, samples should be collected from surface sections and examined under the microscope for properties observable also in well cuttings.

258. Supplementary Core Holes

When all outcrops in an area have been examined and mapped it may be found that no surface control is obtainable in critical stratigraphic or structural localities. If depths to definitive horizons are not too great, shallow wells (called core holes) are drilled to supply the required geological information. Although the data obtained from core holes are basically subsurface in character, the locations of the wells and interpretation of the samples or electric logs should be the responsibility of the geologist who does the surface work, for he will be most familiar with stratigraphic and lithologic details and the broader requirements of the project. Inasmuch as core holes are costly, every effort should be made to gain the utmost from the least possible number of wells. The surface maps should be studied critically to ascertain exactly where the wells must be situated to provide the required information. Accessibility of the terrain, availability of drilling water, and other operational requirements must be considered in relation to the most advantageous pattern for the subsurface tests.

259. Organic Constituents

The organic constituents of sedimentary rocks are sometimes difficult to analyze by methods and equipment generally available to the geologist who turns to subsurface methods only occasionally. Nevertheless, the organic matter in the rocks may be significant either in appraising certain economic aspects of a region or as an indication of the environment in which the sediments were deposited. Brown to black stains from iron and manganese oxides commonly have the appearance of bituminous or carbonaceous stains, especially in fine-grained or dense rocks. Simple tests will distinguish between the organic and inorganic constituents.

Lignitic or Carbonaceous Matter

Normally these materials can be recognized under the binocular microscope and no specific tests are required. (Testing by ignition has already been mentioned.) However, some types of shales contain large percentages of carbonaceous matter which is so finely divided its presence may not be suspected by microscopic observation. There are two methods for separating these materials from the clay and silt or carbonate constituents.

If the material occurs in *limestone, dolomite,* or *marl,* crush the specimen to fine, but not pulverized, particles and dissolve the soluble constituents in boiling hydrochloric acid. This frees the organic matter, which will float to the surface of the acid, where it may be skimmed off and dried for examination under the microscope or tested by ignition.

Where the carbonaceous material occurs in *shales* or *siltstones,* the finely crushed sample is boiled in a strong solution of sodium carbonate until completely disaggregated. The organic matter is skimmed off the surface and tested, as stated in the preceding paragraph.

Approximation of the relative quantities can be made if the crushed rock is measured and the dried "float" is compared with the bulk quantity of the original sample.

SOLUBLE HYDROCARBONS

Petroleum, asphalt, and a number of solid hydrocarbons are readily dissolved in ether, acetone, and carbon tetrachloride.

For ether and carbon tetrachloride tests, crush the rock to fine particles and blow away the powdered material, which may interfere with the test. Place a small portion of the rock in the center of a two- or three-inch watch glass and immerse in the solvent. Roll the chips about with a clean metal or plastic stirrer. These solvents evaporate rapidly, leaving a film of the dissolved hyrocarbon on the surface of the watch glass, which may be examined for minute globules of oil under the microscope.

A method employing acetone as the solvent is as follows. This is a very sensitive test.

Wash and *thoroughly dry* a test tube, being careful that no grease or oil is left anywhere on the inside surface. Place the crushed specimen in the tube and half fill with C.P. acetone and agitate with a glass rod for a few minutes. If the solvent is quite clear, pour it off into another clean dry tube. If it is cloudy, filter into the second tube. To the solvent add a small quantity of distilled water and thoroughly mix. If dissolved hydrocarbons are present the solution will become milky and the density of the cloudiness is a relative measure of the amount of soluble hyrocarbon present.

CHAPTER X

Geologic Illustrations

260. Introductory Comments

Nearly all forms of illustration have been utilized in an effort to clarify the complexities of geology, but as the science itself develops the problems of adequate illustration become more difficult. The greatest obstacle to intelligible illustration is that the three-dimensional aspects of physical geology must be shown on the two dimensions of the drawing board, and some geologists possess neither the skill nor the perception to master the problems. It is a serious handicap for a geologist not to be able mentally to assemble the incremental data of geology into a concrete three-dimensional image. It is fundamental to illustration that one must be able to observe accurately and objectively before he can draw correctly. A nebulous mental image simply cannot be transferred to the drawing board as a straightforward picture.

Two basic factors must be considered together: perception of form and skill in mechanical and freehand drawing; and, as mentioned earlier, perception must come first. Although everything we look upon we perceive in three dimensions, only artists are trained specifically in the analysis of depth perception. The geologist is fully as much concerned with depth perception as is the artist and his problems are vastly greater because they extend from the observable to the mental images which must come into play when he deals with geologic forms lying far below the surface. Some persons are endowed with exceptional three-dimensional perception, and as geologists, they are fortunate. Those in whom this faculty is weak, must *dicipline their observations* of form so that the *memory* of form is retained as a vivid image. The retention of mental images is an essential attribute of the field geologist.

Skill in drawing is acquired by learning a few fundamental rules, and practice—much practice. Practice in drawing directly from observation also aids greatly in the development of observational dicipline; the two go hand in hand, and in this respect, even though one never becomes proficient in illustration, he will have gained something worthwhile by much practice in sketching.

261. The Purpose of Geologic Illustrations

Geologic drawings are made for three principal reasons: (1) to record observations made in the field for future reference, (2) to solve various kinds of three-dimensional problems by graphic methods, and (3) to convey to others those concepts which are difficult to express by words alone. Nearly all of the usual forms of illustration employed in geology are made to satisfy one or more of these purposes. Drawings should not be used purely for decoration; they must fulfill a useful purpose.

The variety of maps, sections, diagrams, and sketches that are usefully and commonly employed in geological work is almost limitless, and the methods and techniques by which they are constructed are many. The space in this manual does not permit even a list of all types; therefore, the remainder of this chapter is devoted to those kinds of illustrations that are of greatest use to the *field* geologist.

262. Definitions and Uses of Maps

The field geologist is concerned with relatively few types of maps, except in so far as the data which he collects and processes are utilized in map work by others. It is in order, then, to consider the maps which he may actually use or construct in the field, or during the post-seasonal period normally allotted for the preparation of maps and reports.

TOPOGRAPHIC MAPS

A topographic map is one which shows the configuration of the surface of the ground by means of hachures, shading, elevations or contours, or combinations thereof. A topographic map is usually understood to be a *contour* map, the geologic applications of which are considered here.

Topographic maps have long served as the best base on which to map areal geology, though air photographs are now used in the same manner. As explained in another chapter, structural data can be derived from a combination of topography and areal geology. Inasmuch as the basic reasons for most topographic forms are geological, rather extensive geologic deductions can be made from critical study of topographic maps. For the field geologist, a good topographic map is an invaluable asset.

AREAL GEOLOGIC MAPS

An areal geologic map, as the name suggests, is one which shows by colors or black-line patterns the areal distribution of geologic formations. Most credit is due the U.S. Geological Survey for standardizing the colors, patterns, and letter symbols which indicate on the map the geologic systems, epochs, and formations cropping out at or near the surface. Like the topographic map, the areal geologic map is valuable to the field man in that it enables him quickly to become oriented with respect to regional geologic features. Topography and areal geology are closely related, both genetically and pictorially. This subject is treated in some detail in Chapter V.

STRUCTURAL MAPS

The structural map indicates geologic structure either by symbols or contours. The methods employed in the field in the construction of structural maps are given in Chapter VI.

The basic map of the oil industry is the structure contour map. Although other maps are widely used by oil companies, ever since the formulation of the anticlinal theory, this map has been predominant in the search for new oil fields. Every conceivable means has been directed to the search for structural anomalies and new data bearing on the subject. In a purely geologic sense, structure maps are basic to a variety of others. Sometimes the solutions to difficult stratigraphic problems are reached through analytical study of local and regional structure maps. Changing environments of sedimentation have been the direct or indirect result of tectonic processes. The patterns of formational distribution are due in large part to the structure. The depth at which a well will penetrate a given horizon or at what point a mine tunnel will intersect a vein can be calculated only on the basis of accurate structural analysis and mapping.

ISOPACH MAPS

An isopach map shows the changing thickness of a stratigraphic interval by means of "contours," or *isopachs*. Isopach maps are useful to the field man in reducing the elevations on key beds to datum values. Isopach maps are probably the best means of delineating the areal extent, or zero line, of a formation. This information may be quite important in problems of structure, stratigraphy, or areal geology.

263. Cross Sections

Although cross sections vary greatly in details of construction and appearance, they fall into one of two general classes—structural and stratigraphic. In the structural section the *datum* or reference from which formation boundaries are scaled and plotted is an elevation (level) line. In a stratigraphic section, the datum is a stratigraphic horizon, drawn as a straight horizontal line across the sheet, and other stratigraphic boundaries are scaled and plotted upward or downward from this datum according to stratigraphic intervals.

It is quite common practice to exaggerate the vertical scale with reference to the horizontal. Where structural dips or the rates of stratigraphic thinning are quite small, increasing the vertical scale emphasizes these factors so that they are more apparent on casual observation. Also, if it is necessary to show details of stratigraphy without extending the length of the drawing, the vertical scale must be larger than the horizontal. However, except in special cases, as suggested, natural scale (vertical and horizontal equal) sections are superior. Exaggeration of the vertical scale distorts the rate of dip or the rate of convergence, as the case may be, thus giving a distorted view of actual relationships.

264. Block Diagrams

The field geologist rarely needs to construct block diagrams; but occasionally the complexities of structural and stratigraphic relationships cannot be shown clearly on maps or cross-sections. Block diagrams are three-dimensional projections, and therefore, present the spatial relationships of geologic features. Excepting rough freehand sketches, there is only one type of block diagram of general use to the field geologist; this is the isometric projection.

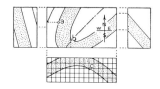

Fig. 202. View of a disassembled three-dimensional block showing areal geology on the top, cross sections on the two ends, and a gridded cross section on the front side.

ISOMETRIC BLOCK DIAGRAM

An isometric projection differs from other types of block drawings in that it produces the illusion of perspective and depth without introducing scale distortions inherent in most three-dimensional figures.

When viewing an actual rectangular block, such as a model, it is possible to see only three of the six sides from any one point of observation. The usual practice is to show the top, front, and either the right or left side.

Figure 202 shows the disassembled elements of a block model. The top element is an areal geologic map, and the three sides shown in the figure are cross sections. The dotted lines indicate the relationships of geologic features as seen in plan and section. Each of these elements is in a form of presentation commonly employed in geologic work. The problem is to put the data to-

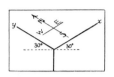

FIG. 203. Construction axes of an isometric block diagram.

gether in an isometric block diagram. In Fig. 203 is a system of axes which are the framework for the diagram. In this example, the southwest corner of the map will be placed at the central angle of the axes, and the south and west sides will lie along the *x* and *y* axes. The *x* and *y* axes are inclined on the paper at angles of 30 degrees to the horizontal. The projection is thus called a 30-degree isometric, though in practice any angle of projection may be used.

Along all lines parallel to the projection axes the scale in the isometric projection is the same as that of the map and sections.

Consider first the transfer of data from the map to the top face of the block, as shown in Fig. 204. Points for control of sketching are plotted by means of coördinates. Section and township lines are usually sufficient, but any grid may be drawn on the map in pencil for the purpose. In the figure, points *a* and *b* are located on the map by scaling north and west from the southwest corner. The same distances are scaled along corresponding coördinates to locate the points on the projection. The geologic boundaries are sketched by means of control located in this manner. Bearings

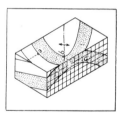

FIG. 204. Isometric block diagram constructed from an areal geologic map and cross sections shown in Fig. 203. Compare the gridded section with that in the figure cited.

and angles cannot be used because the four 90-degree corners of the block become two 60-degree and two 120-degree angles on the projection.

Details of the vertical sides of the projection are scaled from the appropriate cross sections. The simplest way is to draw a rectangular grid on the section and a corresponding oblique grid on the projection. The coördinate position of point *c* in Fig. 202 is exactly the same on the section and the isometric projection in Fig. 204.

It should be borne in mind that the *only* directions in which distances may be scaled are those parallel to the three principal axes.

265. Panel Diagrams

Basically, a panel diagram consists of cross sections drawn in their correct positions on a map or isometric base. They are used primarily to show three-dimensional variations in stratigraphy. Figure 205 is a simple map-panel diagram. Briefly, the construction is as follows.

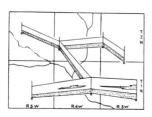

FIG. 205. Stratigraphic panel diagram drawn on a map base.

The plane of the map is the datum for the diagram. If the diagram is to show structure, the datum is a level surface. If relationships of stratigraphy are to be illustrated, structure is disregarded and the map plane becomes a selected stratigraphic horizon. Referring again to the figure, vertical lines are erected at the map locations of the sections. Treat these points as the base of the stratigraphic interval to be shown. Plot formation tops to the desired vertical scale, upward from the base of the basal unit, and then connect these points of correlation from well to well, as in the figure.

The panel diagram may be plotted on an isometric perspective base. The procedure is the same as for a map-panel diagram. It can be seen in the illustration that only east-west sections, or panels, are shown in true dimensions, all others being foreshortened because of the angle of the view. The isometric base is used for two purposes: to heighten the illusion of perspective and to present nearly north-south panels in full view, at the sacrifice of east-west sections. This would be desirable where the most significant changes occurred in a north-south direction. It is entirely a matter of choice which sections are joined to form a panel.

266. Stratigraphic Boundary Lines and Patterns

Cross sections, panel diagrams, and isometric blocks are more useful and legible if the lines representing boundaries of members, formations and systems are differentiated by weight, dashes, and dots.

Black-line patterns and colors are used to emphasize stratigraphic units and to produce an effect of solidity in the sections. A wide variety of black-line patterns on very thin cellophane is marketed under several trade names. The backs of these sheets are coated with a hard wax-like adhesive which will adhere strongly to any type of drawing material when rubbed with a bone buffer. The patterns reproduce well by either photographic and photostatic or offset printing methods.

267. Field Photographs

A good, compact camera is an important piece of equipment for the field geologist. Good photos not only serve admirably as illustrations for reports, but also aid the geologist in recalling and reviewing certain specific field relationships observed some time in the past.

There are many brands and types of cameras that are more than adequate for the field geologist's purposes, and it would be impossible to obtain agreement on which are best. Despite individual preferences, certain factors should be considered in the selection of a camera for field use.

The camera should be compact and sturdily built. The field geologist commonly carries a very considerable amount of essential equipment, and every additional piece increases this burden. In rough country, all such equipment is subject to hard knocks, and it must be well constructed to withstand field usage.

Depending to some degree on the nature of the field work, it may be desirable to take close-up pictures of small features, such as fossils, rock granularity, and fracturing. This type of work requires a camera than can be sharply focused on minute detail. Similarly, the broad, distant views are often important, and therefore a suitable lens and filters are necessary.

Color is not only an important rock property, but it may be the most useful basis for differentiating formations on a broad scale. Two stratigraphic units similar in weathering characteristics but different in overall color effect may photograph alike in black and white, yet be quite distinct on color film. There can be no doubt that color film provides a better geologic record.

Three-dimensional, or stereoscopic cameras are now widely used in the field. With this type of photo the geologist can review the spatial relationships of features observed throughout the field season. The cost of the camera and processing of film are somewhat higher than ordinary single exposures, but the value of information in this form is likewise greater.

268. Stereoscopic Views with a Single Lens Camera

A stereopair of photos may be taken with any kind of single lens camera, but in order to obtain satisfactory results, it is essential to follow strict procedures in the field.

A stereopair consists of two exposures of the same object or scene taken from different camera stations. It is essential that the camera be oriented in space precisely the same at both stations; otherwise the prints cannot be properly aligned under the stereoscope.

For obtaining a stereopair of a distant view the procedure is as follows:

(1) Place the camera on a flat surface a foot or two wide. A plane table is ideal.

(2) Lay a Brunton alongside the camera and read the bearing exactly. Hold the camera base firmly on the plane table (or other flat surface) and make the exposure.

(3) Roll the film for the next exposure. Move the camera sidewise about one foot. Reorient with the Brunton and take the picture. These two pictures will appear in three dimensions when placed under an ordinary pocket stereoscope.

The spacing between camera stations determines the apparent relief in the stereoscopic view—the wider the separation, the greater will be the exaggeration of the third dimension. Try various spacings until the desired effect is obtained.

269. Composition in Field Photographs

Photos are taken primarily for the purpose of illustration, but the effectiveness of any picture rests not only on the clarity of detail but also on the composition of lines and tones or masses. The subject of composition is complex, and there is no necessity for delving into its intricacies here. Nevertheless, it should be mentioned that a photo can be an excellent display of geologic data and at the same time be either a poor or a good picture. Small booklets on landscape composition can be purchased at small cost. One need know only a few basic principles of composition to obtain snapshots that are pleasing to the eye without sacrificing a single detail of geologic illustration.

A broad landscape should consist of three *related* elements: foreground, middle distance, and far distance. Each of these elements is related to the adjacent one by *repetition* of features or by *continuity* of line, such as a stream, road, ridge, or meadow. When taking a picture of outcropping formations or topographic forms, one should look for the repetition of details such as ledges, trees, and the like from the foreground into the distance, and, as mentioned, lines which carry through.

Heavy masses placed entirely in one corner or on one side of a picture produce an effect of unbalance. Move the camera slightly so that a small, very dense shadow on one side of the picture may be balanced by a larger area of intermediate density. Get into the picture some object in the foreground—a bush, rocks, or the dead branch or stump of a tree. The difference in a fine picture or a poor one may be only a matter of a few steps to one side or the other.

A common failure, and a fatal one for an otherwise good picture, is to cut the picture in half by the skyline. The skyline should be no nearer the middle than $\frac{2}{5}$ the distance from top to bottom. An effect of vast space and distance is gotten when the skyline is placed quite near the bottom of the picture, and close proximity is the result when only a thin band or small patch of sky appears at the top. As in the example of skyline, no line should divide the picture in left and right halves, such as a straight road leading from the foreground into the distance. It is generally bad practice to decapitate trees along the lower edge of the picture, thus detaching them from the familiar stability of a ground setting.

270. Relative Scales

The sizes of features in a photograph are indicated only by comparison with some familiar object whose approximate size is known. The photograph of a scene built on a table top can appear as vast and spacious as a similar scene actually photographed out of doors. But if a watch, pencil, or similar object were in juxtaposition to a model hill or tree, the miniature character of the photo would be clearly apparent.

A person, pine tree, or surveying tripod will give the scale of a landscape. A geologist's pick or notebook provides a scale for the thicknesses of beds or sizes of boulders; and a lead pencil, watch, or pocket knife will indicate the order of magnitude of fractures, grains, or fossils in a close-up picture of outcrop detail. The field photograph should always include some sort of scale gauge.

271. Systematic Photography

A procedure developed by L. W. LeRoy, which he calls *photostratigraphy,* can be applied generally to field photography. It consists in systematizing the arrangement of photo stations in the field so that increasing detail is developed when the photos are viewed in consecutive order. A base map or aerial mosaic is required for locating camera stations. In the following example the numbers refer to consecutive stations as shown in Fig. 206.

EXAMPLE:

(1) *Distant view*—shows the broad setting of the area of primary interest. Bearing to central point and distance indicated on the map.

(2) *Middle view*—Large stratigraphic units, massive cliffs, and so forth, are distinct.

(3) *Near view*—Two exposures, one above the other, may be needed to cover the field. These shots show formations, members, individual beds, and the like.

(4) *On the outcrops*—The distance, eight to 20 feet, is such that thin beds are distinct.

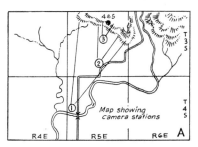

Fig. 206. A. Camera stations for a succession of field photographs taken from a distant point at station 1, and from a few inches at 4 and 5. B. A pick and Brunton are used for scales in photos 4 and 5.

(5) *Close-up*—The distance, three to five feet, permits distinguishing grains, laminae, minor features, large fossils, etc. Hand specimens may be broken out and laid on the outcrop to illustrate certain details.

(6) *Photomicrographs*—Made from typical hand specimens, polished sections, and thin sections to show textural, paleontologic, and other minute aspects of the rock.

Complete notes are made to show precisely where each of the close-up shots is taken, as for example:

Photo Number 15:—In Juniper Formation, approximately 45 feet above basal conglomerate. Limestone member 4 feet thick, underlain by gray shales, overlain by shales and gypsum.

Photos taken systematically have much greater value, both as illustrations and as a reference library, than do an equally large number of random snapshots. The number of photos needed to insure adequate illustration is actually reduced by this scheme.

272. Field Sketching

Despite the wide use of cameras in geological work, a geologist should be able to make accurate field sketches. Even the best cameras are subject to occasional failure of one kind or another. Furthermore, the vagaries of light and shade sometimes mislead the most experienced photographers.

Freehand drawing properly belongs in the field of art, yet it can be one of the most useful tools of the field geologist or topographer. Being one of the graphic arts, it is a subject simple in theory and complex in application. But in relation to geology, only a few basic points need be mentioned.

273. Perspective

Perception of relative size and distance is primarily a function of angles between the lines of sight in rapidly progressive glances. We actually see clearly at a given instant, only a very small area, which varies somewhat in size among individuals. Select any letter in the middle of a word on this page and scrutinize its details. You are conscious of the remainder of the letters to the extent of recognition of each, and of the word; but you cannot, *while focusing attention on the middle letter,* discern the *details* of the other letters. This deficiency in vision is overcome by a

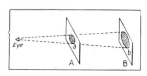

Fig. 207. Relation of apparent size of an object and distance to the object.

continuous series of minute jerky movements of the eyes by which you read the words in this sentence. Now the area in which you see sharply has been called the area of *instantaneous vision.* It is an *area* only in the sense of the angle subtended. Figure 207 illustrates this concept. At *A*, the angle of instant vision permits sharp comprehension of the object *a*. At *B*, an object *b* is twice as large as *a*, but it is also twice the distance; so, excepting conditions of atmosphere, it is seen with equal sharpness and apparently at the same distance.

For reasons not completely understood the eyes "measure" the angle swept across the field of vision. If the angle referred to in the figure cited be considered zero and objects *a* and *b* as having large dimensions, the following remarks will be more readily understood. Things appear large or small, near or distant, depending upon the angle swept by the eyes in viewing the object from top to bottom or side to side. Another factor of importance is familiarity with the size of the particular thing being viewed— in other words, a scale of reference.

The preceding remarks intimate some of the conditions which stimulate the faculty of sight in a manner that causes the brain to translate relative angles into relative size or distance. A similar response can be obtained from simple line drawings.

Figure 208 is a simple sketch of a straight railroad and a line of telegraph poles, representing horizontal and vertical planes, respectively. The horizontal line is the *horizon*, at which visibility ceases. The *vanishing*

Fig. 208. One-point perspective sketch. All parallel lines converge to the vanishing point.

point is the point of convergence of all parallel lines. The horizon is considered level with the observer's eyes, and the vanishing point lies on this horizon.

It can be seen that ties and telegraph poles not only become shorter into the distance, but they are also progressively closer together. This, again is a function of angles. In Fig. 209 the equally spaced railroad ties are viewed from a point at *a*. The vertical plane of the drawing is the line *xy,* and the converging lines are lines of sight as they would appear in vertical section. The spacing of these lines on the vertical plane is the spacing that appears in the perspective drawing cited above. The horizon is placed where the converging lines are essentially coincident, as indicated in the figure.

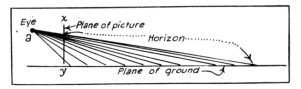

FIG. 209. Vertical projection illustrating the perspective spacing of equally spaced lines parallel to the plane of the picture.

The illusion of a high or low viewpoint is created by the *rate* of convergence, or of spacing. Various effects of distance and point of observation can be produced simply by changing the angles of paralled lines and the spacing of points on the drawing.

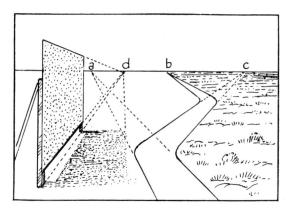

FIG. 210. Showing relationships of several vanishing points to pairs of parallel lines in a landscape.

In the preceding discussion only one vanishing point was considered, the reason being that the rails, the course of the telegraph line, and the tops and bases of the poles are parallel to each other. Now we will examine a more usual case where pairs or groups of parallel lines have different bearings. Figure 210 shows a road whose bearing changes three times, thus resulting in the three vanishing points *a, b,* and *c.* The *rate* of convergence, however, is constant. The billboard illustrates several points which must be considered in the construction of a perspective sketch. Inasmuch as the billboard is parallel to no part of the road, the vanishing point is at *d,* rather than at one of those mentioned above. Notice that the space beneath the billboard and the shadow cast on the ground are also governed by the vanishing point at *d.* That portion of the billboard extending above the horizon is above the eye level of the observer. It is very important to keep this principle in mind when making field sketches.

When one face of a three-dimensional object is normal to the observer's direction of sight (parallel to the plane of the picture), horizontal lines in this plane are also horizontal on the drawing, as illustrated by the cube in Fig. 211. But all planes not normal to the line of sight are subject to the rules of convergence, as demonstrated in the obelisk of the figure. Each plane has its own vanishing point (*a, b,* and *c*). It is also evident in the figure that shadows on the horizontal plane,

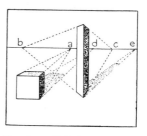

Fig. 211. Relating various elements of a perspective sketch to the horizon and vanishing points.

falling directly opposite the source of light, converge toward vanishing points *d* and *e,* the relative lengths of the shadows being determined by the height of the object and the light source.

Fig. 212. Application of the principles of perspective to a canyon lanscape where portions of the natural objects are situated both above and below eye level.

The simple sketch in Fig. 212 shows how the principles of perspective are applied in field drawings. The horizontal stratification in the high spires must be shown converging toward the distant horizon in order to produce the effect of height. Notice that "one-point" perspective controls the sketch of the butte on the left because the frontal face is parallel to the plane of the drawing and, therefore, lines in the drawing are parallel; it is only the right side which is subject to convergence. The butte on the right is in "two-point" perspective because the planes are neither parallel to each other nor to the plane of the picture.

When preparing to make a detailed sketch in the field it is well to contemplate the following suggestions.

(1) The position of the perspective horizon determines the elevation of the observer's viewpoint. If you are on a high vantage point, then the horizon will fall low on the picture. If your position is low, relative to the general landscape, the horizon will be in the upper part of the sketch. If the most distant visible feature is many miles away, the *actual* horizon and the perspective horizon will be coincident, as in the canyon sketch cited.

(2) Try to see the land forms as lying in imaginary planes. Lightly sketch these planes on the paper, ignoring minor details of the landscape until the overall framework of the drawing is made.

(3) Next, sketch the outlines of the major topographic features within the perspective frame.

(4) Fill in the secondary features, but keep in mind the fact that all elements within a plane are subject to the perspective of that plane as a whole.

(5.) Include a tree, bush, or similar object in the foreground and again in the middle distance to serve a scale.

(6) The darkest shadows are always directly opposite the strongest light. Shadows reveal the forms, not only of the objects which cast them, but also those upon which they fall; therefore, it is extremely important to lay out the forms of "shaded" areas very carefully. Large areas in strong light exhibit little more detail than those in dark shadow. Draw the details of the landscape in the zones of intermediate light and shade, and *suggest* detail with very few lines in the zones of high light and deep shadow.

274. Surface Texture and Topographic Grain

The topographic sketches of Holmes, Davis, and others of the U.S. Geological Survey in the late 1800's capture the essence of western topography. These panoramic views are as precisely correct in line and structure as the draftsman's drawing of a gear. But the vitality and realism of their work is due not so much to the precision but to the "touch" of the artist. A critical study of these superb drawings discloses only one element that is capable of expressing the "feel" of the country they portrayed. This element is topographic and surface *texture*.

Textures may be roughly classified. There is the coarsest, which might include the hummocky topography of sand dunes and morainal deposits; and there are finer textures such as shale slopes and outwash sands and silts. The character of these surface textures is expressed in the sketch by bold solid lines, light wavy lines, rows of broken lines and dots, stippling, and various other techniques.

In addition to the ground surface, one must be cognizant of the vegetation cover. Areas covered by deciduous trees have an entirely different texture from those supporting evergreen forests, and neither resembles grassy slopes and plains. Inasmuch as the vegetal cover commonly is related to the stratigraphy, the distinction in plant cover is often important. Figure 213 illustrates the uses of a few patterns to simulate various textures.

A cursory examination of *low-angle oblique* aerial photos of

Fig. 213. Textures in drawings. Shading of the middle and background is in harmony with detail of the foreground.

different types of topography will show that certain prominent lines or bands of light and shadow conform to the topographic forms. In rolling or flat plains the lines are nearly straight and horizontal; in rolling, hilly regions, lines are gently arched; and in rugged canyon country, the lines are jagged and many prominent lines are vertical. A line drawn generally horizontal but following the directions of the shadow lines, approximates a profile of the surface. When sketching the broad relief features of an area it is helpful to visualize the surface as consisting of a series of profiles. Light profile lines may be sketched as guides at several places on the sheet.

275. The Sketching Frame

A sketching frame is a device than can be carried in the field for sketching directly any object or scene with an accuracy comparable to a photograph. It consists of two open rectangular frames, similar to a picture frame, mounted on a slat at the base in such a manner that the spacing between the frames can be adjusted. The larger forward frame contains a wire rectangular grid. Fig. 214 is a sketch of one type of frame that can easily be constructed in a home workshop.

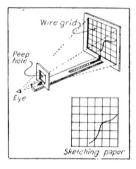

When in use, the spacing is adjusted until the desired scope of the view is seen in the forward frame when the rear frame is exactly coincident with it, as shown in Fig. 214. Of course the distance from the eye to the rear frame must also be

Fig. 214. Topograhic sketching frame for making precise sketches in the field.

compatible. When these conditions have been met, details of the landscape are related to each other according to where they appear on the coördinates of the grid. The drawing paper is prepared by ruling in a coördinate system having the same number of lines as the frame. If tracing paper is used, the coördinates can be inked on another sheet which is placed beneath the translucent material, thus serving for any number of sketches.

The main points and lines of the landscape appear at definite coördinate positions and they are sketched at the same relative coördinate positions on the drawing paper, as suggested in the figure.

The sketching frame is an aid to learning proportion and

perspective. A method sometimes employed in the classroom involves the same principle, as follows:

Heavy black coördinates are drawn on a large sheet of white paper, such as showcard stock. This sheet is a screen on to which any photographic slide can be projected. Drawing paper ruled in a similar fashion is the base for sketching details as seen in the projected image. This method is also excellent for constructing accurate line drawings for black and white illustrations for reports, theses, and the like.

276. Reproducible Drawings

A great amount of effort and time may go into the preparation of geologic illustrations; and it is indeed unfortunate if it is found, too late, that they are unsuitable for reproduction. For this reason it is well to plan for this eventuality by ascertaining *before* the drawings are made just what processes of reproduction will be used, the capacities of available reproduction machines, costs, and scale requirements. These factors may have much bearing on the methods, styles, and techniques that will be practical. The following items should be considered.

DIRECT PRINTING PROCESSES

These processes include Van Dyke, Ozalid, sepia, blue line, and blue print.

The *Van Dyke* is a "wet" method. A negative is made first and positive prints are made from this negative. The exposed sensitized paper is developed in a chemical bath, dried, and run through a mangle to iron out the wrinkles. Prints are clear and legible and the paper is a tough, high grade rag stock; therefore, the prints are quite durable. However, because of the liquid bath, the scale is always somewhat distorted. Original drawings must be on translucent material.

The *Ozalid* is a dry method and the scale remains fairly constant. After exposure of the original, the paper is exposed to ammonia fumes which develop the line detail. Ozalid paper comes in various weights and grades. The kind most commonly used is not quite so tough as the Van Dyke. The lines of drawings may be reproduced in several colors: blue, purple, brown, near black, *etc*. This method requires translucent originals.

Sepia prints are made by the ammonia, or dry process; hence, the scale is distorted but little. Lines are dark brown on a thin translucent paper that is moderately tough. Sepia prints, being translucent, may be used as the original tracings. This attribute is quite important to the geologist who may wish to make a number of different kinds of maps from the same base map. Undesirable details on the original can be eradicated from the sepia print and other data may be added in ink. The Sepia is then essentially the same as an original tracing and Ozalid or other types of prints can be made directly from this composite. Sepia prints can be made only from translucent drawings.

Certain processes, such as blue print, reverse the black and white of the original; i.e., the print has white lines on a dark blue background. This type of print serves as a record but is generally unsatisfactory for geologic work.

Indirect Processes

The commonest of these methods are metal lithograph, zinc offset, and half-tone.

These processes require the making of plates from which prints are made. Costs are much higher than for direct prints if only a few copies are needed. However, once the plate is made, printing costs are low. Therefore, if more than 100 copies of a drawing are required, one of the plate processes is better than direct printing. By these methods the original drawings may be reduced to any desired size.

Originals for zinc offset or lithograph reproduction must be in black and white on either opaque or translucent material. Intermediate tones of gray are not reproducible.

The half-tone is the process by which pencil, water color wash, and other shaded drawings and photographs are reproduced. The process is somewhat more expensive than the offset or lithograph. Original drawings are on opaque paper. A wide range of tonal values is required for a good half-tone print. Original drawings shaded in only the middle-tone grays will generally be quite flat in the half-tone print. Be sure the lights and darks in the original are in high contrast.

PHOTOGRAPHIC PROCESSES

These methods include photographs and photostats. The principal advantages in these methods is that the original drawing may be reduced or enlarged to any desired scale at moderate cost. Because of the emulsion covering the surface of the paper, prints are difficult to work on in pencil, ink, or color, though the surface can be improved by rubbing with drafting pounce.

Colored slides or prints can be made by photographing colored originals, and uncolored reproductions can be made from either black-line or shaded drawings. Originals may be made on either opaque or translucent materials.

Photostats can be made from only black- (or dark-) line originals. Colored or shaded areas are likely to be blotchy in the prints.

There is some scale distortion in these methods, though not significantly large. The paper used in both photographic and photostatic methods tends to harden with age, and for this reason it is a nuisance in bound reports.

277. Scale and Line Weight

Before maps and other drawings are made, the dimensions of reproducing machines should be ascertained. A 45-inch map cannot be printed in a 42-inch Ozalid machine.

A wide variety of tracing papers is available in sizes $8\frac{1}{2}$ x 11 and $8\frac{1}{2}$ x 14 inches. These are the standard letter-size and legal-size dimensions. Much inconvenience can be avoided if drawings are made on these standardized materials, not only in the preparation of the original sketches, but also in utilizing the prints in the finished report.

The small irregularities and roughness in inked lines are minimized or eliminated in prints on a reduced scale. For this reason, drawings to be reproduced by indirect or photographic methods should be made somewhat larger than desired in the prints. When a drawing is reduced to, say, one-half the scale of the original, every line, letter, and other detail is likewise reduced. This fact must be kept in mind when making the drawing, or certain portions may be illegible in the print. As a general rule, the best amount of reduction is one-fourth to one-half; i.e., the reproduction will be three-fourths or one-half the size of the original. A reduction in this amount is sufficient to "clean up" the lines, but not so great as to reduce fine detail to illegibility.

Extremely thin or poorly inked lines are likely to disappear by any of the processes of reproduction mentioned. Be sure that the lines are not too thin and are jet black, for light passes through or cuts out a thinly inked line. Very small enclosures, such as the letter *o* or the figures *4* and *9,* tend to fill in by any of the reproduction processes. Carefully check these features before sending the maps and drawings to the printer.

Excessively large drawings require more time in preparation than small ones and the appearance of the reduced reproduction is more difficult to visualize. The sketches in this book are reproduced at either the same scale as the original drawings or but slightly smaller.

Appendix

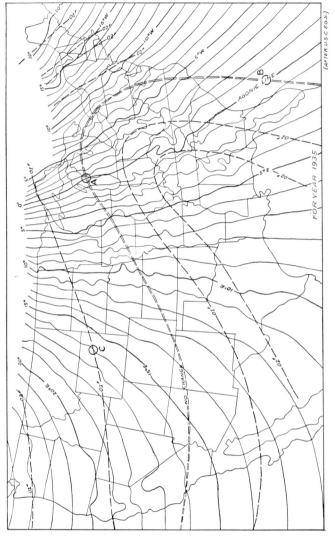

(AFTER U.S.C.&G.S.)

FOR YEAR 1935

AGONIC LINE

NO CHANGE

500 Miles

440

TABLE 1. The Isogonic Chart

Lines of equal magnetic declination are shown as solid lines. The values of these lines apply without correction only to the year 1935, the date of the chart. East of the AGONIC, or zero, line declinations are west; west of this line declinations are east; along the agonic line the compass needle points to true north (on the date of the chart).

The dashed lines indicate the annual rate of change in declination. Along the double dashed line there is no annual change in the amount of declination. North and east of this line the needle shifts to the west at a yearly rate indicated by the one-minute lines; and south and west of the double line the needle shifts to the east. At points *A* and *B* the needle points to true north year after year.

Example:

Year: 1950 (15 years after date of chart)
Location: At *C* in Wyoming
Indicated declination is 16°00′ East
Rate of annual change is 01′
Corrected declination is
16°00′−(15×01′)=15°45′ East

From Julian W. Low, *Plane Table Mapping*, Harper & Brothers, 1952, pp. 332-333.

TABLE 2. Stadia Conversion Tables

For computing difference of elevation and horizontal distance.
Anderson's: U.S. Geological Survey

\u0020 0°		1°		2°		3°		4°	
′	100	′	100	′	100	′	100	′	100
1	0.03	0	1.74	0	3.49	0	5.23	0	6.96
2	0.06	1	1.77	1	3.52	1	5.26	1	6.99
3	0.09	2	1.80	2	3.55	2	5.29	2	7.02
4	0.12	3	1.83	3	3.58	3	5.31	3	7.05
5	0.15	4	1.86	4	3.60	4	5.34	4	7.08
6	0.18	5	1.89	5	3.63	5	5.37	5	7.10
7	0.20	6	1.92	6	3.66	6	5.40	6	7.13
8	0.23	7	1.95	7	3.69	7	5.43	7	7.16
9	0.26	8	1.98	8	3.72	8	5.46	8	7.19
		9	2.01	9	3.75	9	5.49	9	7.22
10	0.29	10	2.04	10	3.78	10	5.52	10	7.25
11	0.32	11	2.06	11	3.81	11	5.54	11	7.28
12	0.38	12	2.09	12	3.84	12	5.58	12	7.30
13	0.38	13	2.12	13	3.86	13	5.60	13	7.33
14	0.41	14	2.15	14	3.89	14	5.63	14	7.36
15	0.44	15	2.18	15	3.92	15	5.66	15	7.39
16	0.47	16	2.21	16	3.95	16	5.69	16	7.42
17	0.49	17	2.24	17	3.98	17	5.72	17	7.45
18	0.52	18	2.27	18	4.01	18	5.75	18	7.48
19	0.55	19	2.30	19	4.04	19	5.77	19	7.51
20	0.58	20	2.33	20	4.07	20	5.80	20	7.53
21	0.61	21	2.36	21	4.10	21	5.83	21	7.56
22	0.64	22	2.38	22	4.13	22	5.86	22	7.59
23	0.67	23	2.41	23	4.16	23	5.89	23	7.62
24	0.70	24	2.44	24	4.18	24	5.92	24	7.65
25	0.73	25	2.47	25	4.21	25	5.95	25	7.68
26	0.76	26	2.50	26	4.24	26	5.98	26	7.71
27	0.79	27	2.53	27	4.27	27	6.01	27	7.74
28	0.81	28	2.56	28	4.30	28	6.04	28	7.76
29	0.84	29	2.59	29	4.33	29	6.06	29	7.79
30	0.87	30	2.62	30	4.36	30	6.09	30	7.82
31	0.90	31	2.65	31	4.39	31	6.12	31	7.85
32	0.93	32	2.68	32	4.42	32	6.15	32	7.88
33	0.96	33	2.70	33	4.44	33	6.18	33	7.91
34	0.99	34	2.73	34	4.47	34	6.21	34	7.94
35	1.02	35	2.76	35	4.50	35	6.24	35	7.97
36	1.05	36	2.79	36	4.53	36	6.27	36	7.99
37	1.08	37	2.82	37	4.56	37	6.30	37	8.02
38	1.11	38	2.85	38	4.59	38	6.32	38	8.05
39	1.13	39	2.88	39	4.62	39	6.35	39	8.08
40	1.16	40	2.91	40	4.65	40	6.38	40	8.11
41	1.19	41	2.94	41	4.68	41	6.41	41	8.14
42	1.22	42	2.97	42	4.71	42	6.44	42	8.17
43	1.25	43	3.00	43	4.73	43	6.47	43	8.20
44	1.28	44	3.02	44	4.76	44	6.50	44	8.22
45	1.31	45	3.05	45	4.79	45	6.53	45	8.25
46	1.34	46	3.08	46	4.82	46	6.56	46	8.28
47	1.37	47	3.11	47	4.85	47	6.59	47	8.31
48	1.40	48	3.14	48	4.88	48	6.61	48	8.34
49	1.42	49	3.17	49	4.91	49	6.64	49	8.37
50	1.45	50	3.20	50	4.94	50	6.67	50	8.40
51	1.48	51	3.23	51	4.97	51	6.70	51	8.43
52	1.51	52	3.26	52	5.00	52	6.73	52	8.45
53	1.54	53	3.29	53	5.02	53	6.76	53	8.48
54	1.57	54	3.31	54	5.05	54	6.79	54	8.51
55	1.60	55	3.34	55	5.08	55	6.81	55	8.54
56	1.63	56	3.37	56	5.11	56	6.85	56	8.57
57	1.66	57	3.40	57	5.14	57	6.88	57	8.60
58	1.69	58	3.43	58	5.17	58	6.90	58	8.63
59	1.72	59	3.46	59	5.20	59	6.93	59	8.65
Horz. Dist.	99.99	Horz. Dist.	99.93	Horz. Dist.	99.81	Horz. Dist.	99.63	Horz. Dist.	99.38

From Julian W. Low, *Plane Table Mapping,* Harper & Brothers 1952, pp. 354-359.

TABLE 2 (Continued)

5°		6°		7°		8°		9°	
′	100	′	100	′	100	′	100	′	100
0	8.68	0	10.40	0	12.10	0	13.78	0	15.45
1	8.71	1	10.42	1	12.12	1	13.81	1	15.48
2	8.74	2	10.45	2	12.15	2	13.84	2	15.51
3	8.77	3	10.48	3	12.18	3	13.87	3	15.53
4	8.80	4	10.51	4	12.21	4	13.89	4	15.56
5	8.82	5	10.54	5	12.24	5	13.92	5	15.59
6	8.85	6	10.57	6	12.27	6	13.95	6	15.62
7	8.88	7	10.59	7	12.29	7	13.98	7	15.64
8	8.91	8	10.62	8	12.32	8	14.01	8	15.67
9	8.94	9	10.65	9	12.35	9	14.03	9	15.70
10	8.97	10	10.68	10	12.38	10	14.06	10	15.73
11	9.00	11	10.71	11	12.41	11	14.09	11	15.76
12	9.03	12	10.74	12	12.43	12	14.12	12	15.78
13	9.06	13	10.76	13	12.46	13	14.14	13	15.81
14	9.08	14	10.79	14	12.49	14	14.17	14	15.84
15	9.11	15	10.82	15	12.52	15	14.20	15	15.86
16	9.14	16	10.85	16	12.55	16	14.23	16	15.89
17	9.17	17	10.88	17	12.58	17	14.26	17	15.92
18	9.20	18	10.91	18	12.60	18	14.28	18	15.95
19	9.23	19	10.94	19	12.63	19	14.31	19	15.98
20	9.25	20	10.96	20	12.66	20	14.34	20	16.00
21	9.28	21	10.99	21	12.69	21	14.37	21	16.03
22	9.31	22	11.02	22	12.72	22	14.40	22	16.06
23	9.34	23	11.05	23	12.74	23	14.42	23	16.09
24	9.37	24	11.08	24	12.77	24	14.45	24	16.11
25	9.40	25	11.11	25	12.80	25	14.48	25	16.14
26	9.43	26	11.13	26	12.83	26	14.51	26	16.17
27	9.46	27	11.16	27	12.86	27	14.54	27	16.20
28	9.48	28	11.19	28	12.88	28	14.56	28	16.22
29	9.51	29	11.22	29	12.91	29	14.59	29	16.25
30	9.54	30	11.25	30	12.94	30	14.62	30	16.28
31	9.57	31	11.28	31	12.97	31	14.65	31	16.31
32	9.60	32	11.30	32	13.00	32	14.67	32	16.33
33	9.63	33	11.32	33	13.02	33	14.70	33	16.36
34	9.65	34	11.36	34	13.05	34	14.73	34	16.39
35	9.68	35	11.39	35	13.08	35	14.76	35	16.42
36	9.71	36	11.42	36	13.11	36	14.79	36	16.44
37	9.74	37	11.45	37	13.14	37	14.81	37	16.47
38	9.77	38	11.47	38	13.17	38	14.84	38	16.50
39	9.80	39	11.50	39	13.20	39	14.87	39	16.53
40	9.83	40	11.53	40	13.22	40	14.90	40	16.55
41	9.86	41	11.56	41	13.25	41	14.92	41	16.58
42	9.88	42	11.59	42	13.28	42	14.95	42	16.61
43	9.91	43	11.62	43	13.31	43	14.98	43	16.64
44	9.94	44	11.64	44	13.33	44	15.01	44	16.66
45	9.97	45	11.67	45	13.36	45	15.04	45	16.69
46	10.00	46	11.70	46	13.39	46	15.06	46	16.72
47	10.02	47	11.73	47	13.42	47	15.09	47	16.74
48	10.05	48	11.76	48	13.45	48	15.12	48	16.77
49	10.08	49	11.79	49	13.47	49	15.15	49	16.80
50	10.11	50	11.81	50	13.50	50	15.17	50	16.83
51	10.14	51	11.84	51	13.53	51	15.20	51	16.86
52	10.17	52	11.87	52	13.56	52	15.23	52	16.88
53	10.20	53	11.90	53	13.59	53	15.26	53	16.91
54	10.22	54	11.93	54	13.61	54	15.28	54	16.94
55	10.25	55	11.96	55	13.64	55	15.31	55	16.96
56	10.28	56	11.98	56	13.67	56	15.34	56	16.99
57	10.31	57	12.01	57	13.70	57	15.37	57	17.02
58	10.34	58	12.04	58	13.73	58	15.40	58	17.05
59	10.37	59	12.07	59	13.75	59	15.42	59	17.08
Horz. Dist.	99.08	Horz. Dist.	98.72	Horz. Dist.	98.29	Horz. Dist.	97.82	Horz. Dist.	97.28

TABLE 2 (*Continued*)

10°		11°		12°		13°		14°	
′	100	′	100	′	100	′	100	′	100
0	17.10	0	18.73	0	20.34	0	21.92	0	23.47
1	17.13	1	18.76	1	20.36	1	21.94	1	23.50
2	17.16	2	18.78	2	20.39	2	21.97	2	23.52
3	17.18	3	18.81	3	20.42	3	22.00	3	23.55
4	17.21	4	18.84	4	20.44	4	22.02	4	23.58
5	17.24	5	18.86	5	20.47	5	22.05	5	23.60
6	17.26	6	18.89	6	20.50	6	22.08	6	23.63
7	17.29	7	18.92	7	20.52	7	22.10	7	23.65
8	17.32	8	18.95	8	20.55	8	22.13	8	23.68
9	17.35	9	18.97	9	20.58	9	22.15	9	23.70
10	17.37	10	19.00	10	20.60	10	22.18	10	23.73
11	17.40	11	19.03	11	20.63	11	22.21	11	23.76
12	17.43	12	19.05	12	20.66	12	22.23	12	23.78
13	17.46	13	19.08	13	20.68	13	22.26	13	23.81
14	17.48	14	19.11	14	20.71	14	22.28	14	23.83
15	17.51	15	19.13	15	20.73	15	22.31	15	23.86
16	17.54	16	19.16	16	20.76	16	22.34	16	23.88
17	17.56	17	19.19	17	20.79	17	22.36	17	23.91
18	17.59	18	19.22	18	20.81	18	22.39	18	23.94
19	17.62	19	19.24	19	20.84	19	22.41	19	23.96
20	17.65	20	19.27	20	20.87	20	22.44	20	23.98
21	17.67	21	19.30	21	20.89	21	22.47	21	24.01
22	17.70	22	19.32	22	20.92	22	22.49	22	24.04
23	17.73	23	19.35	23	20.95	23	22.52	23	24.06
24	17.76	24	19.38	24	20.97	24	22.54	24	24.09
25	17.78	25	19.40	25	21.00	25	22.57	25	24.11
26	17.81	26	19.43	26	21.03	26	22.60	26	24.14
27	17.84	27	19.46	27	21.05	27	22.62	27	24.16
28	17.86	28	19.48	28	21.08	28	22.65	28	24.19
29	17.89	29	19.51	29	21.10	29	22.67	29	24.22
30	17.92	30	19.54	30	21.13	30	22.70	30	24.24
31	17.95	31	19.56	31	21.16	31	22.73	31	24.27
32	17.97	32	19.59	32	21.18	32	22.75	32	24.29
33	18.00	33	19.62	33	21.21	33	22.78	33	24.32
34	18.03	34	19.64	34	21.24	34	22.80	34	24.34
35	18.05	35	19.67	35	21.26	35	22.83	35	24.37
36	18.08	36	19.70	36	21.29	36	22.86	36	24.39
37	18.11	37	19.72	37	21.32	37	22.88	37	24.42
38	18.14	38	19.75	38	21.34	38	22.91	38	24.44
39	18.16	39	19.78	39	21.37	39	22.94	39	24.47
40	18.19	40	19.80	40	21.39	40	22.96	40	24.50
41	18.22	41	19.83	41	21.42	41	22.98	41	24.52
42	18.24	42	19.86	42	21.45	42	23.01	42	24.54
43	18.27	43	19.88	43	21.47	43	23.04	43	24.57
44	18.30	44	19.91	44	21.50	44	23.06	44	24.60
45	18.32	45	19.94	45	21.53	45	23.09	45	24.62
46	18.35	46	19.96	46	21.55	46	23.11	46	24.65
47	18.38	47	19.99	47	21.58	47	23.14	47	24.67
48	18.41	48	20.02	48	21.60	48	23.17	48	24.70
49	18.43	49	20.04	49	21.63	49	23.19	49	24.72
50	18.46	50	20.07	50	21.66	50	23.22	50	24.75
51	18.49	51	20.10	51	21.68	51	23.24	51	24.77
52	18.51	52	20.12	52	21.71	52	23.27	52	24.80
53	18.54	53	20.15	53	21.74	53	23.29	53	24.82
54	18.57	54	20.18	54	21.76	54	23.32	54	24.85
55	18.60	55	20.20	55	21.79	55	23.34	55	24.87
56	18.62	56	20.23	56	21.81	56	23.37	56	24.90
57	18.65	57	20.26	57	21.84	57	23.40	57	24.92
58	18.68	58	20.28	58	21.87	58	23.42	58	24.95
59	18.70	59	20.31	59	21.89	59	23.45	59	24.98
Horz. Dist.	96.68	Horz. Dist.	96.03	Horz. Dist.	95.32	Horz. Dist.	94.55	Horz. Dist.	93.73

TABLE 2 (*Continued*)

15°		16°		17°		18°		19°	
′	100	′	100	′	100	′	100	′	100
0	25.00	0	26.50	0	27.96	0	29.39	0	30.78
1	25.02	1	26.52	1	27.99	1	29.42	1	30.81
2	25.05	2	26.55	2	28.01	2	29.44	2	30.83
3	25.08	3	26.57	3	28.04	3	29.47	3	30.85
4	25.10	4	26.60	4	28.06	4	29.49	4	30.87
5	25.13	5	26.62	5	28.08	5	29.51	5	30.90
6	25.15	6	26.64	6	28.10	6	29.53	6	30.92
7	25.18	7	26.67	7	28.13	7	29.56	7	30.94
8	25.20	8	26.69	8	28.15	8	29.58	8	30.97
9	25.23	9	26.72	9	28.18	9	29.60	9	30.99
10	25.25	10	26.74	10	28.20	10	29.62	10	31.01
11	25.28	11	26.77	11	28.22	11	29.65	11	31.04
12	25.30	12	26.79	12	28.25	12	29.67	12	31.06
13	25.33	13	26.82	13	28.27	13	29.69	13	31.08
14	25.35	14	26.84	14	28.30	14	29.72	14	31.10
15	25.38	15	26.86	15	28.32	15	29.74	15	31.13
16	25.40	16	26.89	16	28.34	16	29.76	16	31.15
17	25.43	17	26.91	17	28.37	17	29.79	17	31.17
18	25.45	18	26.94	18	28.39	18	29.81	18	31.19
19	25.48	19	26.96	19	28.42	19	29.83	19	31.22
20	25.50	20	26.99	20	28.44	20	29.86	20	31.24
21	25.53	21	27.01	21	28.47	21	29.88	21	31.26
22	25.55	22	27.04	22	28.49	22	29.90	22	31.28
23	25.58	23	27.06	23	28.51	23	29.93	23	31.30
24	25.60	24	27.09	24	28.54	24	29.95	24	31.33
25	25.63	25	27.11	25	28.56	25	29.97	25	31.35
26	25.65	26	27.13	26	28.58	26	30.00	26	31.38
27	25.68	27	27.16	27	28.61	27	30.02	27	31.40
28	25.70	28	27.18	28	28.63	28	30.04	28	31.42
29	25.73	29	27.21	29	28.66	29	30.07	29	31.44
30	25.75	30	27.23	30	28.68	30	30.09	30	31.47
31	25.78	31	27.26	31	28.70	31	30.11	31	31.49
32	25.80	32	27.28	32	28.73	32	30.14	32	31.51
33	25.83	33	27.30	33	28.75	33	30.16	33	31.54
34	25.85	34	27.33	34	28.77	34	30.19	34	31.56
35	25.88	35	27.35	35	28.80	35	30.21	35	31.58
36	25.90	36	27.38	36	28.82	36	30.23	36	31.60
37	25.93	37	27.40	37	28.85	37	30.26	37	31.63
38	25.95	38	27.43	38	28.87	38	30.28	38	31.65
39	25.98	39	27.45	39	28.89	39	30.30	39	31.67
40	26.00	40	27.48	40	28.92	40	30.32	40	31.69
41	26.02	41	27.50	41	28.94	41	30.36	41	31.72
42	26.05	42	27.52	42	28.96	42	30.37	42	31.74
43	26.08	43	27.55	43	28.99	43	30.39	43	31.76
44	26.10	44	27.57	44	29.01	44	30.41	44	31.78
45	26.12	45	27.60	45	29.04	45	30.44	45	31.81
46	26.15	46	27.62	46	29.06	46	30.46	46	31.83
47	26.18	47	27.65	47	29.08	47	30.49	47	31.85
48	26.20	48	27.67	48	29.11	48	30.51	48	31.87
49	26.22	49	27.69	49	29.13	49	30.53	49	31.90
50	26.25	50	27.72	50	29.15	50	30.55	50	31.92
51	26.27	51	27.74	51	29.18	51	30.58	51	31.94
52	26.30	52	27.77	52	29.20	52	30.60	52	31.96
53	26.32	53	27.79	53	29.23	53	30.62	53	31.99
54	26.35	54	27.82	54	29.25	54	30.65	54	32.01
55	26.37	55	27.84	55	29.27	55	30.67	55	32.03
56	26.40	56	27.86	56	29.30	56	30.69	56	32.05
57	26.42	57	27.89	57	29.32	57	30.72	57	32.07
58	26.45	58	27.91	58	29.34	58	30.74	58	32.09
59	26.47	59	27.94	59	29.37	59	30.76	59	32.12
Horz. Dist.	92.86	Horz. Dist.	91.93	Horz. Dist.	90.96	Horz. Dist.	89.93	Horz. Dist.	88.86

TABLE 2 (*Continued*)

20°		21°		22°		23°		24°	
′	100	′	100	′	100	′	100	′	100
0	32.14	0	33.46	0	34.73	0	35.97	0	37.16
1	32.16	1	33.48	1	34.75	1	35.99	1	37.18
2	32.18	2	33.50	2	34.77	2	36.01	2	37.20
3	32.21	3	33.52	3	34.80	3	36.03	3	37.22
4	32.23	4	33.54	4	34.82	4	36.05	4	37.23
5	32.25	5	33.57	5	34.84	5	36.07	5	37.25
6	32.27	6	33.59	6	34.86	6	36.09	6	37.27
7	32.30	7	33.61	7	34.88	7	36.11	7	37.29
8	32.32	8	33.63	8	34.90	8	36.13	8	37.31
9	32.34	9	33.65	9	34.92	9	36.15	9	37.33
10	32.36	10	33.67	10	34.94	10	36.17	10	37.35
11	32.39	11	33.70	11	34.96	11	36.19	11	37.37
12	32.41	12	33.72	12	34.98	12	36.21	12	37.39
13	32.43	13	33.74	13	35.00	13	36.23	13	37.41
14	32.45	14	33.76	14	35.02	14	36.25	14	37.43
15	32.47	15	33.78	15	35.05	15	36.27	15	37.45
16	32.49	16	33.80	16	35.07	16	36.29	16	37.47
17	32.51	17	33.82	17	35.09	17	36.31	17	37.49
18	32.54	18	33.84	18	35.11	18	36.33	18	37.51
19	32.56	19	33.87	19	35.13	19	36.35	19	37.53
20	32.58	20	33.89	20	35.15	20	36.37	20	37.54
21	32.61	21	33.91	21	35.17	21	36.39	21	37.56
22	32.63	22	33.93	22	35.19	22	36.41	22	37.58
23	32.65	23	33.95	23	35.21	23	36.43	23	37.60
24	32.67	24	33.97	24	35.23	24	36.45	24	37.62
25	32.70	25	33.99	25	35.25	25	36.47	25	37.64
26	32.72	26	34.01	26	35.27	26	36.49	26	37.66
27	32.74	27	34.04	27	35.29	27	36.51	27	37.68
28	32.76	28	34.06	28	35.31	28	36.53	28	37.70
29	32.78	29	34.08	29	35.34	29	36.55	29	37.72
30	32.80	30	34.10	30	35.36	30	36.57	30	37.74
31	32.83	31	34.12	31	35.38	31	36.59	31	37.76
32	32.85	32	34.14	32	35.40	32	36.61	32	37.77
33	32.87	33	34.16	33	35.42	33	36.63	33	37.79
34	32.89	34	34.18	34	35.44	34	36.65	34	37.81
35	32.91	35	34.21	35	35.46	35	36.67	35	37.83
36	32.93	36	34.23	36	35.48	36	36.69	36	37.85
37	32.96	37	34.25	37	35.50	37	36.71	37	37.87
38	32.98	38	34.27	38	35.52	38	36.73	38	37.89
39	33.00	39	34.29	39	35.54	39	36.75	39	37.91
40	33.02	40	34.31	40	35.56	40	36.77	40	37.93
41	33.05	41	34.33	41	35.58	41	36.79	41	37.95
42	33.07	42	34.35	42	35.60	42	36.80	42	37.96
43	33.09	43	34.38	43	35.62	43	36.82	43	37.98
44	33.11	44	34.40	44	35.64	44	36.84	44	38.00
45	33.13	45	34.42	45	35.66	45	36.86	45	38.02
46	33.15	46	34.44	46	35.68	46	36.88	46	38.04
47	33.18	47	34.46	47	35.70	47	36.90	47	38.06
48	33.20	48	34.48	48	35.72	48	36.92	48	38.08
49	33.22	49	34.50	49	35.74	49	36.94	49	38.10
50	33.24	50	34.52	50	35.76	50	36.96	50	38.11
51	33.26	51	34.54	51	35.78	51	36.98	51	38.13
52	33.28	52	34.57	52	35.80	52	37.00	52	38.15
53	33.31	53	34.59	53	35.83	53	37.02	53	38.17
54	33.33	54	34.61	54	35.85	54	37.04	54	38.19
55	33.35	55	34.63	55	35.87	55	37.06	55	38.21
56	33.37	56	34.65	56	35.89	56	37.08	56	38.23
57	33.39	57	34.67	57	35.91	57	37.10	57	38.25
58	33.41	58	34.69	58	35.93	58	37.12	58	38.26
59	33.44	59	34.71	59	35.95	59	37.14	59	38.28
Horz. Dist.	87.74	Horz. Dist.	86.57	Horz. Dist.	85.36	Horz. Dist.	84.10	Horz. Dist.	82.80

TABLE 2 (*Continued*)

25°	100	26°	100	27°	100	28°	100	29°	100
′		′		′		′		′	
0	38.30	0	39.40	0	40.45	0	41.45	0	42.40
1	38.32	1	39.42	1	40.47	1	41.47	1	42.42
2	38.34	2	39.44	2	40.49	2	41.48	2	42.43
3	38.36	3	39.46	3	40.51	3	41.50	3	42.45
4	38.38	4	39.47	4	40.52	4	41.52	4	42.46
5	38.40	5	39.49	5	40.54	5	41.54	5	42.48
6	38.41	6	39.51	6	40.55	6	41.55	6	42.49
7	38.43	7	39.53	7	40.57	7	41.57	7	42.51
8	38.45	8	39.55	8	40.59	8	41.58	8	42.53
9	38.47	9	39.56	9	40.61	9	41.60	9	42.54
10	38.49	10	39.58	10	40.62	10	41.61	10	42.56
11	38.51	11	39.60	11	40.64	11	41.63	11	42.58
12	38.53	12	39.61	12	40.66	12	41.65	12	42.59
13	38.55	13	39.63	13	40.68	13	41.67	13	42.60
14	38.56	14	39.65	14	40.69	14	41.68	14	42.62
15	38.58	15	39.67	15	40.71	15	41.70	15	42.64
16	38.60	16	39.69	16	40.72	16	41.71	16	42.65
17	38.62	17	39.71	17	40.74	17	41.73	17	42.66
18	38.64	18	39.72	18	40.76	18	41.74	18	42.68
19	38.66	19	39.74	19	40.78	19	41.76	19	42.70
20	38.67	20	39.76	20	40.79	20	41.77	20	42.71
21	38.69	21	39.78	21	40.81	21	41.79	21	42.72
22	38.71	22	39.79	22	40.82	22	41.81	22	42.74
23	38.73	23	39.81	23	40.84	23	41.83	23	42.76
24	38.75	24	39.83	24	40.86	24	41.84	24	42.77
25	38.76	25	39.85	25	40.88	25	41.86	25	42.78
26	38.78	26	39.86	26	40.89	26	41.87	26	42.80
27	38.80	27	39.88	27	40.91	27	41.89	27	42.82
28	38.82	28	39.90	28	40.92	28	41.90	28	42.83
29	38.84	29	39.92	29	40.94	29	41.92	29	42.85
30	38.86	30	39.93	30	40.96	30	41.93	30	42.86
31	38.88	31	39.95	31	40.98	31	41.95	31	42.88
32	38.89	32	39.97	32	40.99	32	41.97	32	42.89
33	38.91	33	39.99	33	41.01	33	41.99	33	42.91
34	38.93	34	40.00	34	41.02	34	42.00	34	42.92
35	38.95	35	40.02	35	41.04	35	42.02	35	42.94
36	38.97	36	40.04	36	41.06	36	42.03	36	42.95
37	38.99	37	40.06	37	41.08	37	42.05	37	42.97
38	39.00	38	40.07	38	41.09	38	42.06	38	42.98
39	39.02	39	40.09	39	41.11	39	42.08	39	43.00
40	39.04	40	40.11	40	41.12	40	42.09	40	43.01
41	39.06	41	40.13	41	41.14	41	42.11	41	43.03
42	39.08	42	40.14	42	41.16	42	42.12	42	43.04
43	39.10	43	40.16	43	41.18	43	42.14	43	43.06
44	39.11	44	40.18	44	41.19	44	42.15	44	43.07
45	39.13	45	40.20	45	41.21	45	42.17	45	43.09
46	39.15	46	40.21	46	41.22	46	42.19	46	43.10
47	39.17	47	40.23	47	41.24	47	42.21	47	43.12
48	39.18	48	40.24	48	41.26	48	42.22	48	43.13
49	39.20	49	40.26	49	41.28	49	42.24	49	43.15
50	39.22	50	40.28	50	41.29	50	42.25	50	44.16
51	39.24	51	40.30	51	41.31	51	42.26	51	43.17
52	39.26	52	40.31	52	41.32	52	42.28	52	43.18
53	39.27	53	40.33	53	41.34	53	42.30	53	43.20
54	39.29	54	40.35	54	41.35	54	42.31	54	43.21
55	39.31	55	40.37	55	41.37	55	42.33	55	43.23
56	39.33	56	40.38	56	41.39	56	42.34	56	43.24
57	39.35	57	40.40	57	41.41	57	42.36	57	43.26
58	39.36	58	40.42	58	41.42	58	42.37	58	43.27
59	39.38	59	40.44	59	41.43	59	42.39	59	43.29
Horz. Dist.	81.47	Horz. Dist.	80.09	Horz. Dist.	78.68	Horz. Dist.	77.23	Horz. Dist.	75.75

447

TABLE 3.   Corrections for Curvature and Refraction

Correction in feet $= 0.0206 \left(\dfrac{d}{1000}\right)^2$ (When d is in feet)

Dist. in Feet	Cor. in Feet		Dist.	Cor.		Dist.	Cor.
2,000	00.1		18,000	06.6		34,000	23.7
3,000	00.2		19,000	07.4		35,000	25.2
4,000	00.3		20,000	08.2		36,000	26.7
5,000	00.4		21,000	09.0		37,000	28.2
6,000	00.6		22,000	09.9		38,000	29.7
7,000	00.8		23,000	10.8		39,000	31.3
8,000	01.2		24,000	11.8		40,000	32.9
9,000	01.6		25,000	12.8		41,000	34.6
10,000	02.1		26,000	13.9		42,000	36.3
11,000	02.5		27,000	14.9		43,000	38.1
12,000	03.0		28,000	16.0		44,000	39.9
13,000	03.5		29,000	17.2		45,000	41.7
14,000	04.0		30,000	18.4		46,000	43.6
15,000	04.6		31,000	19.7		47,000	45.5
16,000	05.2		32,000	20.9		48,000	47.5
17,000	05.9		33,000	22.2		49,000	49.5
						50,000	51.5

Correction in feet $= 0.574D^2$ (When D is in miles)

Distance in Miles	Cor. in Feet	Distance in Miles	Cor. in Feet
1	00.6	13	97.0
2	02.3	14	112.5
3	05.2	15	129.1
4	09.2	16	146.9
5	14.4	17	165.8
6	20.6	18	185.9
7	28.1	19	207.2
8	36.7	20	229.5
9	46.4	21	253.1
10	57.4	22	277.7
11	69.4	23	303.6
12	82.7	24	330.5
		25	358.6

From Julian W. Low, *Plane Table Mapping,* Harper & Brothers, 1952, p. 331.

TABLE 4. Stratigraphic Thickness and Dip Migration from Horizontal Distance Measurements

$T = h\ sine\ \theta$

$m = (h\ sine\ \theta)\cdot sine\ \theta, \quad m = h\ sine^2\ \theta$

$\alpha = \theta$

$m = T\ sine\ \alpha$

Rate of Dip	Horizontal Distance Stratigraphic Thickness										Normal to Strike Migration of Dip									
	100	200	300	400	500	600	700	800	900	1000	100	200	300	400	500	600	700	800	900	1000
2°	3	7	10	14	17	21	24	28	31	35	0	0	0	0	0	0	0	1	1	1
4	7	14	21	28	35	42	49	56	63	70	0	1	1	2	2	3	3	4	4	5
6	10	21	31	42	52	62	73	83	93	104	1	2	3	4	5	6	8	9	10	11
8	14	28	42	56	70	84	98	112	126	140	2	4	6	8	10	12	14	16	18	20
10	17	35	52	70	87	104	122	139	157	174	3	6	9	12	15	18	21	24	27	30
12	21	42	62	83	104	124	146	166	187	208	4	9	13	17	22	26	30	34	39	43
14	24	48	76	97	121	145	169	194	218	242	6	12	18	23	29	35	41	47	53	59
16	28	56	84	112	140	168	196	224	252	280	8	16	23	31	39	47	55	63	71	78
18	31	62	93	124	155	186	217	248	279	310	10	19	29	38	48	58	67	77	86	96
20	34	68	103	137	171	205	239	274	308	342	12	23	35	47	58	70	81	93	105	117
22	37	74	112	150	187	225	262	300	337	375	14	28	42	56	70	84	98	112	126	141
24	41	81	122	163	203	245	286	326	367	408	17	33	50	66	83	100	116	133	149	166
26	44	88	128	175	219	263	307	350	394	438	19	38	56	77	96	115	134	153	172	192
28	47	94	141	188	235	281	328	375	422	469	22	44	66	88	110	132	154	176	198	220
30	50	100	150	200	250	300	350	400	450	500	25	50	75	100	125	150	175	200	225	250
32	53	106	159	212	265	318	371	424	477	530	28	56	84	112	140	168	197	225	253	281
34	56	112	168	224	279	335	391	447	503	559	31	63	94	125	156	187	218	250	281	312
36	59	118	176	235	294	353	412	470	529	588	35	69	103	138	173	207	242	276	311	346
38	62	123	185	246	308	370	431	493	554	616	38	76	114	152	190	228	265	304	341	379
40	64	129	193	257	321	386	450	514	579	643	41	83	124	165	206	248	289	330	372	413
42	67	134	201	268	334	401	468	535	602	669	45	90	134	179	223	268	313	358	403	447
44	70	139	208	278	347	417	486	556	625	695	48	97	144	193	241	290	338	386	434	483
46	72	144	215	288	359	431	503	575	647	719	51	102	152	204	254	305	357	408	459	510
48	74	149	223	297	371	446	520	594	669	743	55	110	166	220	276	331	386	441	497	552
50	77	153	230	306	383	460	536	613	689	766	59	117	176	234	293	352	410	469	528	587
52	79	158	236	315	394	473	552	630	709	788	62	124	186	248	310	373	435	496	559	621
54	81	162	243	324	404	485	566	647	728	809	65	131	197	262	327	392	458	523	589	654
56	83	165	249	332	414	497	580	663	746	829	69	137	206	275	343	412	481	550	618	687
58	85	170	254	339	424	509	594	678	763	848	72	144	215	287	359	432	504	575	647	719
60	87	173	260	346	433	520	606	693	780	866	75	150	225	300	375	450	525	600	675	750

Example: Dip 32°, Distance 1250 ft. Thickness 530 (from 10th column), 106 (from 2nd column), 26 (from 5th column), Total 662. Migration 281, 56, 14, Total 351.

Compiled by J.W.Low, 1954

449

TABLE 5. Conversion of Brunton Observations to Stratigraphic Thicknesses

Dip in Degrees	Height of Eyes Above Ground Point							
	4.6	4.8	5.0	5.2	5.4	5.6	5.8	6.0
0	4.6	4.8	5.0	5.2	5.4	5.6	5.8	6.0
2	4.6	4.8	5.0	5.2	5.4	5.6	5.8	6.0
4	4.6	4.8	5.0	5.2	5.4	5.6	5.8	6.0
6	4.6	4.8	5.0	5.2	5.4	5.6	5.8	6.0
8	4.5	4.7	4.9	5.1	5.3	5.5	5.7	5.9
10	4.5	4.7	4.9	5.1	5.3	5.5	5.7	5.9
12	4.5	4.7	4.9	5.1	5.3	5.5	5.7	5.9
14	4.5	4.6	4.8	5.0	5.2	5.4	5.6	5.8
16	4.5	4.6	4.8	5.0	5.2	5.4	5.6	5.8
18	4.4	4.5	4.7	4.9	5.1	5.3	5.5	5.7
20	4.4	4.5	4.7	4.9	5.1	5.3	5.4	5.6
22	4.4	4.5	4.7	4.9	5.1	5.3	5.4	5.6
24	4.2	4.4	4.5	4.7	4.9	5.1	5.2	5.4
26	4.1	4.3	4.5	4.6	4.8	5.0	5.2	5.4
28	4.0	4.2	4.4	4.6	4.7	4.9	5.1	5.3
30	4.0	4.2	4.3	4.5	4.7	4.9	5.0	5.2
32	3.9	4.1	4.2	4.4	4.6	4.8	4.9	5.1
34	3.8	4.0	4.2	4.4	4.6	4.8	4.9	5.1
36	3.8	3.9	4.1	4.3	4.4	4.6	4.7	4.9
38	3.6	3.8	4.0	4.2	4.3	4.4	4.6	4.7
40	3.5	3.7	3.9	4.0	4.2	4.3	4.5	4.6
42	3.4	3.5	3.7	3.8	4.0	4.1	4.3	4.4
44	3.3	3.4	3.6	3.7	3.9	4.0	4.2	4.3
46	3.2	3.3	3.4	3.6	3.7	3.9	4.0	4.1
48	3.1	3.2	3.3	3.5	3.6	3.7	3.8	4.0
50	2.9	3.1	3.2	3.3	3.5	3.6	3.7	3.9
52	2.8	3.0	3.1	3.2	3.3	3.4	3.6	3.7
54	2.7	2.8	2.9	3.0	3.2	3.3	3.4	3.5
56	2.6	2.7	2.8	2.9	3.0	3.1	3.2	3.3
58	2.4	2.5	2.6	2.8	2.9	3.0	3.1	3.2
60	2.3	2.4	2.5	2.6	2.7	2.8	2.9	3.0

Example 1. Height from eyes to ground, 5.4 feet; dip 20 degrees. Set the Brunton arc at 20°, sight to ground points as if Brunton were a hand level along line of section normal to strike. Stratigraphic thickness for each "step" is 5.1 ft. (from table).

Example 2: Measurement parallel to strike. Set Brunton at zero or use a Locke hand level. Height to eyes, 5.8 ft ; dip 30°. Stratigraphic thickness is 5.0 feet per step (from table).

TABLE 6. Natural Secants

For computing the vertical distance to specific horizons where the rate of dip and the stratigraphic interval are known

Degrees (Dip)	Factor	Degrees (Dip)	Factor
0	1.000	36	1.236
1	1.000	37	1.252
2	1.000	38	1.269
3	1.001	39	1.287
4	1.002	40	1.305
5	1.004		
6	1.006	41	1.325
7	1.008	42	1.346
8	1.010	43	1.367
9	1.012	44	1.390
10	1.015	45	1.414
		46	1.439
11	1.019	47	1.466
12	1.022	48	1.494
13	1.026	49	1.524
14	1.030	50	1.556
15	1.035		
16	1.040	51	1.589
17	1.046	52	1.624
18	1.051	53	1.661
19	1.058	54	1.701
20	1.064	55	1.743
		56	1.788
21	1.071	57	1.836
22	1.078	58	1.887
23	1.086	59	1.941
24	1.095	60	2.000
25	1.103		
26	1.113	61	2.063
27	1.122	62	2.130
28	1.133	63	2.203
29	1.143	64	2.281
30	1.155	65	2.366
		66	2.499
31	1.167	67	2.599
32	1.179	68	2.669
33	1.192	69	2.790
34	1.206	70	2.924
35	1.221		

Example: Angle of dip, 18 degrees
Stratigraphic interval, 1240 feet
Drilling thickness = 1240 × 1.051 = 1303 feet

451

TABLE 7. Conversion of True Dip to Component in the Line of Section

Angle Between Section Line and Strike of Strata — Degrees	Apparent Dips in the Line of Section — Degrees																
	5	10	15	20	25	30	35	40	45	50	55	60	65	70	75	80	85
5	0.5	1.0	1.5	2.0	2.5	3.0	3.5	4.0	5.0	6.0	7.0	8.5	10.0	13.0	18.0	26.0	44.0
10	1.0	2.0	3.0	4.0	5.0	6.0	7.0	8.5	10.0	12.0	14.0	16.5	20.0	25.0	32.0	44.0	62.0
15	1.5	3.0	4.0	5.5	7.0	8.5	10.5	12.0	15.0	17.5	20.0	24.0	29.5	35.0	43.0	55.0	70.0
20	1.5	3.5	5.5	7.0	9.0	11.0	13.5	16.0	19.0	22.5	26.0	31.0	36.0	42.5	51.0	62.0	75.0
25	2.0	4.5	6.5	9.0	11.0	13.5	17.0	19.5	22.5	27.0	31.0	36.5	42.0	48.5	57.0	67.0	78.0
30	2.5	5.0	8.0	10.5	13.0	16.0	19.0	23.0	26.0	31.0	35.5	41.0	46.5	53.0	61.0	70.5	80.0
35	3.0	6.0	9.0	12.0	15.0	18.0	23.0	26.0	29.0	34.5	39.5	45.0	50.5	57.5	65.0	73.0	82.0
40	3.0	6.5	10.0	13.5	16.5	20.5	24.0	28.0	32.0	37.5	43.0	48.0	54.0	61.0	67.0	75.0	83.0
45	3.5	7.0	11.0	14.5	18.0	22.0	26.5	31.0	35.5	40.0	45.5	51.0	56.5	63.0	69.0	76.5	83.5
50	3.5	7.5	11.5	16.0	19.5	24.0	28.0	33.0	37.5	42.5	47.5	53.0	59.0	65.0	71.0	77.5	84.0
55	4.0	8.0	12.0	17.0	21.0	25.0	30.0	35.0	39.5	44.5	49.5	55.0	60.5	66.5	72.0	78.0	84.0
60	4.5	9.0	13.0	18.0	22.0	27.0	31.5	36.5	41.0	46.0	51.0	56.5	61.5	67.5	73.0	79.0	84.0
65	4.5	9.0	13.5	18.5	23.0	28.0	32.5	37.5	42.0	47.0	52.0	57.5	62.5	68.5	73.5	79.5	84.5
70	4.5	9.0	14.0	19.0	23.5	28.5	33.5	38.0	43.0	48.0	53.0	58.5	63.5	69.0	74.0	79.5	85.0
75	5.0	9.5	14.5	19.5	24.0	29.0	34.0	39.0	44.0	49.0	54.0	59.0	64.0	69.5	74.5	80.0	85.0
80	5.0	10.0	15.0	20.0	24.5	29.5	34.5	39.5	44.5	49.5	54.5	59.5	64.5	69.5	74.5	80.0	85.0
85	5.0	10.0	15.0	20.0	25.0	30.0	35.0	40.0	44.5	49.5	54.5	59.5	64.5	69.5	75.0	80.0	85.0
Degrees	5	10	15	20	25	30	35	40	45	50	55	60	65	70	75	80	85

True Dips at 90° to the Strike

Example 1: Strike N 10° E, Dip 30° SE, line of section N 50° E. Find apparent dip along line of section. Angle between strike and line of section is 50° − 10° = 40°. Find 40° in left column, 30° on bottom row; dip component in line of section is 20.5°.

Example 2: Strike of strata N 15° E, component of dip along a line bearing N 40° E is 20°. Find true dip. Angle between strike and line of component is 40° − 15° = 25°. From left column at 25° find 20° to the right (19.5 is nearest point). From 19.5, read true dip at bottom: 40°, approximate.

Reprinted with permission from J. Donald Forrester, *Principles of Field and Mining Geology*, 1946, John Wiley & Sons, Inc.

TABLE 8. Useful Trigonometric Formulas

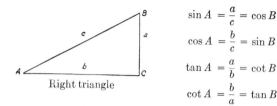

$$\sin A = \frac{a}{c} = \cos B$$

$$\cos A = \frac{b}{c} = \sin B$$

$$\tan A = \frac{a}{b} = \cot B$$

$$\cot A = \frac{b}{a} = \tan B$$

Right triangle

$$a = c \sin A = c \cos B = b \tan A = b \cot B$$
$$b = c \cos A = c \sin B = a \cot A = a \tan B$$
$$c = \frac{a}{\sin A} = \frac{a}{\cos B} = \frac{b}{\sin B} = \frac{b}{\cos A}$$

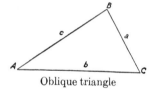

Oblique triangle

Known
a, B, A

$$b = \frac{a}{\sin A} \cdot \sin B$$

$$c = \frac{a}{\sin A} \cdot \sin (A + B)$$

Known
a, b, A

$$\sin B = \frac{\sin A}{a} \cdot b$$

$$c = \frac{a}{\sin A} \cdot \sin C$$

$$\frac{a}{\sin A} = \frac{b}{\sin B} = \frac{c}{\sin C}$$

$$a = \frac{b}{\sin B} \cdot \sin A = \frac{c}{\sin C} \cdot \sin A$$

$$b = \frac{a}{\sin A} \cdot \sin B = \frac{c}{\sin C} \cdot \sin B$$

$$c = \frac{a}{\sin A} \cdot \sin C = \frac{b}{\sin B} \cdot \sin C$$

From Julian W. Low, *Plane Table Mapping,* Harper & Brothers, 1952, p. 353.

TABLE 9. Natural Sines, Cosines, Tangents, and Cotangents

′	0°		1°		2°		3°		4°		′
	N. sine	N. cos.	N. sine	N. cos.	N.sine	N.cos.	N.sine	N.cos.	N.sine	N.cos.	
0	.00000	1.00000	.01745	.99985	.03490	.99939	.05234	.99863	.06976	.99756	60
1	029	000	774	984	519	938	263	861	.07005	754	59
2	058	000	803	984	548	937	292	860	034	752	58
3	087	000	832	983	577	936	321	858	063	750	57
4	116	000	862	983	606	935	350	857	092	748	56
5	145	000	891	982	635	934	379	855	121	746	55
6	175	000	920	982	664	933	408	854	150	744	54
7	204	000	949	981	693	932	437	852	179	742	53
8	233	000	978	980	723	931	466	851	208	740	52
9	262	000	.02007	980	752	930	495	849	237	738	51
10	.00291	1.00000	.02036	.99979	.03781	.99929	.05524	.99847	.07266	.99736	50
11	320	.99999	065	979	810	927	553	846	295	734	49
12	349	999	094	978	839	926	582	844	324	731	48
13	378	999	123	977	868	925	611	842	353	729	47
14	407	999	152	977	897	924	640	841	382	727	46
15	436	999	181	976	926	923	669	839	411	725	45
16	465	999	211	976	955	922	698	838	440	723	44
17	495	999	240	975	984	921	727	836	469	721	43
18	524	999	269	974	.04013	919	756	834	498	719	42
19	553	998	298	974	042	918	785	833	527	716	41
20	00582	.99998	.02327	.99973	.04071	.99917	.05814	.99831	.07556	.99714	40
21	611	998	356	972	100	916	844	829	585	712	39
22	640	998	385	972	129	915	873	827	614	710	38
23	669	998	414	971	159	913	902	826	643	708	37
24	698	998	443	970	188	912	931	824	672	705	36
25	727	997	472	969	217	911	960	822	701	703	35
26	756	997	501	969	246	910	989	821	730	701	34
27	785	997	530	968	275	909	.06018	819	759	699	33
28	814	997	560	967	304	907	047	817	788	696	32
29	844	996	589	966	333	906	076	815	817	694	31
30	.00873	.99996	.02618	.99966	.04362	.99905	.06105	.99813	.07846	.99692	30
31	902	996	647	965	391	904	134	812	875	689	29
32	931	996	676	964	420	902	163	810	904	687	28
33	960	995	705	963	449	901	192	808	933	685	27
34	989	995	734	963	478	900	221	806	962	683	26
35	.01018	995	763	962	507	898	250	804	991	680	25
36	047	995	792	961	536	897	279	803	.08020	678	24
37	076	994	821	960	565	896	308	801	049	676	23
38	105	994	850	959	594	894	337	799	078	673	22
39	134	994	879	959	623	893	366	797	107	671	21
40	.01164	.99993	.02908	.99958	.04653	.99892	.06395	.99795	.08136	.99668	20
41	193	993	938	957	682	890	424	793	165	666	19
42	222	993	967	956	711	889	453	792	194	664	18
43	251	992	996	955	740	888	482	790	223	661	17
44	280	992	.03025	954	769	886	511	788	252	659	16
45	309	991	054	953	798	885	540	786	281	657	15
46	338	991	083	952	827	883	569	784	310	654	14
47	367	991	112	952	856	882	598	782	339	652	13
48	396	990	141	951	885	881	627	780	368	649	12
49	425	990	170	950	914	879	656	778	397	647	11
50	.01454	.99989	.03199	.99949	.04943	.99878	.06685	.99776	.08426	.99644	10
51	483	989	228	948	972	876	714	774	455	642	9
52	513	989	257	947	.05001	875	743	772	484	639	8
53	542	988	286	946	030	873	773	770	513	637	7
54	571	988	316	945	059	872	802	768	542	635	6
55	600	987	345	944	088	870	831	766	571	632	5
56	629	987	374	943	117	869	860	764	600	630	4
57	658	986	403	942	146	867	889	762	629	627	3
58	687	986	432	941	175	866	918	760	658	625	2
59	716	985	461	940	205	864	947	758	687	622	1
60	.01745	.99985	.03490	.99939	.05234	.99863	.06976	.99756	.08716	.99619	0
	N. cos.	N. sine	N. cos.	N. sine	N.cos.	N.sine	N.cos.	N.sine	N.cos.	N.sine	
′	89°		88°		87°		86°		85°		′

From Julian W. Low, *Plane Table Mapping*, Harper & Brothers, 1952, pp. 334-351.

TABLE 9 (Continued)

′	0° Tang	0° Cotg	1° Tang	1° Cotg	2° Tang	2° Cotg	3° Tang	3° Cotg	4° Tang	4° Cotg	′
0	.0000	Infinite	.0175	57.2900	.0349	28.6363	.0524	19.0811	.0699	14.3007	60
1	03	3437.75	77	56.3506	52	3994	27	18.9755	.0702	2411	59
2	06	1718.87	80	55.4415	55	1664	30	8711	05	1821	58
3	09	1145.92	83	54.5613	58	27.9372	33	7678	08	1235	57
4	12	859.436	86	53.7086	61	7117	36	6656	11	0655	56
5	15	687.549	89	52.8821	64	4899	39	5645	14	0079	55
6	17	572.957	92	0807	67	2715	42	4645	17	13.9507	54
7	20	491.106	95	51.3032	70	0566	44	3655	20	8940	53
8	23	429.718	98	50.5485	73	26.8450	47	2677	23	8378	52
9	26	381.971	.0201	49.8157	75	6367	50	1708	26	7821	51
10	.0029	343.774	.0204	49.1039	.0378	26.4316	.0553	18.0750	.0729	13.7267	50
11	32	312.521	07	48.4121	81	2296	56	17.9802	31	6719	49
12	35	286.478	09	47.7395	84	0307	59	8863	34	6174	48
13	38	264.441	12	0853	87	25.8348	62	7934	37	5634	47
14	41	245.552	15	46.4489	90	6418	65	7015	40	5098	46
15	44	229.182	18	45.8294	93	4517	68	6106	43	4566	45
16	47	214.858	21	2261	96	2644	71	5205	46	4039	44
17	49	202.219	24	44.6386	99	0798	74	4314	49	3515	43
18	52	190.984	27	0661	.0402	24.8978	77	3432	52	2996	42
19	55	180.932	30	43.5081	05	7185	80	2558	55	2480	41
20	.0058	171.885	.0233	42.9641	.0407	24.5418	.0582	17.1693	.0758	13.1969	40
21	61	163.700	36	4335	10	3675	85	0837	61	1461	39
22	64	156.259	39	41.9158	13	1957	88	16.9990	64	0958	38
23	67	149.465	41	4106	16	0263	91	9150	67	0458	37
24	70	143.237	44	40.9174	19	23.8593	94	8319	69	12.9962	36
25	73	137.507	47	4358	22	6945	97	7496	72	9469	35
26	76	132.219	50	39.9655	25	5321	.0600	6681	75	8981	34
27	79	127.321	53	5059	28	3718	03	5874	78	8496	33
28	81	122.774	56	0568	31	2137	06	5075	81	8014	32
29	84	118.540	59	38.6177	34	0577	09	4283	84	7536	31
30	.0087	114.589	.0262	38.1885	.0437	22.9038	.0612	16.3499	.0787	12.7062	30
31	90	110.892	65	37.7686	40	7519	15	2722	90	6591	29
32	93	107.426	68	3579	42	6020	17	1952	93	6124	28
33	96	104.171	71	36.9560	45	4541	20	1190	96	5660	27
34	99	101.107	74	5627	48	3081	23	0435	99	5199	26
35	.0102	98.2179	76	1776	51	1640	26	15.9687	.0802	4742	25
36	05	95.4895	79	35.8006	54	0217	29	8945	05	4288	24
37	08	92.9085	82	4313	57	21.8813	32	8211	08	3838	23
38	11	90.4633	85	0695	60	7426	35	7483	10	3390	22
39	13	88.1436	88	34.7151	63	6056	38	6762	13	2946	21
40	.0116	85.9398	.0291	34.3678	.0466	21.4704	.0641	15.6048	.0816	12.2505	20
41	19	83.8435	94	0273	69	3369	44	5340	19	2067	19
42	22	81.8470	97	33.6935	72	2049	47	4638	22	1632	18
43	25	79.9434	.0300	3662	75	0747	50	3943	25	1201	17
44	28	78.1263	03	0452	77	20.9460	53	3254	28	0772	16
45	31	76.3900	06	32.7303	80	8188	55	2571	31	0346	15
46	34	74.7292	08	4213	83	6932	58	1893	34	11.9923	14
47	37	73.1390	11	1181	86	5691	61	1222	37	9504	13
48	40	71.6151	14	31.8205	89	4465	64	0557	40	9087	12
49	43	70.1533	17	5284	92	3253	67	14.9898	43	8673	11
50	.0145	68.7501	.0320	31.2416	.0495	20.2056	.0670	14.9244	.0846	11.8262	10
51	48	67.4019	23	30.9599	98	0872	73	8596	49	7853	9
52	51	66.1055	26	6833	.0501	19.9702	76	7954	51	7448	8
53	54	64.8580	29	4116	04	8546	79	7317	54	7045	7
54	57	63.6567	32	1446	07	7403	82	6685	57	6645	6
55	60	62.4992	35	29.8823	09	6273	85	6059	60	6248	5
56	63	61.3829	38	6245	12	5156	88	5438	63	5853	4
57	66	60.3058	40	3711	15	4051	90	4823	66	5461	3
58	69	59.2659	43	1220	18	2959	93	4212	69	5072	2
59	72	58.2612	46	28.8771	21	1879	96	3607	72	4685	1
60	.0175	57.2900	.0349	28.6363	.0524	19.0811	.0699	14.3007	.0875	11.4301	0
	Cotg	Tang	Cotg	Tang	Cotg	Tang	Cotg	Tang	Cotg	Tang	′
		89°		88°		87°		86°		85°	

TABLE 9 (Continued)

'	5°		6°		7°		8°		9°		'
	N.sine	N. cos.	N.sine	N. cos.	N.sine	N. cos.	N.sine	N. cos.	N.sine	N. cos.	
0	.08716	.99619	.10453	.99452	.12187	.99255	.13917	.99027	.15643	.98769	60
1	745	617	482	449	216	251	946	023	672	764	59
2	774	614	511	446	245	248	975	019	701	760	58
3	803	612	540	443	274	244	.14004	015	730	755	57
4	831	609	569	440	302	240	033	011	758	751	56
5	860	607	597	437	331	237	061	006	787	746	55
6	889	604	626	434	360	233	090	002	816	741	54
7	918	602	655	431	389	230	119	.98998	845	737	53
8	947	599	684	428	418	226	148	994	873	732	52
9	976	596	713	424	447	222	177	990	902	728	51
10	.09005	.99594	.10742	.99421	.12476	.99219	.14205	.98986	.15931	.98723	50
11	034	591	771	418	504	215	234	982	959	718	49
12	063	588	800	415	533	211	263	978	988	714	48
13	092	586	829	412	562	208	292	973	.16017	709	47
14	121	583	858	409	591	204	320	969	046	704	46
15	150	580	887	406	620	200	349	965	074	700	45
16	179	578	916	402	649	197	378	961	103	695	44
17	208	575	945	399	678	193	407	957	132	690	43
18	237	572	973	396	706	189	436	953	160	686	42
19	266	570	.11002	393	735	186	464	948	189	681	41
20	.09295	.99567	.11031	.99390	.12764	.99182	.14493	.98944	.16218	.98676	40
21	324	564	060	386	793	178	522	940	246	671	39
22	353	562	089	383	822	175	551	936	275	667	38
23	382	559	118	380	851	171	580	931	304	662	37
24	411	556	147	377	880	167	608	927	333	657	36
25	440	553	176	374	908	163	637	923	361	652	35
26	469	551	205	370	937	160	666	919	390	648	34
27	498	548	234	367	966	156	695	914	419	643	33
28	527	545	263	364	995	152	723	910	447	638	32
29	556	542	291	360	.13024	148	752	906	476	633	31
30	.09585	.99540	.11320	.99357	.13053	.99144	.14781	.98902	.16505	.98629	30
31	614	537	349	354	081	141	810	897	533	624	29
32	642	534	378	351	110	137	838	893	562	619	28
33	671	531	407	347	139	133	867	889	591	614	27
34	700	528	436	344	168	129	896	884	620	609	26
35	729	526	465	341	197	125	925	880	648	604	25
36	758	523	494	337	226	122	954	876	677	600	24
37	787	520	523	334	254	118	982	871	706	595	23
38	816	517	552	331	283	114	.15011	867	734	590	22
39	845	514	580	327	312	110	040	863	763	585	21
40	.09874	.99511	.11609	.99324	.13341	.99106	.15069	.98858	.16792	.98580	20
41	903	508	638	320	370	102	097	854	820	575	19
42	932	506	667	317	399	098	126	849	849	570	18
43	961	503	696	314	427	094	155	845	878	565	17
44	990	500	725	310	456	091	184	841	906	561	16
45	.10019	497	754	307	485	087	212	836	935	556	15
46	048	494	783	303	514	083	241	832	964	551	14
47	077	491	812	300	543	079	270	827	992	546	13
48	106	488	840	297	572	075	299	823	.17021	541	12
49	135	485	869	293	601	071	327	818	050	536	11
50	.10164	.99482	.11898	.99290	.13629	.99067	.15356	.98814	.17078	.98531	10
51	192	479	927	286	658	063	385	809	107	526	9
52	221	476	956	283	687	059	414	805	136	521	8
53	250	473	985	279	716	055	442	800	164	516	7
54	279	470	.12014	276	744	051	471	796	193	511	6
55	308	467	043	272	773	047	500	791	222	506	5
56	337	464	071	269	802	043	529	787	250	501	4
57	366	461	100	265	831	039	557	782	279	496	3
58	395	458	129	262	860	035	586	778	308	491	2
59	424	455	158	258	889	031	615	773	336	486	1
60	.10453	.99452	.12187	.99255	.13917	.99027	.15643	.98769	.17365	.98481	0
	N.cos.	N. sine	N.cos.	N. sine	N.cos.	N. sine	N.cos.	N. sine	N.cos.	N. sine	
'	84°		83°		82°		81°		80°		'

456

TABLE 9 (Continued)

′	5° Tang.	5° Cotg.	6° Tang.	6° Cotg.	7° Tang.	7° Cotg.	8° Tang.	8° Cotg.	9° Tang.	9° Cotg.	′
0	.0875	11.4301	.1051	9.5144	.1228	8.1443	.1405	7.1154	.1584	6.3138	60
1	78	11.3919	54	9.4878	31	248	08	004	87	019	59
2	81	540	57	614	34	054	11	7.0855	90	6.2901	58
3	84	163	60	352	37	8.0860	14	706	93	783	57
4	87	11.2789	63	090	40	667	17	558	96	666	56
5	90	417	66	9.3831	43	476	20	410	99	549	55
6	92	048	69	572	46	285	23	264	.1602	432	54
7	95	11.1681	72	315	49	095	26	117	05	316	53
8	98	316	75	060	51	7.9906	29	6.9972	08	200	52
9	.0901	11.0954	78	9.2806	54	718	32	827	11	085	51
10	.0904	11.0594	.1080	9.2553	.1257	7.9530	.1435	6.9682	.1614	6.1970	50
11	07	237	83	302	60	344	38	538	17	856	49
12	10	10.9882	86	052	63	158	41	395	20	742	48
13	13	529	89	9.1803	66	7.8973	44	252	23	628	47
14	16	178	92	555	69	789	47	110	26	515	46
15	19	10.8829	95	309	72	606	50	6.8969	29	402	45
16	22	483	98	065	75	424	53	828	32	290	44
17	25	139	.1101	9.0821	78	243	56	687	35	178	43
18	28	10.7797	04	579	81	062	59	548	38	066	42
19	31	457	07	338	84	7.7882	62	408	41	6.0955	41
20	.0934	10.7119	.1110	9.0098	.1287	7.7704	.1465	6.8269	.1644	6.0844	40
21	36	10.6783	13	8.9860	90	525	68	131	47	734	39
22	39	450	16	623	93	348	71	6.7994	50	624	38
23	42	118	19	387	96	171	74	856	53	514	37
24	45	10.5789	22	152	99	7.6996	77	720	55	405	36
25	48	462	25	8.8919	1302	821	80	584	58	296	35
26	51	136	28	686	05	647	83	448	61	188	34
27	54	10.4813	31	455	08	473	86	313	64	080	33
28	57	491	33	225	11	301	89	179	67	5.9972	32
29	60	172	36	8.7996	14	129	92	045	70	865	31
30	.0963	10.3854	.1139	8.7769	.1317	7.5958	.1495	6.6912	.1673	5.9758	30
31	66	538	42	542	19	787	97	779	76	651	29
32	69	224	45	317	22	618	1500	646	79	545	28
33	72	10.2913	48	093	25	449	03	514	82	439	27
34	75	602	51	8.6870	28	281	06	383	85	333	26
35	78	294	54	648	31	113	09	252	88	228	25
36	81	10.1988	57	427	34	7.4947	12	122	91	124	24
37	83	683	60	208	37	781	15	6.5992	94	019	23
38	86	381	63	8.5989	40	615	18	863	97	5.8915	22
39	89	080	66	772	43	451	21	734	.1700	811	21
40	.0992	10.0780	.1169	8.5555	.1346	7.4287	.1524	6.5606	.1703	5.8708	20
41	95	483	72	340	49	124	27	478	06	605	19
42	98	187	75	126	52	7.3962	30	350	09	502	18
43	.1001	9.9893	78	8.4913	55	800	33	223	12	400	17
44	04	601	81	701	58	639	36	097	15	298	16
45	07	310	84	490	61	479	39	6.4971	18	197	15
46	10	021	87	280	64	319	42	846	21	095	14
47	13	9.8734	89	071	67	160	45	721	24	5.7994	13
48	16	448	92	8.3863	70	002	48	596	27	894	12
49	19	164	95	656	73	7.2844	51	472	30	794	11
50	.1022	9.7882	.1198	8.3450	.1376	7.2687	.1554	6.4348	.1733	5.7694	10
51	25	601	.1201	245	79	531	57	225	36	594	9
52	28	322	04	041	82	375	60	103	39	495	8
53	30	044	07	8.2838	85	220	63	6.3980	42	396	7
54	33	9.6768	10	636	88	066	66	859	45	297	6
55	36	493	13	434	91	7.1912	69	737	48	199	5
56	39	220	16	234	94	759	72	617	51	101	4
57	42	9.5949	19	035	97	607	75	496	54	004	3
58	45	679	22	8.1837	99	455	78	376	57	5.6906	2
59	48	411	25	640	.1402	304	81	257	60	809	1
60	.1051	9.5144	.1228	8.1443	.1405	7.1154	.1584	6.3138	.1763	5.6713	0
′	Cotg.	Tang.	Cotg.	Tang.	Cotg.	Tang.	Cotg.	Tang.	Cotg.	Tang.	′
	84°		83°		82°		81°		80°		

457

TABLE 9 (*Continued*)

′	10°		11°		12°		13°		14°		′
	N.sine	N. cos.	N.sine	N. cos.	N.sine	N. cos.	N.sine	N. cos.	N.sine	N. cos.	
0	.17365	.98481	.19081	.98163	.20791	.97815	.22495	.97437	.24192	.97030	60
1	393	476	109	157	820	809	523	430	220	023	59
2	422	471	138	152	848	803	552	424	249	015	58
3	451	466	167	146	877	797	580	417	277	008	57
4	479	461	195	140	905	791	608	411	305	001	56
5	508	455	224	135	933	784	637	404	333	.96994	55
6	537	450	252	129	962	778	665	398	362	987	54
7	565	445	281	124	990	772	693	391	390	980	53
8	594	440	309	118	.21019	766	722	384	418	973	52
9	623	435	338	112	047	760	750	378	446	966	51
10	.17651	.98430	.19366	.98107	.21076	.97754	.22778	.97371	.24474	.96959	50
11	680	425	395	101	104	748	807	365	503	952	49
12	708	420	423	096	132	742	835	358	531	945	48
13	737	414	452	090	161	735	863	351	559	937	47
14	766	409	481	084	189	729	892	345	587	930	46
15	794	404	509	079	218	723	920	338	615	923	45
16	823	399	538	073	246	717	948	331	644	916	44
17	852	394	566	067	275	711	977	325	672	909	43
18	880	389	595	061	303	705	.23005	318	700	902	42
19	909	383	623	056	331	698	033	311	728	894	41
20	.17937	.98378	.19652	.98050	.21360	.97692	.23062	.97304	.24756	.96887	40
21	966	373	680	044	388	686	090	298	784	880	39
22	995	368	709	039	417	680	118	291	813	873	38
23	.18023	362	737	033	445	673	146	284	841	866	37
24	052	357	766	027	474	667	175	278	869	858	36
25	081	352	794	021	502	661	203	271	897	851	35
26	109	347	823	016	530	655	231	264	925	844	34
27	138	341	851	010	559	648	260	257	954	837	33
28	166	336	880	004	587	642	288	251	982	829	32
29	195	331	908	.97998	616	636	316	244	.25010	822	31
30	.18224	.98325	.19937	.97992	.21644	.97630	.23345	.97237	.25038	.96815	30
31	252	320	965	987	672	623	373	230	066	807	29
32	281	315	994	981	701	617	401	223	094	800	28
33	309	310	.20022	975	729	611	429	217	122	793	27
34	338	304	051	969	758	604	458	210	151	786	26
35	367	299	079	963	786	598	486	203	179	778	25
36	395	294	108	958	814	592	514	196	207	771	24
37	424	288	136	952	843	585	542	189	235	764	23
38	452	283	165	946	871	579	571	182	263	756	22
39	481	277	193	940	899	573	599	176	291	749	21
40	.18509	.98272	.20222	.97934	.21928	.97566	.23627	.97169	.25320	.96742	20
41	538	267	250	928	956	560	656	162	348	734	19
42	567	261	279	922	985	553	684	155	376	727	18
43	595	256	307	916	.22013	547	712	148	404	719	17
44	624	250	336	910	041	541	740	141	432	712	16
45	652	245	364	905	070	534	769	134	460	705	15
46	681	240	393	899	098	528	797	127	488	697	14
47	710	234	421	893	126	521	825	120	516	690	13
48	738	229	450	887	155	515	853	113	545	682	12
49	767	223	478	881	183	508	882	106	573	675	11
50	.18795	.98218	.20507	.97875	.22212	.97502	.23910	.97100	.25601	.96667	10
51	824	212	535	869	240	496	938	093	629	660	9
52	852	207	563	863	268	489	966	086	657	653	8
53	881	201	592	857	297	483	995	079	685	645	7
54	910	196	620	851	325	476	.24023	072	713	638	6
55	938	190	649	845	353	470	051	065	741	630	5
56	967	185	677	839	382	463	079	058	769	623	4
57	995	179	706	833	410	457	108	051	798	615	3
58	.19024	174	734	827	438	450	136	044	826	608	2
59	052	168	763	821	467	444	164	037	854	600	1
60	.19081	.98163	.20791	.97815	22495	.97437	.24192	.97030	.25882	.96593	0
	N. cos.	N. sine	N.cos.	N. sine	N.cos.	N. sine	N.cos.	N. sine	N.cos.	N. sine	′
′	79°		78°		77°		76°		75°		

TABLE 9 (*Continued*)

′	10° Tang.	10° Cotg.	11° Tang.	11° Cotg.	12° Tang.	12° Cotg.	13° Tang.	13° Cotg.	14° Tang.	14° Cotg.	′
0	.1763	5.6713	.1944	5.1446	.2126	4.7046	.2309	4.3315	.2493	4.0108	60
1	66	617	47	366	29	4.6979	12	257	96	058	59
2	69	521	50	286	32	912	15	200	99	009	58
3	72	425	53	207	35	845	18	143	.2503	3.9959	57
4	75	329	56	128	38	779	21	086	06	910	56
5	78	234	59	049	41	712	24	029	09	861	55
6	81	140	62	5.0970	44	646	27	4.2972	12	812	54
7	84	045	65	892	47	580	30	916	15	763	53
8	87	5.5951	68	814	50	514	33	859	18	714	52
9	90	857	71	736	53	448	36	803	21	665	51
10	.1793	5.5764	.1974	5.0658	.2156	4.6382	.2339	4.2747	.2524	3.9617	50
11	96	671	77	581	59	317	42	691	27	568	49
12	99	578	80	504	62	252	45	635	30	520	48
13	.1802	485	83	427	65	187	49	580	33	471	47
14	05	393	86	350	68	122	52	524	37	423	46
15	08	301	89	273	71	057	55	468	40	375	45
16	11	209	92	197	74	4.5993	58	413	43	327	44
17	14	118	95	121	77	928	61	358	46	279	43
18	17	026	98	045	80	864	64	303	49	232	42
19	20	5.4936	.2001	4.9969	83	800	67	248	52	184	41
20	.1823	5.4845	.2004	4.9894	.2186	4.5736	.2370	4.2193	.2555	3.9136	40
21	26	755	07	819	89	673	73	139	58	089	39
22	29	665	10	744	93	609	76	084	61	042	38
23	32	575	13	669	96	546	79	030	64	3.8995	37
24	35	486	16	594	99	483	82	4.1976	68	947	36
25	38	397	19	520	.2202	420	85	922	71	900	35
26	41	308	22	446	05	357	88	868	74	854	34
27	44	219	25	372	08	294	92	814	77	807	33
28	47	131	28	298	11	232	95	760	80	760	32
29	50	043	31	225	14	169	98	706	83	714	31
30	.1853	5.3955	.2035	4.9152	.2217	4.5107	.2401	4.1653	.2586	3.8667	30
31	56	868	38	078	20	045	04	600	89	621	29
32	59	781	41	006	23	4.4983	07	547	92	575	28
33	62	694	44	4.8933	26	922	10	493	95	528	27
34	65	607	47	860	29	860	13	441	99	482	26
35	68	521	50	788	32	799	16	388	2602	436	25
36	71	435	53	716	35	737	19	335	05	391	24
37	74	349	56	644	38	676	22	282	08	345	23
38	77	263	59	573	41	615	25	230	11	299	22
39	80	178	62	501	44	555	28	178	14	254	21
40	.1883	5.3093	.2065	4.8430	.2247	4.4494	.2432	4.1126	.2617	3.8208	20
41	87	008	68	359	51	434	35	074	20	163	19
42	90	5.2924	71	288	54	374	38	022	23	118	18
43	93	839	74	218	57	313	41	4.0970	27	073	17
44	96	755	77	147	60	253	44	918	30	028	16
45	99	672	80	077	63	194	47	867	33	3.7983	15
46	.1902	588	83	007	66	134	50	815	36	938	14
47	05	505	86	4.7937	69	075	53	764	39	893	13
48	08	422	89	867	72	015	56	713	42	848	12
49	11	339	92	798	75	4.3956	59	662	45	804	11
50	.1914	5.2257	.2095	4.7729	.2278	4.3897	.2462	4.0611	.2648	3.7760	10
51	17	174	98	659	81	838	65	560	51	715	9
52	20	092	.2101	591	84	779	69	509	55	671	8
53	23	011	04	522	87	721	72	459	58	627	7
54	26	5.1929	07	453	90	662	75	408	61	583	6
55	29	848	10	385	93	604	78	358	64	539	5
56	32	767	13	317	96	546	81	308	67	495	4
57	35	686	16	249	99	488	84	257	70	451	3
58	38	606	19	181	.2303	430	87	207	73	408	2
59	41	526	23	114	06	372	90	158	76	364	1
60	.1944	5.1446	.2126	4.7046	.2309	4.3315	.2493	4.0108	.2679	3.7321	0
	Cotg.	Tang.	Cotg.	Tang.	Cotg.	Tang.	Cotg.	Tang.	Cotg.	Tang.	
′	79°		78°		77°		76°		75°		′

TABLE 9 (Continued)

′	15°		16°		17°		18°		19°		′
	N.sine	N. cos.	N.sine	N. cos.	N.sine	N. cos.	N.sine	N. cos.	N.sine	N. cos.	
0	.25882	.96593	.27564	.96126	.29237	.95630	.30902	.95106	.32557	.94552	60
1	910	585	592	118	265	622	929	097	584	542	59
2	938	578	620	110	293	613	957	088	612	533	58
3	966	570	648	102	321	605	985	079	639	523	57
4	994	562	676	094	348	596	.31012	070	667	514	56
5	.26022	555	704	086	376	588	040	061	694	504	55
6	050	547	731	078	404	579	068	052	722	495	54
7	079	540	759	070	432	571	095	043	749	485	53
8	107	532	787	062	460	562	123	033	777	476	52
9	135	524	815	054	487	554	151	024	804	466	51
10	.26163	.96517	.27843	.96046	.29515	.95545	.31178	.95015	.32832	.94457	50
11	191	509	871	037	543	536	206	006	859	447	49
12	219	502	899	029	571	528	233	.94997	887	438	48
13	247	494	927	021	599	519	261	988	914	428	47
14	275	486	955	013	626	511	289	979	942	418	46
15	303	479	983	005	654	502	316	970	969	409	45
16	331	471	.28011	.95997	682	493	344	961	997	399	44
17	359	463	039	989	710	485	372	952	.33024	390	43
18	387	456	067	981	737	476	399	943	051	380	42
19	415	448	095	972	765	467	427	933	079	370	41
20	.26443	.96440	.28123	.95964	.29793	.95459	.31454	.94924	.33106	.94361	40
21	471	433	150	956	821	450	482	915	134	351	39
22	500	425	178	948	849	441	510	906	161	342	38
23	528	417	206	940	876	433	537	897	189	332	37
24	556	410	234	931	904	424	565	888	216	322	36
25	584	402	262	923	932	415	593	878	244	313	35
26	612	394	290	915	960	407	620	869	271	303	34
27	640	386	318	907	987	398	648	860	298	293	33
28	668	379	346	898	.30015	389	675	851	326	284	32
29	696	371	374	890	043	380	703	842	353	274	31
30	.26724	.96363	.28402	.95882	.30071	.95372	.31730	.94832	.33381	.94264	30
31	752	355	429	874	098	363	758	823	408	254	29
32	780	347	457	865	126	354	786	814	436	245	28
33	808	340	485	857	154	345	813	805	463	235	27
34	836	332	513	849	182	337	841	795	490	225	26
35	864	324	541	841	209	328	868	786	518	215	25
36	892	316	569	832	237	319	896	777	545	206	24
37	920	308	597	824	265	310	923	768	573	196	23
38	948	301	625	816	292	301	951	758	600	186	22
39	976	293	652	807	320	293	979	749	627	176	21
40	.27004	.96285	.28680	.95799	.30348	.95284	.32006	.94740	.33655	.94167	20
41	032	277	708	791	376	275	034	730	682	157	19
42	060	269	736	782	403	266	061	721	710	147	18
43	088	261	764	774	431	257	089	712	737	137	17
44	116	253	792	766	459	248	116	702	764	127	16
45	144	246	820	757	486	240	144	693	792	118	15
46	172	238	847	749	514	231	171	684	819	108	14
47	200	230	875	740	542	222	199	674	846	098	13
48	228	222	903	732	570	213	227	665	874	088	12
49	256	214	931	724	597	204	254	656	901	078	11
50	.27284	.96206	.28959	.95715	.30625	.95195	.32282	.94646	.33929	.94068	10
51	312	198	987	707	653	186	309	637	956	058	9
52	340	190	.29015	698	680	177	337	627	983	049	8
53	368	182	042	690	708	168	364	618	.34011	039	7
54	396	174	070	681	736	159	392	609	038	029	6
55	424	166	098	673	763	150	419	599	065	019	5
56	452	158	126	664	791	142	447	590	093	009	4
57	480	150	154	656	819	133	474	580	120	.93999	3
58	508	142	182	647	846	124	502	571	147	989	2
59	536	134	209	639	874	115	529	561	175	979	1
60	.27564	.96126	.29237	.95630	.30902	.95106	.32557	.94552	.34202	.93969	0
	N.cos.	N. sine	N.cos.	N. sine	N.cos.	N. sine	N.cos.	N. sine	N.cos.	N. sine	
′	74°		73°		72°		71°		70°		′

TABLE 9 (Continued)

′	15°		16°		17°		18°		19°		′
	Tang.	Cotg.	Tang.	Cotg.	Tang.	Cotg.	Tang.	Cotg.	Tang.	Cotg.	
0	.2679	3.7321	.2867	3.4874	.3057	3.2709	.3249	3.0777	.3443	2.9042	60
1	83	277	71	836	60	675	52	746	47	015	59
2	86	234	74	798	64	641	56	716	50	2.8987	58
3	89	191	77	760	67	607	59	686	53	960	57
4	92	148	80	722	70	573	62	655	56	933	56
5	95	105	83	684	73	539	65	625	60	905	55
6	98	062	86	646	76	506	69	595	63	878	54
7	.2701	019	90	608	80	472	72	565	66	851	53
8	04	3.6976	93	570	83	438	75	535	69	824	52
9	08	933	96	533	86	405	78	505	73	797	51
10	.2711	3.6891	.2899	3.4495	.3089	3.2371	.3281	3.0475	.3476	2.8770	50
11	14	848	.2902	458	92	338	85	445	79	743	49
12	17	806	05	420	96	305	88	415	82	716	48
13	20	764	08	383	99	272	91	385	86	689	47
14	23	722	12	346	.3102	238	94	356	89	662	46
15	26	680	15	308	05	205	98	326	92	636	45
16	29	638	18	271	08	172	.3301	296	95	609	44
17	33	596	21	234	11	139	04	267	99	582	43
18	36	554	24	197	15	106	07	237	.3502	556	42
19	39	512	27	160	18	073	10	208	05	529	41
20	.2742	3.6470	.2931	3.4124	.3121	3.2041	.3314	3.0178	.3508	2.8502	40
21	45	429	34	087	24	008	17	149	12	476	39
22	48	387	37	050	27	3.1975	20	120	15	449	38
23	51	346	40	014	31	943	23	090	18	423	37
24	54	305	43	3.3977	34	910	27	061	22	397	36
25	58	264	46	941	37	878	30	032	25	370	35
26	61	222	49	904	40	845	33	003	28	344	34
27	64	181	53	868	43	813	36	2.9974	31	318	33
28	67	140	56	832	47	780	39	945	35	291	32
29	70	100	59	796	50	748	43	916	38	265	31
30	.2773	3.6059	.2962	3.3759	.3153	3.1716	.3346	2.9887	.3541	2.8239	30
31	76	018	65	723	56	684	49	858	44	213	29
32	80	3.5978	68	687	59	652	52	829	48	187	28
33	83	937	72	652	63	620	56	800	51	161	27
34	86	897	75	616	66	588	59	772	54	135	26
35	89	856	78	580	69	556	62	743	58	109	25
36	92	816	81	544	72	524	65	714	61	083	24
37	95	776	84	509	75	492	69	686	64	057	23
38	98	736	87	473	79	460	72	657	67	032	22
39	.2801	696	91	438	82	429	75	629	71	006	21
40	.2805	3.5656	.2994	3.3402	.3185	3.1397	.3378	2.9600	.3574	2.7980	20
41	08	616	97	367	88	366	82	572	77	955	19
42	11	576	.3000	332	91	334	85	544	81	929	18
43	14	536	03	297	95	303	88	515	84	903	17
44	17	497	06	261	98	271	91	487	87	878	16
45	20	457	10	226	.3201	240	95	459	90	852	15
46	23	418	13	191	04	209	98	431	94	827	14
47	27	379	16	156	07	178	.3401	403	97	801	13
48	30	339	19	122	11	146	04	375	.3600	776	12
49	33	300	22	087	14	115	08	347	04	751	11
50	.2836	3.5261	.3026	3.3052	.3217	3.1084	.3411	2.9319	.3607	2.7725	10
51	39	222	29	017	20	053	14	291	10	700	9
52	42	183	32	3.2983	23	022	17	263	13	675	8
53	45	144	35	948	27	3.0991	21	235	17	650	7
54	49	105	38	914	30	961	24	208	20	625	6
55	52	067	41	879	33	930	27	180	23	600	5
56	55	028	45	845	36	899	30	152	27	575	4
57	58	3.4989	48	811	40	868	34	125	30	550	3
58	61	951	51	777	43	838	37	097	33	525	2
59	64	912	54	743	46	807	40	070	36	500	1
60	.2867	3.4874	.3057	3.2709	.3249	3.0777	.3443	2.9042	.3640	2.7475	0
	Cotg.	Tang.	Cotg.	Tang.	Cotg.	Tang.	Cotg.	Tang.	Cotg.	Tang.	
′	74°		73°		72°		71°		70°		′

TABLE 9 (*Continued*)

′	20° N.sine	20° N.cos.	21° N.sine	21° N.cos.	22° N.sine	22° N.cos.	23° N.sine	23° N.cos.	24° N.sine	24° N.cos.	′
0	.34202	.93969	.35837	.93358	.37461	.92718	.39073	.92050	.40674	.91355	60
1	229	959	864	348	488	707	100	039	700	343	59
2	257	949	891	337	515	697	127	028	727	331	58
3	284	939	918	327	542	686	153	016	753	319	57
4	311	929	945	316	569	675	180	005	780	307	56
5	339	919	973	306	595	664	207	.91994	806	295	55
6	366	909	.36000	295	622	653	234	982	833	283	54
7	393	899	027	285	649	642	260	971	860	272	53
8	421	889	054	274	676	631	287	959	886	260	52
9	448	879	081	264	703	620	314	948	913	248	51
10	.34475	.93869	.36108	.93253	.37730	.92609	.39341	.91936	.40939	.91236	50
11	503	859	135	243	757	598	367	925	966	224	49
12	530	849	162	232	784	587	394	914	992	212	48
13	557	839	190	222	811	576	421	902	.41019	200	47
14	584	829	217	211	838	565	448	891	045	188	46
15	612	819	244	201	865	554	474	879	072	176	45
16	639	809	271	190	892	543	501	868	098	164	44
17	666	799	298	180	919	532	528	856	125	152	43
18	694	789	325	169	946	521	555	845	151	140	42
19	721	779	352	159	973	510	581	833	178	128	41
20	.34748	.93769	.36379	.93148	.37999	.92499	.39608	.91822	.41204	.91116	40
21	775	759	406	137	.38026	488	635	810	231	104	39
22	803	748	434	127	053	477	661	799	257	092	38
23	830	738	461	116	080	466	688	787	284	080	37
24	857	728	488	106	107	455	715	775	310	068	36
25	884	718	515	095	134	444	741	764	337	056	35
26	912	708	542	084	161	432	768	752	363	044	34
27	939	698	569	074	188	421	795	741	390	032	33
28	966	688	596	063	215	410	822	729	416	020	32
29	993	677	623	052	241	399	848	718	443	008	31
30	.35021	.93667	.36650	.93042	.38268	.92388	.39875	.91706	.41469	.90996	30
31	048	657	677	031	295	377	902	694	496	984	29
32	075	647	704	020	322	366	928	683	522	972	28
33	102	637	731	010	349	355	955	671	549	960	27
34	130	626	758	.92999	376	343	982	660	575	948	26
35	157	616	785	988	403	332	.40008	648	602	936	25
36	184	606	812	978	430	321	035	636	628	924	24
37	211	596	839	967	456	310	062	625	655	911	23
38	239	585	867	956	483	299	088	613	681	899	22
39	266	575	894	945	510	287	115	601	707	887	21
40	.35293	.93565	.36921	.92935	.38537	.92276	.40141	.91590	.41734	.90875	20
41	320	555	948	924	564	265	168	578	760	863	19
42	347	544	975	913	591	254	195	566	787	851	18
43	375	534	.37002	902	617	243	221	555	813	839	17
44	402	524	029	892	644	231	248	543	840	826	16
45	429	514	056	881	671	220	275	531	866	814	15
46	456	503	083	870	698	209	301	519	892	802	14
47	484	493	110	859	725	198	328	508	919	790	13
48	511	483	137	849	752	186	355	496	945	778	12
49	538	472	164	838	778	175	381	484	972	766	11
50	.35565	.93462	.37191	.92827	.38805	.92164	.40408	.91472	.41998	.90753	10
51	592	452	218	816	832	152	434	461	.42024	741	9
52	619	441	245	805	859	141	461	449	051	729	8
53	647	431	272	794	886	130	488	437	077	717	7
54	674	420	299	784	912	119	514	425	104	704	6
55	701	410	326	773	939	107	541	414	130	692	5
56	728	400	353	762	966	096	567	402	156	680	4
57	755	389	380	751	993	085	594	390	183	668	3
58	782	379	407	740	.39020	073	621	378	209	655	2
59	810	368	434	729	046	062	647	366	235	643	1
60	.35837	.93358	.37461	.92718	.39073	.92050	.40674	.91355	.42262	.90631	0
	N.cos.	N.sine	N.cos.	N.sine	N.cos.	N.sine	N.cos.	N.sine	N.cos.	N.sine	
′	69°		68°		67°		66°		65°		′

TABLE 9 (*Continued*)

′	20°		21°		22°		23°		24°		′
	Tang.	Cotg.	Tang.	Cotg.	Tang.	Cotg.	Tang.	Cotg.	Tang.	Cotg.	
0	.3640	2.7475	.3839	2.6051	.4040	2.4751	.4245	2.3559	.4452	2.2460	60
1	43	50	42	28	44	30	48	39	56	43	59
2	46	25	45	06	47	09	52	20	59	25	58
3	50	00	49	2.5983	50	2.4689	55	01	63	08	57
4	53	2.7376	52	61	54	68	58	2.3483	66	2.2390	56
5	56	51	55	38	57	48	62	64	70	73	55
6	59	26	59	16	61	27	65	45	73	55	54
7	63	02	62	2.5893	64	06	69	26	77	38	53
8	66	2.7277	65	71	67	2.4586	72	07	80	20	52
9	69	53	69	48	71	66	76	2.3388	84	03	51
10	.3673	2.7228	.3872	2.5826	.4074	2.4545	.4279	2.3369	.4487	2.2286	50
11	76	04	75	04	78	25	83	51	91	68	49
12	79	2.7179	79	2.5782	81	04	86	32	94	51	48
13	83	55	82	59	84	2.4484	89	13	98	34	47
14	86	30	85	37	88	64	93	2.3294	4501	16	46
15	89	06	89	15	91	43	96	76	05	2.2199	45
16	92	2.7082	92	2.5693	95	23	.4300	57	08	82	44
17	96	58	95	71	98	03	03	38	12	65	43
18	99	34	99	49	.4101	2.4383	07	20	15	48	42
19	.3702	09	.3902	27	05	62	10	01	19	30	41
20	.3706	2.6985	.3906	2.5605	.4108	2.4342	.4314	2.3183	.4522	2.2113	40
21	09	61	09	2.5583	11	22	17	64	26	2.2096	39
22	12	37	12	61	15	02	20	46	29	79	38
23	16	13	16	39	18	2.4282	24	27	33	62	37
24	19	2.6889	19	17	22	62	27	09	36	45	36
25	22	65	22	2.5495	25	42	31	2.3090	40	28	35
26	26	41	26	73	29	22	34	72	43	11	34
27	29	18	29	52	32	02	38	53	47	2.1994	33
28	32	2.6794	32	30	35	2.4182	41	35	50	77	32
29	36	70	36	08	39	62	45	17	54	60	31
30	.3739	2.6746	.3939	2.5386	.4142	2.4142	.4348	2.2998	.4557	2.1943	30
31	42	23	42	65	46	22	52	80	61	26	29
32	45	2.6699	46	43	49	02	55	62	64	09	28
33	49	75	49	22	52	2.4083	59	44	68	2.1892	27
34	52	52	53	00	56	63	62	25	71	76	26
35	55	28	56	2.5279	59	43	65	07	75	59	25
36	59	05	59	57	63	23	69	2.2889	78	42	24
37	62	2.6581	63	36	66	04	72	71	82	25	23
38	65	58	66	14	69	2.3984	76	53	85	08	22
39	69	34	69	2.5193	73	64	79	35	89	2.1792	21
40	.3772	2.6511	.3973	2.5172	.4176	2.3945	.4383	2.2817	.4592	2.1775	20
41	75	2.6488	76	50	80	25	86	2.2799	96	58	19
42	79	64	79	29	83	06	90	81	99	42	18
43	82	41	83	08	87	2.3886	93	63	.4603	25	17
44	85	18	86	2.5086	90	67	97	45	07	08	16
45	89	2.6395	90	65	93	47	.4400	27	10	2.1692	15
46	92	71	93	44	97	28	04	09	14	75	14
47	95	48	96	23	.4200	08	07	2.2691	17	59	13
48	99	25	.4000	02	04	2.3789	11	73	21	42	12
49	.3802	02	03	2.4981	07	70	14	55	24	25	11
50	.3805	2.6279	.4006	2.4960	.4210	2.3750	.4417	2.2637	.4628	2.1609	10
51	09	56	10	39	14	31	21	20	31	2.1592	9
52	12	33	13	18	17	12	24	02	35	76	8
53	15	10	17	2.4897	21	2.3693	28	2.2584	38	60	7
54	19	2.6187	20	76	24	73	31	66	42	43	6
55	22	65	23	55	28	54	35	49	45	27	5
56	25	42	27	34	31	35	38	31	49	10	4
57	29	19	30	13	34	16	42	13	52	2.1494	3
58	32	2.6096	33	2.4792	38	2.3597	45	2.2496	56	78	2
59	35	74	37	72	41	78	49	78	60	61	1
60	.3839	2.6051	.4040	2.4751	.4245	2.3559	.4452	2.2460	.4663	2.1445	0
	Cotg.	Tang.	Cotg.	Tang.	Cotg.	Tang.	Cotg.	Tang.	Cotg.	Tang.	
′	69°		68°		67°		66°		65°		′

TABLE 9 (*Continued*)

′	25°		26°		27°		28°		29°		′
	N.sine	N. cos.	N.sine	N. cos.	N.sine	N. cos.	N.sine	N. cos.	N.sine	N. cos.	
0	.42262	.90631	.43837	.89879	.45399	.89101	.46947	.88295	.48481	.87462	60
1	288	618	863	867	425	087	973	281	506	448	59
2	315	606	889	854	451	074	999	267	532	434	58
3	341	594	916	841	477	061	.47024	254	557	420	57
4	367	582	942	828	503	048	050	240	583	406	56
5	394	569	968	816	529	035	076	226	608	391	55
6	420	557	994	803	554	021	101	213	634	377	54
7	446	545	.44020	790	580	008	127	199	659	363	53
8	473	532	046	777	606	.88995	153	185	684	349	52
9	499	520	072	764	632	981	178	172	710	335	51
10	.42525	.90507	.44098	.89752	.45658	.88968	.47204	.88158	.48735	.87321	50
11	552	495	124	739	684	955	229	144	761	306	49
12	578	483	151	726	710	942	255	130	786	292	48
13	604	470	177	713	736	928	281	117	811	278	47
14	631	458	203	700	762	915	306	103	837	264	46
15	657	446	229	687	787	902	332	089	862	250	45
16	683	433	255	674	813	888	358	075	888	235	44
17	709	421	281	662	839	875	383	062	913	221	43
18	736	408	307	649	865	862	409	048	938	207	42
19	762	396	333	636	891	848	434	034	964	193	41
20	.42788	.90383	.44359	.89623	.45917	.88835	.47460	.88020	.48989	.87178	40
21	815	371	385	610	942	822	486	006	.49014	164	39
22	841	358	411	597	968	808	511	.87993	040	150	38
23	867	346	437	584	994	795	537	979	065	136	37
24	894	334	464	571	.46020	782	562	965	090	121	36
25	920	321	490	558	046	768	588	951	116	107	35
26	946	309	516	545	072	755	614	937	141	093	34
27	972	296	542	532	097	741	639	923	166	079	33
28	999	284	568	519	123	728	665	909	192	064	32
29	.43025	271	594	506	149	715	690	896	217	050	31
30	.43051	.90259	.44620	.89493	.46175	.88701	.47716	.87882	.49242	.87036	30
31	077	246	646	480	201	688	741	868	268	021	29
32	104	233	672	467	226	674	767	854	293	007	28
33	130	221	698	454	252	661	793	840	318	.86993	27
34	156	208	724	441	278	647	818	826	344	978	26
35	182	196	750	428	304	634	844	812	369	964	25
36	209	183	776	415	330	620	869	798	394	949	24
37	235	171	802	402	355	607	895	784	419	935	23
38	261	158	828	389	381	593	920	770	445	921	22
39	287	146	854	376	407	580	946	756	470	906	21
40	.43313	.90133	.44880	.89363	.46433	.88566	.47971	.87743	.49495	.86892	20
41	340	120	906	350	458	553	997	729	521	878	19
42	366	108	932	337	484	539	.48022	715	546	863	18
43	392	095	958	324	510	526	048	701	571	849	17
44	418	082	984	311	536	512	073	687	596	834	16
45	445	070	.45010	298	561	499	099	673	622	820	15
46	471	057	036	285	587	485	124	659	647	805	14
47	497	045	062	272	613	472	150	645	672	791	13
48	523	032	088	259	639	458	175	631	697	777	12
49	549	019	114	245	664	445	201	617	723	762	11
50	.43575	.90007	.45140	.89232	.46690	.88431	.48226	.87603	.49748	.86748	10
51	602	.89994	166	219	716	417	252	589	773	733	9
52	628	981	192	206	742	404	277	575	798	719	8
53	654	968	218	193	767	390	303	561	824	704	7
54	680	956	243	180	793	377	328	546	849	690	6
55	706	943	269	167	819	363	354	532	874	675	5
56	733	930	295	153	844	349	379	518	899	661	4
57	759	918	321	140	870	336	405	504	924	646	3
58	785	905	347	127	896	322	430	490	950	632	2
59	811	892	373	114	921	308	456	476	975	617	1
60	.43837	.89879	.45399	.89101	.46947	.88295	.48481	.87462	.50000	.86603	0
	N.cos.	N. sine	N.cos.	N. sine	N.cos.	N. sine	N.cos.	N. sine	N.cos.	N. sine	
′	64°		63°		62°		61°		60°		′

TABLE 9 (*Continued*)

′	25°		26°		27°		28°		29°		′
	Tang.	Cotg.	Tang.	Cotg.	Tang.	Cotg.	Tang.	Cotg.	Tang.	Cotg.	
0	.4663	2.1445	.4877	2.0503	.5095	1.9626	.5317	1.8807	.5543	1.8040	**60**
1	67	29	81	2.0488	99	12	21	1.8794	47	28	59
2	70	13	85	73	.5103	1.9598	25	81	51	16	58
3	74	2.1396	88	58	06	84	28	68	55	03	57
4	77	80	92	43	10	70	32	55	58	1.7991	56
5	81	64	95	28	14	56	36	41	62	79	55
6	84	48	99	13	17	42	40	28	66	66	54
7	88	32	.4903	2.0398	21	28	43	15	70	54	53
8	91	15	06	83	25	14	47	02	74	42	52
9	95	2.1299	10	68	28	00	51	1.8689	77	30	51
10	.4699	2.1283	.4913	2.0353	.5132	1.9486	.5354	1.8676	.5581	1.7917	**50**
11	.4702	67	17	38	36	72	58	63	·85	05	49
12	06	51	21	23	39	58	62	50	89	1.7893	48
13	09	35	24	08	43	44	66	37	93	81	47
14	13	19	28	2.0293	47	30	69	24	96	68	46
15	16	03	31	78	50	16	73	11	.5600	56	45
16	20	2.1187	35	63	54	02	77	1.8598	04	44	44
17	23	71	39	48	58	1.9388	81	85	08	32	43
18	27	55	42	33	61	75	84	72	12	20	42
19	31	39	46	19	65	61	88	59	16	08	41
20	.4734	2.1123	.4950	2.0204	.5169	1.9347	.5392	1.8546	.5619	1.7796	**40**
21	38	07	53	2.0189	72	33	96	33	23	83	39
22	41	2.1092	57	74	76	19	99	20	27	71	38
23	45	76	60	60	80	06	.5403	07	31	59	37
24	48	60	64	45	84	1.9292	07	1.8495	35	47	36
25	52	44	68	30	87	78	11	82	39	35	35
26	55	28	71	15	91	65	15	69	42	23	34
27	59	13	75	01	95	51	18	56	46	11	33
28	63	2.0997	79	2.0086	98	37	22	43	50	1.7699	32
29	66	81	82	72	.5202	23	26	30	54	87	31
30	.4770	2.0965	.4986	2.0057	.5206	1.9210	.5430	1.8418	.5658	1.7675	**30**
31	73	50	89	42	09	1.9196	33	05	62	63	29
32	77	34	93	28	13	83	37	1.8392	65	51	28
33	80	18	97	13	17	69	41	79	69	39	27
34	84	03	.5000	1.9999	20	55	45	67	73	27	26
35	88	2.0887	04	84	24	42	48	54	77	15	25
36	91	72	08	70	28	28	52	41	81	03	24
37	95	56	11	55	32	15	56	29	85	1.7591	23
38	98	40	15	41	35	01	60	16	88	79	22
39	.4802	25	19	26	39	1.9088	64	03	92	67	21
40	.4806	2.0809	.5022	1.9912	.5243	1.9074	.5467	1.8291	.5696	1.7556	**20**
41	09	2.0794	26	1.9897	46	61	71	78	.5700	44	19
42	13	78	29	83	50	47	75	65	04	32	18
43	16	63	33	68	54	34	79	53	08	20	17
44	20	48	37	54	58	20	82	40	12	08	16
45	23	32	40	40	61	07	86	28	15	1.7496	15
46	27	17	44	25	65	1.8993	90	15	19	85	14
47	31	01	48	11	69	80	94	02	23	73	13
48	34	2.0686	51	1.9797	72	67	98	1.8190	27	61	12
49	38	71	55	82	76	53	.5501	77	31	49	11
50	.4841	2.0655	.5059	1.9768	.5280	1.8940	.5505	1.8165	.5735	1.7437	**10**
51	45	40	62	54	84	27	09	52	39	26	9
52	49	25	66	40	87	13	13	40	43	14	8
53	52	09	70	25	91	00	17	27	46	02	7
54	56	2.0594	73	11	95	1.8887	20	15	50	1.7391	6
55	59	79	77	1.9697	99	73	24	03	54	79	5
56	63	64	81	83	.5302	60	28	1.8090	58	67	4
57	67	49	84	69	06	47	32	78	62	55	3
58	70	33	88	54	10	34	35	65	66	44	2
59	74	18	92	40	13	20	39	53	70	32	1
60	.4877	2.0503	.5095	1.9626	.5317	1.8807	.5543	1.8040	.5774	1.7321	**0**
	Cotg.	Tang.	Cotg.	Tang.	Cotg.	Tang.	Cotg.	Tang.	Cotg.	Tang.	
′	64°		63°		62°		61°		60°		′

465

TABLE 9 (*Continued*)

′	30° N.sine	30° N.cos.	31° N.sine	31° N.cos.	32° N.sine	32° N.cos.	33° N.sine	33° N.cos.	34° N.sine	34° N.cos.	′
0	.50000	.86603	.51504	.85717	.52992	.84805	.54464	.83867	.55919	.82904	60
1	025	588	529	702	.53017	789	488	851	943	887	59
2	050	573	554	687	041	774	513	835	968	871	58
3	076	559	579	672	066	759	537	819	992	855	57
4	101	544	604	657	091	743	561	804	.56016	839	56
5	126	530	628	642	115	728	586	788	040	822	55
6	151	515	653	627	140	712	610	772	064	806	54
7	176	501	678	612	164	697	635	756	088	790	53
8	201	486	703	597	189	681	659	740	112	773	52
9	227	471	728	582	214	666	683	724	136	757	51
10	.50252	.86457	.51753	.85567	.53238	.84650	.54708	.83708	.56160	.82741	50
11	277	442	778	551	263	635	732	692	184	724	49
12	302	427	803	536	288	619	756	676	208	708	48
13	327	413	828	521	312	604	781	660	232	692	47
14	352	398	852	506	337	588	805	645	256	675	46
15	377	384	877	491	361	573	829	629	280	659	45
16	403	369	902	476	386	557	854	613	305	643	44
17	428	354	927	461	411	542	878	597	329	626	43
18	453	340	952	446	435	526	902	581	353	610	42
19	478	325	977	431	460	511	927	565	377	593	41
20	.50503	.86310	.52002	.85416	.53484	.84495	.54951	83549	.56401	.82577	40
21	528	295	026	401	509	480	975	533	425	561	39
22	553	281	051	385	534	464	999	517	449	544	38
23	578	266	076	370	558	448	.55024	501	473	528	37
24	603	251	101	355	583	433	048	485	497	511	36
25	628	237	126	340	607	417	072	469	521	495	35
26	654	222	151	325	632	402	097	453	545	478	34
27	679	207	175	310	656	386	121	437	569	462	33
28	704	192	200	294	681	370	145	421	593	446	32
29	729	178	225	279	705	355	169	405	617	429	31
30	.50754	.86163	.52250	.85264	.53730	.84339	.55194	.83389	.56641	.82413	30
31	779	148	275	249	754	324	218	373	665	396	29
32	804	133	299	234	779	308	242	356	689	380	28
33	829	119	324	218	804	292	266	340	713	363	27
34	854	104	349	203	828	277	291	324	736	347	26
35	879	089	374	188	853	261	315	308	760	330	25
36	904	074	399	173	877	245	339	292	784	314	24
37	929	059	423	157	902	230	363	276	808	297	23
38	954	045	448	142	926	214	388	260	832	281	22
39	979	030	473	127	951	198	412	244	856	264	21
40	.51004	.86015	.52498	.85112	.53975	.84182	.55436	.83228	.56880	.82248	20
41	029	000	522	096	.54000	167	460	212	904	231	19
42	054	.85985	547	081	024	151	484	195	928	214	18
43	079	970	572	066	049	135	509	179	952	198	17
44	104	956	597	051	073	120	533	163	976	181	16
45	129	941	621	035	097	104	557	147	.57000	165	15
46	154	926	646	020	122	088	581	131	024	148	14
47	179	911	671	005	146	072	605	115	047	132	13
48	204	896	696	.84989	171	057	630	098	071	115	12
49	229	881	720	974	195	041	654	082	095	098	11
50	.51254	.85866	.52745	.84959	.54220	.84025	.55678	.83066	.57119	.82082	10
51	279	851	770	943	244	009	702	050	143	065	9
52	304	836	794	928	269	.83994	726	034	167	048	8
53	329	821	819	913	293	978	750	017	191	032	7
54	354	806	844	897	317	962	775	001	215	015	6
55	379	792	869	882	342	946	799	.82985	238	.81999	5
56	404	777	893	866	366	930	823	969	262	982	4
57	429	762	918	851	391	915	847	953	286	965	3
58	454	747	943	836	415	899	871	936	310	949	2
59	479	732	967	820	440	883	895	920	334	932	1
60	.51504	.85717	.52992	.84805	.54464	.83867	.55919	.82904	.57358	.81915	0
′	N.cos.	N.sine	N.cos.	N.sine	N.cos.	N.sine	N.cos.	N.sine	N.cos.	N.sine	′
	59°		58°		57°		56°		55°		

TABLE 9 (*Continued*)

′	30° Tang.	30° Cotg.	31° Tang.	31° Cotg.	32° Tang.	32° Cotg.	33° Tang.	33° Cotg.	34° Tang.	34° Cotg.	′
0	.5774	1.7321	.6009	1.6643	.6249	1.6003	.6494	1.5399	.6745	1.4826	60
1	77	09	13	32	53	1.5993	98	89	49	16	59
2	81	1.7297	17	21	57	83	.6502	79	54	07	58
3	85	86	20	10	61	72	06	69	58	1.4798	57
4	89	74	24	1.6599	65	62	11	59	62	88	56
5	93	62	28	88	69	52	15	50	66	79	55
6	97	51	32	77	73	41	19	40	71	70	54
7	.5801	39	36	66	77	31	23	30	75	61	53
8	05	28	40	55	81	21	27	20	79	51	52
9	08	16	44	45	85	11	31	11	83	42	51
10	.5812	1.7205	.6048	1.6534	.6289	1.5900	.6536	1.5301	.6787	1.4733	50
11	16	1.7193	52	23	93	1.5890	40	1.5291	92	24	49
12	20	82	56	12	97	80	44	82	96	15	48
13	24	70	60	01	.6301	69	48	72	.6800	05	47
14	28	59	64	1.6490	05	59	52	62	05	1.4696	46
15	32	47	68	79	10	49	56	53	09	87	45
16	36	36	72	69	14	39	60	43	13	78	44
17	40	24	76	58	18	29	65	33	17	69	43
18	44	13	80	47	22	18	69	24	22	1.4659	42
19	47	02	84	36	26	08	73	14	26	50	41
20	.5851	1.7090	.6088	1.6426	.6330	1.5798	.6577	1.5204	.6830	1.4641	40
21	55	79	92	15	34	88	81	1.5195	34	32	39
22	59	67	96	04	38	78	85	85	39	23	38
23	63	56	.6100	1.6393	42	68	90	75	43	14	37
24	67	45	04	83	46	57	94	66	47	05	36
25	71	33	08	72	50	47	98	56	51	1.4596	35
26	75	22	12	61	54	37	.6602	47	56	86	34
27	79	11	16	51	58	27	06	37	60	77	33
28	83	1.6999	20	40	63	17	10	27	64	68	32
29	87	88	24	29	67	07	15	18	69	59	31
30	.5890	1.6977	.6128	1.6319	.6371	1.5697	.6619	1.5108	.6873	1.4550	30
31	94	65	32	08	75	87	23	1.5099	77	41	29
32	98	54	36	1.6297	79	77	27	89	81	32	28
33	.5902	43	40	87	83	67	31	80	86	23	27
34	06	32	44	76	87	57	36	70	90	14	26
35	10	20	48	65	91	47	40	61	94	05	25
36	14	09	52	55	95	37	44	51	99	1.4496	24
37	18	1.6898	56	44	99	27	48	42	.6903	87	23
38	22	87	60	34	.6403	17	52	32	07	78	22
39	26	75	64	23	08	07	57	23	11	69	21
40	.5930	1.6864	.6168	1.6212	.6412	1.5597	.6661	1.5013	.6916	1.4460	20
41	34	53	72	02	16	87	65	04	20	51	19
42	38	42	76	1.6191	20	77	69	1.4994	24	42	18
43	42	31	80	81	24	67	73	85	29	33	17
44	45	20	84	70	28	57	78	75	33	24	16
45	49	08	88	60	32	47	82	66	37	15	15
46	53	1.6797	92	49	36	37	86	57	42	06	14
47	57	86	96	39	40	27	90	47	46	1.4397	13
48	61	75	.6200	28	45	17	94	38	50	88	12
49	65	64	04	18	49	07	99	28	54	79	11
50	.5969	1.6753	.6208	1.6107	.6453	1.5497	.6703	1.4919	.6959	1.4370	10
51	73	42	12	1.6097	57	87	07	10	63	61	9
52	77	31	16	87	61	77	11	00	67	52	8
53	81	20	20	76	65	68	15	1.4891	72	44	7
54	85	09	24	66	69	58	20	82	76	35	6
55	89	1.6698	28	55	73	48	24	72	80	26	5
56	93	87	33	45	78	38	28	63	85	17	4
57	97	76	37	34	82	28	32	54	89	08	3
58	.6001	65	41	24	86	18	37	44	93	1.4299	2
59	05	54	45	14	90	08	41	35	98	91	1
60	.6009	1.6643	.6249	1.6003	.6494	1.5399	.6745	1.4826	.7002	1.4281	0
	Cotg.	Tang.	Cotg.	Tang.	Cotg.	Tang.	Cotg.	Tang.	Cotg.	Tang.	
′	59°		58°		57°		56°		55°		′

TABLE 9 (*Continued*)

′	35° N.sine	35° N. cos.	36° N.sine	36° N. cos.	37° N.sine	37° N. cos.	38° N.sine	38° N. cos.	39° N.sine	39° N. cos.	′
0	.57358	.81915	.58779	.80902	.60182	.79864	.61566	.78801	.62932	.77715	60
1	381	899	802	885	205	846	589	783	955	696	59
2	405	882	826	867	228	829	612	765	977	678	58
3	429	865	849	850	251	811	635	747	.63000	660	57
4	453	848	873	833	274	793	658	729	022	641	56
5	477	832	896	816	298	776	681	711	045	623	55
6	501	815	920	799	321	758	704	694	068	605	54
7	524	798	943	782	344	741	726	676	090	586	53
8	548	782	967	765	367	723	749	658	113	568	52
9	572	765	990	748	390	706	772	640	135	550	51
10	.57596	.81748	.59014	.80730	.60414	.79688	.61795	.78622	.63158	.77531	50
11	619	731	037	713	437	671	818	604	180	513	49
12	643	714	061	696	460	653	841	586	203	494	48
13	667	698	084	679	483	635	864	568	225	476	47
14	691	681	108	662	506	618	887	550	248	458	46
15	715	664	131	644	529	600	909	532	271	439	45
16	738	647	154	627	553	583	932	514	293	421	44
17	762	631	178	610	576	565	955	496	316	402	43
18	786	614	201	593	599	547	978	478	338	384	42
19	810	597	225	576	622	530	.62001	460	361	366	41
20	.57833	.81580	.59248	.80558	.60645	.79512	.62024	.78442	.63383	.77347	40
21	857	563	272	541	668	494	046	424	406	329	39
22	881	546	295	524	691	477	069	405	428	310	38
23	904	530	318	507	714	459	092	387	451	292	37
24	928	513	342	489	738	441	115	369	473	273	36
25	952	496	365	472	761	424	138	351	496	255	35
26	976	479	389	455	784	406	160	333	518	236	34
27	999	462	412	438	807	388	183	315	540	218	33
28	.58023	445	436	420	830	371	206	297	563	199	32
29	047	428	459	403	853	353	229	279	585	181	31
30	.58070	.81412	.59482	.80386	.60876	.79335	.62251	.78261	.63608	.77162	30
31	094	395	506	368	899	318	274	243	630	144	29
32	118	378	529	351	922	300	297	225	653	125	28
33	141	361	552	334	945	282	320	206	675	107	27
34	165	344	576	316	968	264	342	188	698	088	26
35	189	327	599	299	991	247	365	170	720	070	25
36	212	310	622	282	.61015	229	388	152	742	051	24
37	236	293	646	264	038	211	411	134	765	033	23
38	260	276	669	247	061	193	433	116	787	014	22
39	283	259	693	230	084	176	456	098	810	.76996	21
40	.58307	.81242	.59716	.80212	.61107	.79158	.62479	.78079	.63832	.76977	20
41	330	225	739	195	130	140	502	061	854	959	19
42	354	208	763	178	153	122	524	043	877	940	18
43	378	191	786	160	176	105	547	025	899	921	17
44	401	174	809	143	199	087	570	007	922	903	16
45	425	157	832	125	222	069	592	.77988	944	884	15
46	449	140	856	108	245	051	615	970	966	866	14
47	472	123	879	091	268	033	638	952	989	847	13
48	496	106	902	073	291	016	660	934	.64011	828	12
49	519	089	926	056	314	.78998	683	916	033	810	11
50	.58543	.81072	.59949	.80038	.61337	.78980	.62706	.77897	.64056	.76791	10
51	567	055	972	021	360	962	728	879	078	772	9
52	590	038	995	003	383	944	751	861	100	754	8
53	614	021	.60019	.79986	406	926	774	843	123	735	7
54	637	004	042	968	429	908	796	824	145	717	6
55	661	.80987	065	951	451	891	819	806	167	698	5
56	684	970	089	934	474	873	842	788	190	679	4
57	708	953	112	916	497	855	864	769	212	661	3
58	731	936	135	899	520	837	887	751	234	642	2
59	755	919	158	881	543	819	909	733	256	623	1
60	.58779	.80902	.60182	.79864	.61566	.78801	.62932	.77715	.64279	.76604	0
	N.cos.	N. sine	N.cos.	N. sine	N.cos.	N. sine	N.cos.	N. sine	N.cos.	N.sine	
′	54°		53°		52°		51°		50°		′

TABLE 9 (*Continued*)

| ′ | 35° | | 36° | | 37° | | 38° | | 39° | | ′ |
	Tang.	Cotg.	Tang.	Cotg.	Tang.	Cotg.	Tang.	Cotg.	Tang.	Cotg.	
0	.7002	1.4281	.7265	1.3764	.7536	1.3270	.7813	1.2799	.8098	1.2349	60
1	06	73	70	55	40	62	18	92	.8103	42	59
2	11	64	74	47	45	54	22	84	07	34	58
3	15	55	79	39	49	46	27	76	12	27	57
4	19	46	83	30	54	38	32	69	17	20	56
5	24	37	88	22	58	30	36	61	22	12	55
6	28	29	92	13	63	22	41	53	27	05	54
7	32	20	97	05	68	14	46	46	32	1.2298	53
8	37	11	.7301	1.3697	72	06	50	38	36	90	52
9	41	02	06	88	77	1.3198	55	31	41	83	51
10	.7046	1.4193	.7310	1.3680	.7581	1.3190	.7860	1.2723	.8146	1.2276	50
11	50	85	14	72	86	82	65	15	51	68	49
12	54	76	19	63	90	75	69	08	56	61	48
13	59	67	23	55	95	67	74	00	61	54	47
14	63	58	28	47	.7600	59	79	1.2693	65	47	46
15	67	50	32	38	04	51	83	85	70	39	45
16	72	41	37	30	09	43	88	77	75	32	44
17	76	32	41	22	13	35	93	70	80	25	43
18	80	24	46	13	18	27	98	62	85	18	42
19	85	15	50	05	23	19	.7902	55	90	10	41
20	.7089	1.4106	.7355	1.3597	.7627	1.3111	.7907	1.2647	.8195	1.2203	40
21	94	1.4097	59	88	32	03	12	40	99	1.2196	39
22	98	89	64	80	36	1.3095	16	32	.8204	89	38
23	.7102	80	68	72	41	87	21	24	09	81	37
24	07	71	73	64	46	79	26	17	14	74	36
25	11	63	77	55	50	72	31	09	19	67	35
26	15	54	82	47	55	64	35	02	24	60	34
27	20	45	86	39	59	56	40	1.2594	29	53	33
28	24	37	91	31	64	48	45	87	34	45	32
29	29	28	95	22	69	40	50	79	38	38	31
30	.7133	1.4019	.7400	1.3514	.7673	1.3032	.7954	1.2572	.8243	1.2131	30
31	37	11	04	06	78	24	59	64	48	24	29
32	42	02	09	1.3498	83	17	64	57	53	17	28
33	46	1.3994	13	90	87	09	69	49	58	09	27
34	51	85	18	81	92	01	73	42	63	02	26
35	55	76	22	73	96	1.2993	78	34	68	1.2095	25
36	59	68	27	65	.7701	85	83	27	73	88	24
37	64	59	31	57	06	77	88	19	78	81	23
38	68	51	36	49	10	70	92	12	83	74	22
39	73	42	40	40	15	62	97	04	87	66	21
40	.7177	1.3934	.7445	1.3432	.7720	1.2954	.8002	1.2497	.8292	1.2059	20
41	81	25	49	24	24	46	07	89	97	52	19
42	86	16	54	16	29	38	12	82	.8302	45	18
43	90	08	58	08	34	31	16	75	07	38	17
44	95	1.3899	63	00	38	23	21	67	12	31	16
45	99	91	67	1.3392	43	15	26	60	17	24	15
46	.7203	82	72	84	47	07	31	52	22	17	14
47	08	74	76	75	52	00	35	45	27	09	13
48	12	65	81	67	57	1.2892	40	37	32	02	12
49	17	57	85	59	61	84	45	30	37	1.1995	11
50	.7221	1.3848	.7490	1.3351	.7766	1.2876	.8050	1.2423	.8342	1.1988	10
51	26	40	95	43	71	69	55	15	46	81	9
52	30	31	99	35	75	61	59	08	51	74	8
53	34	23	.7504	27	80	53	64	01	56	67	7
54	39	14	08	19	85	46	69	1.2393	61	60	6
55	43	06	13	11	89	38	74	86	66	53	5
56	48	1.3798	17	03	94	30	79	78	71	46	4
57	52	89	22	1.3295	99	22	83	71	76	39	3
58	57	81	26	87	.7803	15	88	64	81	32	2
59	61	72	31	78	08	07	93	56	86	25	1
60	.7265	1.3764	.7536	1.3270	.7813	1.2799	.8098	1.2349	.8391	1.1918	0
	Cotg.	Tang.	Cotg.	Tang.	Cotg.	Tang.	Cotg.	Tang.	Cotg.	Tang.	
′	54°		53°		52°		51°		50°		′

TABLE 9 (*Continued*)

′	40°		41°		42°		43°		44°		′
	N.sine	N. cos.	N.sine	N. cos.	N.sine	N. cos.	N.sine	N. cos.	N.sine	N. cos.	
0	.64279	.76604	.65606	.75471	.66913	.74314	.68200	.73135	.69466	.71934	60
1	301	586	628	452	935	295	221	116	487	914	59
2	323	567	650	433	956	276	242	096	508	894	58
3	346	548	672	414	978	256	264	076	529	873	57
4	368	530	694	395	999	237	285	056	549	853	56
5	390	511	716	375	.67021	217	306	036	570	833	55
6	412	492	738	356	043	198	327	016	591	813	54
7	435	473	759	337	064	178	349	.72996	612	792	53
8	457	455	781	318	086	159	370	976	633	772	52
9	479	436	803	299	107	139	391	957	654	752	51
10	.64501	.76417	.65825	.75280	.67129	.74120	.68412	.72937	69675	.71732	50
11	524	398	847	261	151	100	434	917	696	711	49
12	546	380	869	241	172	080	455	897	717	691	48
13	568	361	891	222	194	061	476	877	737	671	47
14	590	342	913	203	215	041	497	857	758	650	46
15	612	323	935	184	237	022	518	837	779	630	45
16	635	304	956	165	258	002	539	817	800	610	44
17	657	286	978	146	280	.73983	561	797	821	590	43
18	679	267	.66000	126	301	963	582	777	842	569	42
19	701	248	022	107	323	944	603	757	862	549	41
20	.64723	.76229	.66044	.75088	.67344	.73924	.68624	.72737	.69883	.71529	40
21	746	210	066	069	366	904	645	717	904	508	39
22	768	192	088	050	387	885	666	697	925	488	38
23	790	173	109	030	409	865	688	677	946	468	37
24	812	154	131	011	430	846	709	657	966	447	36
25	834	135	153	.74992	452	826	730	637	987	427	35
26	856	116	175	973	473	806	751	617	.70008	407	34
27	878	097	197	953	495	787	772	597	029	386	33
28	901	078	218	934	516	767	793	577	049	366	32
29	923	059	240	915	538	747	814	557	070	345	31
30	.64945	.76041	.66262	.74896	.67559	.73728	.68835	.72537	.70091	.71325	30
31	967	022	284	876	580	708	857	517	112	305	29
32	989	003	306	857	602	688	878	497	132	284	28
33	.65011	.75984	327	838	623	669	899	477	153	264	27
34	033	965	349	818	645	649	920	457	174	243	26
35	055	946	371	799	666	629	941	437	195	223	25
36	077	927	393	780	688	610	962	417	215	203	24
37	100	908	414	760	709	590	983	397	236	182	23
38	122	889	436	741	730	570	.69004	377	257	162	22
39	144	870	458	722	752	551	025	357	277	141	21
40	.65166	.75851	.66480	.74703	.67773	.73531	.69046	.72337	.70298	.71121	20
41	188	832	501	683	795	511	067	317	319	100	19
42	210	813	523	664	816	491	088	297	339	080	18
43	232	794	545	644	837	472	109	277	360	059	17
44	254	775	566	625	859	452	130	257	381	039	16
45	276	756	588	606	880	432	151	236	401	019	15
46	298	738	610	586	901	413	172	216	422	.70998	14
47	320	719	632	567	923	393	193	196	443	978	13
48	342	700	653	548	944	373	214	176	463	957	12
49	364	680	675	528	965	353	235	156	484	937	11
50	.65386	.75661	.66697	.74509	.67987	.73333	.69256	.72136	.70505	.70916	10
51	408	642	718	489	.68008	314	277	116	525	896	9
52	430	623	740	470	029	294	298	095	546	875	8
53	452	604	762	451	051	274	319	075	567	855	7
54	474	585	783	431	072	254	340	055	587	834	6
55	496	566	805	412	093	234	361	035	608	813	5
56	518	547	827	392	115	215	382	015	628	793	4
57	540	528	848	373	136	195	403	.71995	649	772	3
58	562	509	870	353	157	175	424	974	670	752	2
59	584	490	891	334	179	155	445	955	690	731	1
60	.65606	.75471	.66913	.74314	.68200	.73135	.69466	.71934	.70711	.70711	0
	N.cos.	N. sine	N.cos.	N. sine	N.cos.	N. sine	N.cos.	N. sine	N.cos.	N. sine	′
	49°		48°		47°		46°		45°		

TABLE 9. (Continued)

′	40°		41°		42°		43°		44°		′
	Tang.	Cotg.	Tang.	Cotg.	Tang.	Cotg.	Tang.	Cotg.	Tang.	Cotg.	
0	.8391	1.1918	.8693	1.1504	.9004	1.1106	.9325	1.0724	.9657	1.0355	60
1	96	10	98	1.1497	09	00	31	17	63	49	59
2	.8401	03	.8703	90	15	1.1093	36	11	68	43	58
3	06	1.1896	08	83	20	87	41	05	74	37	57
4	11	89	13	77	25	80	47	1.0699	79	31	56
5	16	82	18	70	30	74	52	92	85	25	55
6	21	75	24	63	36	67	58	86	91	19	54
7	26	68	29	56	41	61	63	80	96	13	53
8	31	61	34	50	46	54	69	74	.9702	07	52
9	36	54	39	43	52	48	74	68	08	01	51
10	.8441	1.1847	.8744	1.1436	.9057	1.1041	.9380	1.0661	.9713	1.0295	50
11	46	40	49	30	62	35	85	55	19	89	49
12	51	33	54	23	67	28	91	49	25	83	48
13	56	26	59	16	73	22	96	43	30	77	47
14	61	19	65	10	78	16	.9402	37	36	71	46
15	66	12	70	03	83	09	07	30	42	65	45
16	71	06	75	1.1396	89	03	13	24	47	59	44
17	76	1.1799	80	89	94	1.0996	18	18	53	53	43
18	81	92	85	83	99	90	24	12	59	47	42
19	86	85	90	76	.9105	83	29	06	64	41	41
20	.8491	1.1778	.8796	1.1369	.9110	1.0977	.9435	1.0599	.9770	1.0235	40
21	96	71	.8801	63	15	71	40	93	76	30	39
22	.8501	64	06	56	21	64	46	87	81	24	38
23	06	57	11	49	26	58	51	81	87	18	37
24	11	50	16	43	31	51	57	75	93	12	36
25	16	43	21	36	37	45	62	69	98	06	35
26	21	36	27	29	42	39	68	62	.9804	00	34
27	26	29	32	23	47	32	73	56	10	1.0194	33
28	31	22	37	16	53	26	79	50	16	88	32
29	36	15	42	10	58	19	84	44	21	82	31
30	.8541	1.1708	.8847	1.1303	.9163	1.0913	.9490	1.0538	.9827	1.0176	30
31	46	02	52	1.1296	69	07	95	32	33	70	29
32	51	1.1695	58	90	74	00	.9501	26	38	64	28
33	56	88	63	83	79	1.0894	06	19	44	58	27
34	61	81	68	76	85	88	12	13	50	52	26
35	66	74	73	70	90	81	17	07	56	47	25
36	71	67	78	63	95	75	23	01	61	41	24
37	76	60	84	57	.9201	69	28	1.0495	67	35	23
38	81	53	89	50	06	62	34	89	73	29	22
39	86	47	94	43	12	56	40	83	79	23	21
40	.8591	1.1640	.8899	1.1237	.9217	1.0850	.9545	1.0477	.9884	1.0117	20
41	96	33	.8904	30	22	43	51	70	90	11	19
42	.8601	26	10	24	28	37	56	64	96	05	18
43	06	19	15	17	33	31	62	58	.9902	1.0099	17
44	11	12	20	11	39	24	67	52	07	94	16
45	17	06	25	04	44	18	73	46	13	88	15
46	22	1.1599	31	1.1197	49	12	78	40	19	82	14
47	27	92	36	91	55	05	84	34	25	76	13
48	32	85	41	84	60	1.0799	90	28	30	70	12
49	37	78	46	78	66	93	95	22	36	64	11
50	.8642	1.1571	.8952	1.1171	.9271	1.0786	.9601	1.0416	.9942	1.0058	10
51	47	65	57	65	76	80	06	10	48	52	9
52	52	58	62	58	82	74	12	04	54	47	8
53	57	51	67	52	87	68	18	1.0398	59	41	7
54	62	44	72	45	93	61	23	92	65	35	6
55	67	38	78	39	98	55	29	85	71	29	5
56	72	31	83	32	.9303	49	34	79	77	23	4
57	78	24	88	26	09	42	40	73	83	17	3
58	83	17	94	19	14	36	46	67	88	12	2
59	88	10	99	13	20	30	51	61	94	06	1
60	.8693	1.1504	.9004	1.1106	.9325	1.0724	.9657	1.0355	1.0000	1.0000	0
	Cotg.	Tang.	Cotg.	Tang.	Cotg.	Tang.	Cotg.	Tang.	Cotg.	Tang.	
′	49°		48°		47°		46°		45°		′

TABLE 10. Criteria Indicating Faults and Unconformities

	Features Observable in The Field	Fault	Uncon-formity	Other
Structural	Abrupt changes in direction of strike or degree of dip	x	A	Tight folding
	Repetition of known stratigraphic units	x		Erosion of tight folds
	Absence of known stratigraphic units	x	A, D, N	Not deposited
	Abnormal juxaposition of known rock units	x	A, D, N	Landslides
	Abrupt termination of folds, faults, dikes, and like features	x	A, D, N	
	Sharp, abrupt folding (possibly drag along faults)	x	A	Unfaulted tight folds
Lithologic	Marked lithologic changes along strike or dip	x	A	Rapid facies changes
	Gradual lithologic changes from apparent basal conglomerate upward		A, D, N	
	Basal beds contain materials from only older underlying strata		A, D, N	
Physiographic	Linear scarps, faceted spurs, hanging valleys	x		Glaciation
	Stream offsets and wind gaps	x		Stratigraphic peculiarities
	Abrupt changes in stream gradient	x		Resistant strata, dikes
	Landslides, trenches, saddles	x		
	Springs: especially hot, mineralized Seeps: cold, oil, and gas	x	A, D, N	Escape through permeable beds
Rock Condition	Restricted occurrence of clays, rock flour, rock fragments	x		Extreme hydro-thermal action Glaciation
	Slickensides	x		Sharp folding
	Hydrothermal alteration, minerali-zation, silication	x	A, D, N Under tight cover	Permeable stratum
	Gash fractures, intense jointing, fracturing	x		
	Mylonite (microshattering)	x		
	Breccia: sharp, angular fragments, material from both walls	x		

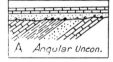 A Angular Uncon.

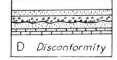 D Disconformity

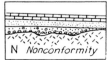 N Nonconformity

472

TABLE 11. Abbreviations for Well Log Strips

Explanation: Although the colored graphic column of a strip log shows the principal differences in lithologies, additional descriptive notes are essential. Where individual stratigraphic units are 20 feet or greater in thickness, descriptive notes may be continued on a second line; however, it is usually necessary to confine the descriptions to a single line about 2½ inches long. This restriction of space makes it necessary to omit all unimportant words and to abbreviate others. There is no established standard for these abbreviations, but those given in the following list are generally acceptable. Periods following abbreviations may be omitted. Commas are used as if the adjectives in a series were complete words; e.g., Ss-crse, rnd, brn-red, hd, calc. Some of the abbreviations may be difficult to interpret if seen alone, but in context they seldom cause any confusion as to meaning. A new abbreviation should not be used without first checking the list to ascertain that it does not conflict with one used for another word.

absorbed—abs	crystal—cryst, xl	large—lge
absorption—absp	crystalline—xln	lavender—lav
abundant—abdt	dark—dk	lignite—lig
accumulation—accum	darker—dkr	limestone—ls or lss
agglomerate—agl	different, difference—diff	limonite—limon
aggregate—ag	diffused—diffus	limy—limy
algae—algae	disseminated—dissem	little—lit
algal—algal	dolomite—dolo	long—long
angular—ang	dolomitic—dolom	magnetite—mag
anhydrite—anhy	drab—drab	massive—mass
arkose, arkosic—ark	elevated, elevation—elev	material—mat
banded—band	fine, finely—fine or f	matted—matted
barite—barite	flint—flint	medium—med
bentonite—bent	fluorescence—fluor	micaceous—mica
biotite—bio	fluorite—fluorite	mudstone—mudst
bituminous—bitum	fossiliferous—fossilif	muscovite—musc
black—bl	fossils—fos	olive—olive
blue—blue	fusulinid—fusul	oölitic—oöl
brachiopod—brach	globular—glob	opaque—op
brown—brn	gradational—grada	opposite—oppos
brownish-gray—brn-gr,	grading—grad	orange—orange
etc.	granular—gran	orthoclase—orth
brecciated—brec	gray—gr	oxidized—ox
calcareous—calc	green—grn	part—pt
chalcedony—chal	gyppy—gyppy	phlogopite—phlog
chalk—chalk	gypsiferous—gypsif	phosphate—phos
chert—cht	gypsum—gyp	pin point—ppt
chlorite—chlor	hard—hd	pink—pink
clay—clay	igneous—ig	plagioclase—plag
coal—coal, coaly	illite—illite	plastic—plast
coarse—crse	inclusion—incl	pores—pores
colloidal—coll	indurated—indur	porous—por
conglomerate—cglm	interstices—interst	purple—purp
conglomeratic—cglmtc	interstitial—interst	quartz—qtz
cream—crm	jasper—jasp	quartzite—qtzte
creamy—crmy	laminated—lam	quartzose—qtzse

From L. W. LeRoy and Julian W. Low, *Graphic Problems in Petroleum Geology,* Harper & Brothers, 1954, pp. 50-51.

TABLE 11. (*Continued*)

random—rand
red—red
round—rnd
rugose—rug
rusty—rusty
salt—salt
sand—sd
sandstone—ss, sss
sandy—sdy
saturated—sat
shale—sh
shaly—shy
siderite—sid

siliceous—sil
silt—silt
siltstone—sltst
slight—slt
slightly—sltly
sphalerite—sphal
spicular—spic
stain—stn
staining—stng
subangular—subang
sucrosic—suc
sulphur—sulf
talc—talc

tarnished—tarn
tripolitic—trip
tubular—tub
undulating—undul
vari-colored—varicol
variegated—varig
vermiculite—vermic
vuggy—vug
water—wat
white—wh
with—w
yellow—yel

INDEX

W''
(
UNI